Warren Cariou, Marilyn Gear Pilling & François Bonneville

COMING ATTRACTIONS
95

This book was written and published with the assistance of the Canada Council, the Ontario Arts Council and others.

Acknowledgements: "Puerto Escondido" by Warren Cariou and "Tib" by Marilyn Gear Pilling first appeared in the *Malahat Review*. "The Necessity of Sleep" by Warren Cariou was originally published in *Fiddlehead*. "Recovering" by Warren Cariou originally appeared in *Grain*. "Digs" by Warren Cariou was first published in *Prairie Fire* and *Stag Line* and broadcast on CBC's "Writers & Company." "Son of Night, Brother of Sleep" by Marilyn Gear Pilling first appeared in *Prism International*.

ISBN 0 7780 1009 0 (hardcover)
ISBN 0 7780 1010 4 (softcover)

Cover art by Noreen Mallory
Book design by Michael Macklem

Printed in Canada

PUBLISHED IN CANADA BY OBERON PRESS

Introduction

In his essay "The Novel and Europe," Milan Kundera once wrote that the novel's essence is complexity, that it expresses "the ancient wisdom of Cervantes, which speaks of the difficulty of knowing and a truth that eludes the grasp." This complexity, the idea that nothing is what it seems, is precisely the quality shared by the three authors included in this year's *Coming Attractions*. All three embody a late-twentieth-century radical doubt, a sense that no situation (story, novel) can be summed up in a single perspective, that the newspapers, pollsters and ideologues have it wrong—we are mysterious beings, the winds of history blow through us fitfully, and the guy who says he's got the goods is either a liar or a fool.

Warren Cariou divides his time between Meadow Lake, Saskatchewan, where he grew up, and the University of Toronto where he is pursuing a PhD on William Blake. He admits the oscillation is befuddling but stimulating, and you can see it informing his stories, which depend for their effect on varying angles of vision and versions of the truth. In "Puerto Escondido," two lovers spend a shocked afternoon remembering how they nearly drowned together in a deadly undertow, how she ignored his warnings, how he threw himself into the waves to rescue her. Their motives and actions are mysterious even to themselves, and neither can remember the name or the face of the surfer who saved them. Now, "They found the true beauty of the place in the warm chiaroscuro of lanternlight, the tantalizing sense of half-glimpsed things."

Marilyn Gear Pilling was born in Waterloo, Ontario, has worked in the Hamilton Public Library for 25 years and claims to have started writing only three years ago. This last is difficult to credit when you read her stories, which flash with an eccentric brilliance and strange passions. In "Tib," a waifish orange-haired child-woman fights for the custody of her daughter Goosey while daydreaming about her fat-bellied father and his cat-like snores. She carries an empty beer bottle like a security blanket, tries to pass a cat off as Goosey's dad and obsesses on that oddly bisexual image of her father's belly. Tib thinks like a dream, and her story has an associative quality that codes truth into the relation between facts and not the facts themselves. "Goosey and her new daddy are breathing in tandem, Daddy's rich round purr ebbing and flowing like the nearby ocean. Tib curls like a foetus at the end of the mattress, and through the night on their small barque, these three drift across the vast, midnight-blue underside of the world."

François Bonneville is Quebecois, born in Halifax, raised mostly in Boston, Massachusetts, where his father worked for NASA. He has studied creative writing at the University of British Columbia, knocked around France as a writer-with-family-in-tow and now lives and teaches in Saratoga Springs, New York. His story "Voyeurism" is a masterful homage to Milan Kundera. Three characters—an American woman, a French businessman and the author—perform a stylish minuet of deflected lust and glances in a Normandy beach town. Even the author can only speculate upon a truth that is a tissue of desire, daydreams and memories. And his half-sister Lucia finally interrupts his reverie, asking, "How do you know why anything?"

DOUGLAS GLOVER

Contributions for *Coming Attractions* 96, published or unpublished, should be sent to the editor, Diane Schoemperlen, at 32 Dunlop Street, Kingston, Ontario, k7l 1l2 before 31 October, 1995. All manuscripts should be accompanied by a stamped, self-addressed envelope.

6

WARREN CARIOU

Puerto Escondido

The air was the temperature of skin.

They walked in the zocalo, Gregory in cutoffs and short sleeves, Alicia in a woven Guatemalan shift she'd found at a roadside market.

With one hand on her hip, he steered her through the crowds of Mexicans and past the occasional clutch of sunburned tourists—forgetting, for the moment, that she hated being steered.

The waves were sounding on the distant beach.

They had come here for the sun, but had switched allegiances after the first day.

Everything in daylight seemed overexposed, like photographs of snow.

They found the true beauty of the place in the warm chiaroscuro of lanternlight, the tantalizing sense of half-glimpsed things.

After sunset, vendors lined the sidewalks of the zocalo, offering silver and lapis lazuli and aquamarine jewellery, batiked cotton dresses and lustrous black pottery.

The dark-muzzled mongrels that lurked in the daytime streets disappeared at nightfall, perhaps to stalk the *campesinos'* chickens.

It was the next best thing to nakedness, this air.

They turned in at the Hotel Cortez and walked through a stuccoed corridor to a beachfront terrace.

The rush and drag of waves on the muddy sand was louder here, though the water was not visible.

Out on the beach, before the boles of the palm trees, was a row of bamboo torches with pale writhing flames.

Alicia tucked her hair behind each ear.

She had nearly killed Gregory, and herself, two days ago.

But this was nothing like the surfing beach, where it had happened.

Here, the little cove that ran the length of the zocalo offered shelter from the deep-sea swells.

They walked past the bar and took a table close to the beach.

She thought she heard voices down there, children playing, laughing like cartoon characters.

The bartender brought red wine in earthenware goblets.

Perhaps these were the same kids they had seen fishing for mackerel from the gunwales of anchored boats, swinging tiny silver hooks above their heads and tossing them out.

The mackerel had moved like swarms of bees, breaking the surface in unison.

One boy had fished by himself from the buttress of volcanic rock that divided the cove from the surfing beach.

Twenty-foot breakers had curled into the rock face and exploded in geysers of spray, and as the water cascaded down, the boy had scampered out onto a jagged promontory and hurled his hook.

One slip on that treacherous surface and he would have been lost.

Alicia was crying again.

"Don't," Gregory said, reaching for her hand.

He had always thought this would be a dangerous place.

He'd read the guidebooks and knew what to expect: malaria, diarrhea, sunburn, earthquakes.

Alicia had laughed at him, but now she brushed her teeth with bottled water.

The undertow was a danger he hadn't considered.

No matter how far the waves flung themselves onto the shore, the ocean always gathered them back in.

He hadn't seen her cry until recently, and didn't know how to react.

The tears were barely visible, trailing down over her cheekbones and underneath her jaw.

"Sorry," she said, trying to laugh.

"You shouldn't be sorry for anything."

She turned to face the beach and inhaled sharply through

9

her nose, then fumbled in her purse for cigarettes.

When Gregory saw that she had no matches he walked to the bar and asked for some.

In mixed English and Spanish, the bartender tried to tell him about a two-hundred-pound sailfish that an *Americano* had caught that afternoon.

"Non quiendo," Gregory said, though he had in fact understood.

Along with the matches, the bartender handed him the business card of a friend who would take *turistas* out fishing for only five thousand pesos an hour.

"Gracias," Gregory said.

When he handed the matches to Alicia, she avoided his gaze.

They were alone on the terrace, which was not surprising since locals never came to these places, and tourist season was already over.

The summer rains would be here soon.

She dried her eyes on a tiny pink napkin, then rolled it into a wad and dropped it in her purse.

According to her mother, her grandfather had died of cigarettes.

"Cigarettes are not a disease," Alicia had told her.

The sounds on the beach came again, boys playing tag among the palm trees.

She wanted to have a child, but she hadn't told Gregory because she didn't want to scare him off.

They had only been seeing each other for three months.

She put the cigarettes back in her purse without taking one.

"I like how the people here smoke," she said, "as if they didn't know it was bad for them."

"They have no concept of safety," he said.

She wondered if he thought the same thing about her.

She had talked him into coming here in the first place, had discounted every one of his excuses.

She almost always got what she wanted.

That was what she told him the first time they went out, and he had laughed, thinking it was a come-on.

He was not at all like her ex-husband, who would have sat there on the beach drinking tequila while she drowned.

She would have almost preferred that.

Gregory took his sunglasses from his shirt pocket and cleaned them on the edge of the tablecloth.

In the lenses he saw reflections of himself.

The Mexicana DC-10 they had taken from San Francisco to Mexico City had shuddered during takeoff, and the engines had wailed like huge saws.

The cars here had no seatbelts, no emissions controls.

Every female dog in the place was either pregnant or nursing, the rows of shrivelled black teats swaying under their concave bellies as they loped from one piece of shade to the next.

Alicia touched her tongue against the glazed edge of the goblet.

She was 32.

Gregory was only 27, and though they both said age didn't matter, she wondered if maybe it did.

Eveyone said they made a beautiful couple.

She had almost killed him.

She remembered his hand gripping her wrist, the riptide sweeping them out toward a breaker that was lifting itself above them.

He could have swam back to shore on his own but refused to let go of her.

That was why she'd screamed for help.

She had never imagined herself screaming, but it had come easily, even with salt water in her throat.

Afterward, she hadn't properly thanked the surfer who rescued her, had instead collapsed on her beach blanket, coughing violently and shivering.

Gregory would have kept holding onto her.

Two beautiful young women had walked by, wearing string

bikinis and carrying expensive cameras.

She couldn't remember what the surfer looked like.

Gregory had thanked him for her, but that wasn't the same.

When she had climbed on the surfboard, she had spread her knees across the back of it and paddled weakly with her feet.

The surfer had pushed the board from behind, and could have looked right up between her legs.

The beach was quiet now, except for the waves.

The children here always went home at the same time, without being called.

When Alicia was a child and spent summers at Manitou Lake, she used to hide in the bushes near the public beach every warm evening, stealing a few more minutes of the night while her mother called out her name again and again.

Gregory leaned forward on the table and looked into her empty goblet.

"Another?" he said.

"Please."

He waved to the bartender, who was leaning against the cash register, eyeing Alicia, like they all did.

"*Dos otros, por favor,*" Gregory said.

Of course, he had eyed her himself when he first saw her.

It was at the welcoming reception for the new Minister of Justice, whom Gregory had supported in the election.

She was standing with her husband in the foyer of the Minister's office, talking to a policy analyst.

She had a slender neck and large grey dissipated eyes, though she spoke with quick authority like all the other lawyers.

The husband stood sullenly beside her, staring into his glass of rye and water.

Gregory thought: this is the kind of man who could be violent.

After the separation, Alicia never once mentioned his name, as if she was afraid of invoking him.

She looked at Gregory now, over the rim of her goblet.

"What are you thinking?" she said.

"I don't know. That we're still here."

"A miracle, is it? We've survived four days."

He took a short breath and exhaled through his teeth, a washing sound.

"Time is going slower than I thought."

She had a crack in her lower lip from sunburn or salt water, and the wine had seeped in, so it looked like she was bleeding.

He would rather taste his own blood than salt water.

He had gone into the ocean before her, diving beneath the cresting breakers and drifting out with the backflow.

The water was as warm as the air.

It was surprisingly shallow for a long way out.

They had watched the surfers slide down those glistening walls all morning.

Some of the Mexican children were playing in the surf, running just ahead of the upwashing waves.

When he turned back toward shore he felt the undertow dragging him further away.

It quickened to the strength of gravity.

Then the next breaker extinguished it, tumbling him shoreward.

He recovered in time to body-surf on the next wave, windmilling his arms to stay on top of the water as long as possible.

The salt made his tongue swell up like a blowfish.

He rode several more waves, until his foot brushed against the bottom and he stood up in waist-deep water.

Alicia was lounging in the surf only a few yards away.

"Go back," he said. "Go in!"

She smiled and splashed frothy water in his direction as the riptide pulled her further out.

"This isn't funny," he said.

He was already swimming out to her when he felt another surge of undertow.

It swept her out thirty feet before a huge wave broke over her head and rolled her under.

She couldn't find the surface.

She inhaled anyway, found air mixed with foam that caught in her windpipe like gravel.

When she opened her eyes she saw Gregory standing on a sand bar in front of her, the water only chest-deep.

She stretched out her hand and he grabbed it as the undertow started again.

He pulled against it, but the sand sifted out from under his feet and in a second he was floating with her, rushing out toward the next wave.

"Swim!" he said, but already he felt her sinking.

The sand had dissolved like a pillar of salt.

They were lost in the surge and heave of the ocean, casting pieces of itself on the shore and gathering them back in.

She knew he wouldn't let go.

The ocean always gathered them back in.

Gregory sipped the last drop of his wine and felt it evaporate from his tongue.

There was a hint of rust in the aftertaste.

Alicia looked past him and saw the bartender leaning on the stump of a straw broom, watching her.

"He must think I'm a goddess or something," she said.

"Finish your wine, and we'll go," Gregory answered.

She swirled it in her goblet for a few seconds, staring back at the bartender.

"If only he knew," she said.

She placed the goblet on the table without drinking from it.

They stood up and Gregory led the way from the south end of the terrace and down a concrete staircase to the beach.

The wind was picking up, bending the palm trees like reeds.

They took off their sandals and walked toward the water.

When they reached the wet sand at the water's edge, they turned down the coast toward the string of orange patio lanterns that marked their hotel's poolside bar.

Shaggy whitecaps bore down on them out of the darkness, and the spray flew with the wind.

Gregory wondered what would have happened if the surfer hadn't been there.

He put his arm around Alicia's waist and she leaned against him.

He should have known he couldn't save her by himself.

At some point he would have had to decide: either let go and watch her drown, or keep holding on and join her.

When they reached the rock where the boy had been fishing, they turned toward the road.

The surfing beach was unlit, and bandits were said to wait there for tourists.

It was safer to walk near the lights of the private cottages.

The only things Alicia remembered about the surfer were his suntanned arms, his California accent, and the word "Pipefitter," which was scrawled across the front of his surfboard in hot pink lettering.

They passed a tiny rust-pitted sign that they hadn't noticed until the day after the incident: *Playa Peligrosa*.

Dangerous beach.

The waves were a few hundred yards away, but they seemed to travel through the sand like tiny earthquakes.

At the edge of the hotel grounds, bougainvillaeas and birds of paradise shuddered in the wind.

A group of young couples sat near the pool, sipping colourful drinks and talking lazily.

Perhaps the surfer was among them.

Alicia found the key in her purse and walked ahead of Gregory to unlock the door.

It was cooler in the room than previous nights.

She flipped off her sandals and padded across the concrete floor to the bathroom.

Gregory chained the door behind himself, then he lay down on the bed.

He would have let go of her.

Whether he'd wanted to or not, he would have let go.

The fan above him wobbled, as if one of the blades was about to fly off.

Alicia came out of the bathroom carrying her shift, which she draped over a chair.

The tan lines on her shoulders and along her neckline gave the impression that she was still clothed.

She lay down beside Gregory and kissed his temple.

The sand sifted out from under his feet and he was swept out with her.

She switched off the bedside lamp.

She unfastened the buttons of his shirt, then opened it and kissed his chest, circling his nipples with her tongue.

Pipefitter.

She pulled his shorts and underwear down to his knees, and he kicked them off.

The fan whirled like a child's fishing line.

She moved onto him and they made love slowly, eyes closed, listening to the muted concussions of the waves.

The ocean always gathered them back in.

The Necessity of Sleep

A young woman in my hometown had an operation. Since she came back from the hospital last spring, she's been living with her parents in the same tidy bungalow she grew up in. On warm evenings they wrap her in mottled afghans and set her in a wooden rocking-chair on the porch. When somebody sees her there, the stories filter through town. Her jaw is slack as a wet rag. Her eyelids are half shut. Saliva collects on her lower lip, spools down to her chest.

The surgery was a breast reduction. Something went wrong with the anaesthetic and she didn't wake up for seven months.

More accurately: her *response* to the anaesthetic was wrong. No-one could have foreseen that she would be the one person in ten thousand to have a malignant hyperthermic reaction. The doctors didn't know until half way through the surgery. They did as much as they could to save her, but it was beyond their control. I've written papers on this type of complication, so I know. When I'm finished medical school next year, I'm going to specialize in anaesthesia.

She's a legend now, a reminder of the dangers of vanity, mentioned by grim parents every time a daughter wears too much makeup or starts a new diet. If the problem had occurred during an appendectomy or a cyst removal or a kidney transplant, the parents would see things differently. But it was, they say, a frivolous operation.

Elsa was not a vain person when I knew her. We attended elementary school together, went to the same birthday parties, saw the same movies. She was an ally: both of us were fat. The boys used to tease us, but not in the same way they teased the pretty girls. We chose not to see the difference. We talked about which boys we liked, which ones we would marry.

In Grade 5, I saw the cutest boy in our class looking down Elsa's shirt. We were making string art, and Elsa was leaning over a black piece of plywood with nails pounded into it in the shape of a five-pointed star. She was winding turquoise thread from one protruding nail to another. I had gone to the teacher's desk to ask for another colour of thread, and when I turned around, there was Darin Myers, staring across two rows of desks into the space where Elsa's blouse had come unbuttoned. She had no breasts, of course. From where I was, I could see one brownish nipple not much bigger than a boy's. Yet Darin gazed, holding his breath.

I told her at recess, in the bathroom. She clamped both hands over her chest.

"He saw me?"

"I think he was ... excited, or something," I said. "He just kept *standing* there."

"God," she breathed, fumbling with the buttons. When they were fastened, she patted the front of her blouse back down and leaned over to look in the mirror. Her pudgy face was so red her freckles were invisible. I had thought she would cry or even faint, but instead she was grinning at herself.

"What're you smiling about?" I said. But she wouldn't tell me.

Last term I did a placement with a cosmetic surgeon in Vancouver. One of our patients was Nathan, a male model who displayed the gracious confidence of a man fully aware of his own beauty. His features were symmetrical, his skin taut, his eyes dark and steady. Whenever I glanced at him, his lips peeled back to unveil luminous teeth.

The surgery Nathan wanted would be his eighth cosmetic operation in eleven years. His agency wanted to have scars from previous surgeries removed, and to have his cheekbones raised to suit the current fashion. He signed the waiver, said he understood the risks. It was part of his job.

I'm ashamed to admit that he was attracted to me. And I to him. Of course it didn't develop beyond juvenile banter, a lingering pause when our eyes met, a readiness to smile. But still, the belief that he liked me was enough to distract me from my work. I spent more time than necessary going through his file, studying before-and-after photographs from each of his surgeries. In the beginning his face had been narrow, with a thin wedge of a nose and a receding chin.

Just before the surgery, I visited him on the ward. He was sitting up on the bed, curls of black hair sticking out from the neck of his hospital gown. I sat in a green vinyl chair by the window and looked over his charts. I wanted to tell him about Elsa, to ask him why he could get away with eight of these surgeries when she couldn't have one.

"What's it like," he asked, "putting people to sleep for a living?"

"I'm not an anaesthetist yet."

"Right." He swung his bare feet idly. The ridges in his ears were curled in a perfect spiral, like the inside of a seashell. His second or third surgery had been an ear tuck. I wondered if it was possible to shape ear ridges surgically.

"Tell me about *your* job," I said. "How does it feel when everyone's staring at you?"

He shrugged. "You're a beautiful woman—you should know. People stare at you too, only you don't get paid for it."

The mask closed over Nathan's face and the oxygen hissed into his windpipe. Dr. Pindar made incisions where the edge of the hairline met the temples, down in front of the ears, and along the curvature of the jaw. Then he peeled back the corners of the face. A pale film of fat gleamed on the underside of the skin. Bands of dark, striated muscle tissue and glistening white tendons were laced around the bone structure.

The flayed human face has always repulsed me. I had seen enough cadavers and textbook illustrations. I shouldn't have been surprised at the apelike musculature of his jaw, the snarling corners of his muzzle. But I was. I hadn't considered that he would be anything but beautiful.

19

Dr. Pindar once saw me reading a copy of the cosmetic surgery brochure he gave to prospective patients. It contained before-and-after photographs of rhinoplasty, liposuction, breast augmentation and other procedures. The subjects were ordinary people. There was the woman with saddlebags on her thighs, the man with protruding ears, the ageing cosmetologist with crow's-feet. In the "before" photographs they quailed, tried to shrink the defective parts away from the camera. In the "after" column they had not become beautiful, but their demeanour had changed. They smiled thinly, like rows of Mona Lisas.

Dr. Pindar had come to the outer office looking for the receptionist, and he found me standing by the desk instead. He studied the brochure from behind my shoulder, breathing a mixture of musty pipe smoke and Clorets past me.

"Doing your homework?" he said.

"Sort of."

He moved in front of me and sat down on the reception desk. His hands, dark on the backs and light on the palms, lurked around his mouth. "Do you want to have something done?"

He smiled, and the Cloret snicked against his teeth. He fixed his eyes on mine. Even though I knew he wasn't looking at my body, I felt scrutinized in a way I hadn't felt since childhood. I was no longer overweight, but at that moment I was ashamed of my awkward, drooping breasts and the fleshiness that remained on my thighs. He would see my body as a flawed thing, in need of tucks and augmentations.

"No thanks," I said. I turned away from his gaze and placed the brochure back on the desk. He laughed, loud enough that some of the patients in the lobby looked up from their magazines. He patted my shoulder three times.

"You don't need it," he whispered.

As he scuttled back down the hall, I remembered what was so disquieting about the way he had looked at me. It was the same way my mother used to stare whenever I told her the kids at school were calling me fat. She would look directly into my eyes, blocking out her view of my body. Her face would show no tension, except for the cluster of wrinkles pinched between her arching eyebrows. She would hold me in her eyes for several seconds while she formulated the lie. "You're not fat, sweetheart," she'd say. "You're just right."

It took me all of Grade 6 to realize that puberty was stretching my body. At first there were only pains. I limped, and I wore tensor bandages on my wrists. Elsa was in awe of my pain—she winced with me, and I could see my own desperate grimaces reflected in her face. Sometimes she massaged my ankles with her chubby fingers.

I began to study myself every day in the bathroom mirror. I was troubled by the side effects—the beginnings of breasts, the first hints of body hair. But I was ecstatic when I noticed I was getting thinner. "It's really happening," I told Elsa. "It'll happen to you, too!"

In the following months, Elsa's body did change. But I could see from the beginning that it wasn't the same as what was happening to me. She was turning into a larger version of her former self, with breasts and hips added on like afterthoughts. She knew it too. I could tell by the way she looked at me.

The next year I skipped a grade, and I became part of a different group. I grew my hair long, the way my mother had always wanted. The boys began to play elaborate games with me—hiding my pencils, erasers, combs.

In high school, Elsa's body was still too large to be attractive. She tried diets, she tried swimming, but they didn't have much effect. Her breasts were balloons that swayed in front of her when she walked. Her arms and legs were marbled with cellulite. She did have a few girlfriends, but for some reason they all seemed to look like her. The boys made jokes about them, dared each other to ask them out.

When I heard about the operation, I hadn't seen Elsa in four years. I went home for my summer break, and instead of asking her parents if I could visit, I walked past their house every evening. After more than a week, I saw her in the rocking-chair. She was alone, so I took a few steps toward her in the long grass.

Her eyes were hidden beneath pale puckers of skin, and they didn't seem to pick up my movement. Yet I was sure she could see me. The blankets over her chest undulated in time with her open-mouthed breathing. Her lips were scaly, and her tongue hung out over her lower teeth like a damp sponge.

"So?" I said, my voice too high. I watched the movement of her chest for a change in rhythm, but it was hard to tell. Thick bundles of skin encircled her neck like ornaments. There was no evidence of a shape beneath the blankets.

I hated my body for the way it contrasted with hers. I didn't deserve my slim legs, my dainty fingers. And yet I knew this body was what I had dreamed of as a girl, what Elsa had dreamed of. What if I hadn't become thin?

"I would have had one too," I said, meaning the operation.

I cried there for a long time. Elsa's mother came out onto the porch and looked at me for a minute, then she went back inside and left us alone. I wanted to believe that Elsa would communicate with me. But she didn't move, and her eyes remained hidden. Maybe she didn't even know I was there.

Finally I started walking home. Night was coming. I thought about Elsa's last seconds before consciousness. When she felt the cold anaesthetic travelling up her arm, was she thinking of the journey into darkness? Or of how it would feel to wake up, changed?

When I was young, my mother used to sing me to sleep. I don't remember the words to the song, but I know it was the same one every time. The melody rose steadily, and every phrase ended on a high note, as if the whole song was a series of questions. She sat on my bedside in the darkness and I could see the silhouette of her face against the light that came through the half-open door.

The melody swirled in my head, climbed to a dark place behind my ears. I allowed my eyes to roll back into dreaming position, and I let my body relax until it was numb. Then I seemed to be floating away from the music and from my mother's warm body. As I succumbed to this drifting, I tried to control its direction, to steer the dream toward my coming transformation.

Recovering

Jake looks out his uncurtained window at the young men painting the west wing. Two of them are using brushes for the delicate spots, and the other is following with a roller. The bright yellow paint is not appropriate for a building that houses grey old people like him. He prefers the milky brown they're covering up.

He hears the throb of Mrs. Dillon's television through the wall. Watching her soaps again, no doubt. Who needs relatives to keep track of when there's so much happening on tv? Sometimes he wishes he had a tv, even a little black-and-white, to keep him company. He and his wife Helen used to have one, but it stopped working just before she died, and he didn't have the energy to fix it. He could afford a new one now, with the money from the sale of the house. But he would have to ask his niece Donna to take the money out of the bank. She has so many questions whenever he needs money.

He hears the rumble of footsteps in the hallway, then a knock at the door.

"Mr. Anderson?"

Today is a weekday, which means the home-care nurse is bringing his hot noon meal. He isn't hungry, but he goes to the door and opens it anyway. A white-uniformed young lady is standing in his doorway with a smile clenched onto her face. She's a new one. She has a green tray in one hand, and her hip is cocked to the other side to balance the tray.

"Hi," she says. The smile intensifies until her eyes become creases. "I brought your hot meal. I'm just coming in to check that everything's all right. My name is Laura."

He moves aside and she steps into the suite. She puts the tray down on the kitchen table, then performs a pirouette as she inspects the room. She says something as she turns, spraying her words into the corners. He doesn't hear, but pretends he understands. He nods in case it was a question.

24

"Mail?" he asks.

"Sorry?"

"My mail."

She shakes her head. "I don't bring the mail, just the food. You can go down to the end of the hall and get the mail yourself. It's just at the end of the hall."

Her eyes stray toward his bottle collection on the window and remain there for several seconds. The harsh outside light makes the coloured ones glow coolly. He wonders if she's counting them, if someone has asked her to find out if there are any recent additions. It would not be beyond Donna to do that. She would think he was stupid enough to add the new ones to his collection.

"Well, everything's okay," the nurse says. She peeks into the bathroom, and he hears her flush the toilet. He turns away in shame, pretends to be looking back out the window at the painters. Her heels tick on the linoleum behind him, and he hears her pick up yesterday's tray from the kitchen counter.

"Be sure to eat everything," she says on her way out. "Goodbye."

"Goodbye," he says. The door closes behind him.

The last nurse brought the mail for him—or *someone* did, a visitor maybe. But he can't recall having any visitors in the past few days. Even Donna, with her weekly cleaning and interrogation sessions, has not been here for quite a while.

He decides he will get the mail himself. It's just down the hall, like the girl said, and he wants to prove to himself that he can do it. He finds the keys and stuffs them into his pocket, then goes out into the hall and closes the door behind him. He moves along the wall with his right hand on the railing.

He advances toward the common-room, where several ladies peer at him from behind fans of playing-cards. They stop talking when he approaches. They're still suspicious, still wondering about his motive in the incident with Mrs. Dillon. There was of course no motive; it was a simple mistake. If anyone was to blame it was Mrs. Dillon herself, for leaving her door unlocked while she was parading around in her girdle.

He keeps his eyes on the upcoming doorway and tries to block the ladies out of his field of vision. They're nothing but gossips, just like all the others who have blamed him for his drinking, his messy house, even Helen's death from cancer. Everyone wants him to reform.

Donna even talked him into going to an alcoholics meeting once. The speakers there talked about recovery as if it was a place. A guy named Gordon told everyone how miserable his life had been, before his arrival at the straight and narrow pathway to recovery. Gordon now had a good job and was back living with his wife and kids. Every day is another door to open, he said, another challenge. Nobody can open those doors for you.

After the meeting Jake told Donna, "The only thing I need to recover from is age. Can they help me out with that?"

The porch is alarmingly sunny, and his head feels weak. He fumbles in his pocket for the keys, then finds his name on the third mailbox from the end and tries to insert a key. It doesn't fit, so he tries several more until one of them turns and the aluminum door pops open. The only thing inside is a blue slip of paper advertising a new kind of denture adhesive. He lets it drift to the floor.

He needs to rest, and decides he should go outside. He opens the heavy glass door and walks to the west side of the building, where a thin shadow leans out from under the eaves. His head begins to stabilize as soon as the shadow overtakes him. He lowers himself to the grass, then leans back against the building.

He remembers red wine mixed in a tumbler with Coke: the way it fizzed when the Coke was added to the wine but not when the wine was added to the Coke. The syrupy taste, the smoothness of it in the back of his throat—he calls these memories, but wonders if they are something stronger. He has no wine now and no money to buy it. Donna has kept him broke for as long as he has lived here.

There was a time when he sat in a homemade lawn chair in his backyard and drank as much wine and Coke as he wanted. Helen sat across from him with her knitting. He recited poems he had memorized as a boy, or he sang old songs. Sometimes he just speculated about the weather. When it got dark and the whole yard was thrumming with crickets, Helen helped him to bed.

It's hard to recover the good memories now that he lives here. Donna has never understood this. When he lived in the house, everything reminded him of Helen: the warm cinnamon smell that had sunk into the wood of the kitchen cupboards, the sunlight in the dining-room on clear mornings, the lurching din of washing-machine in the porch. These things touched off memories in him hundreds of times a day.

Now he recalls only the nightmares. He's tried to erase the memory of Helen's fall, but it keeps coming back. She had climbed up and down those cellar stairs for 28 years, knew the sound each step made with a footfall, knew the exact width of each board. Yet once, when she was bringing a bottle of wine up for Jake, she fell. People said later he shouldn't have let her climb those stairs. But the doctors told him it was a dizzy spell, the first symptom of her tumour. He couldn't have done anything.

There was the hollow sound of her body on the wooden floor, the clashing noise of the bottle breaking. He ran to the cellar door, where he saw a thin leg sticking out from under her dress. He scrambled downstairs and saw the green shards of the wine bottle, a few pieces clinging to the sodden label. Her head was tucked under one arm, like a sleeping swan. He knew he couldn't carry her up the stairs, was unsure if he should even touch her. A swan asleep. The doorway hung above him, curtained with yellow light.

Across the courtyard he can see into some of the apartments. The only signs of life are the tv sets, all of them tuned to the same station. Young people move in unison across the screens, talking earnestly and sweeping their arms in extravagant arcs. If he bought a TV he could be just like all the other tenants, sitting in their reclining chairs and peering in on the lives of strangers.

That's how they forget, he supposes. It doesn't take long for the people on tv to become more important than your memories. He's noticed that the tenants here don't talk much about their families, their personal histories. Maybe tv characters are more interesting, or maybe they're just easier to talk about.

He doesn't want to lose any more of Helen than he's already lost. He isn't sure how much of her is left in him, and he's almost scared to test himself, to find out. Sometimes all he can bring up is a static image of her, standing by the petunia bed on the south side of the house with a watering can, or perhaps younger, scrubbing vegetables in the porcelain sink of the farmhouse they left in '62. She doesn't speak, doesn't even look at him.

He decides to go back inside, but when he tries to stand up he hears a tearing sound as his shirt comes away from the wall. He reaches for his back. The paint is half-congealed like an open wound, and a glob of it sticks to his hand.

"Christ!" he says, and then louder, "Jesus!" He glances around the courtyard for the painters, but doesn't see them. Without stopping to wipe the paint off his hand, he lurches up into the sunlight. His legs move under him, out of synch with this body. He hears breathing from far away. It's too loud, too rasping to be his, and as he reaches for the door he looks back to see if the painters are following him. Still no-one.

He skirts the card party, looks down at the pattern in the carpet, tries to keep his back turned away from the ladies. But the paint is bright as a flag. He goes past doors with numbers on them, but no names. Above the numbers, peepholes peer out at him. He reaches the end of the hall, then comes back one door, two doors, three doors.

The number in front of him is 117.

He hesitates. He can't afford to be wrong again. When he opened the door on Mrs. Dillon, he had mistaken it for his own apartment. He remembers the look of her generous flesh against the tired white of her underclothes as she lumbered from the kitchen to the bedroom. Her skin had been stretched like dough and dropped back into that sorry clothing.

He can see sunlight at the far end of the hallway, past the mailboxes. It paints luminous strips along the segmented bannister and fuzzy patches on the rows of doors. He turns toward the light and places his hand on the railing.

Helen had a beautiful nightgown, white linen embroidered with white flowers. She wore it in the living-room sometimes, even in the afternoon.

Digs

Too bad I'm not majoring in archaeology, with a place like this to study. There's decades worth of filth in here. The floor is carpeted with a mixture of grease and dust that looks like wet velour. The light patches on the tile show where the furniture was, before the fumigators came in and dragged every bed, chair and couch off to the dump. The fridge—which we've only opened once—is webbed inside with purple and orange spore clusters, some of which were sucked into the room during the five seconds the door was open.

I heard about an archaeologist who did a study of American garbage dumps. I should give him a call. I've been keeping a list of artifacts, the way they do at real excavations. So far I've found six bandaids (all used, one with a black scab stuck to it), countless semicircles of fingernails (both bitten and clipped), hair from all bodily regions, mucus in several forms and a half-empty tube of cream marked "for yeast infection."

With a decent lab you could find out a lot about the people who lived here. Their genetic makeup, their diet, daily habits, relationships. It's all a matter of how hard you look.

The only benefit of this job is, when I'm scraping sludge out of a stove or repainting a ceiling or cleaning a toilet, I'm free to think about whatever I want. Lately I've been thinking about the woman who works in the confectionery down the street. For some reason, all this filth and grime makes me want to be with her. I don't even know her name, but I make one up—maybe today she'll be Alice or June or Yvonne.

I don't fantasize about my ex-girlfriend Stacy, even though I saw her yesterday in a pair of cutoffs that barely qualified as clothing. Her legs were the colour of smoked salmon, her hair was oppressively blonde. My throat dropped, like something heavy was sliding into my stomach, and I think I made a little grunting noise when I saw her. I don't know if anyone heard.

I was too busy watching the fringes of denim dangling between her thighs. She was walking to her new boyfriend's house, which is just across the street from here, and she didn't even see me standing at the window, scrubbing the oven rack with steel wool.

The former tenants of this house just up and left. Didn't even bother to take the food out of the cupboards. They were gone for two months before the rental agency realized they weren't coming back.

The neighbours, if they know anything, aren't talking. I've been trying to figure out the disappearance for more than a week now, but all I've got to go on is the archaeological remnants and a handful of bills that came in the mail, addressed to Terence Dixon.

Our foreman Randy is not impressed with my research. He told me people disappear all the time in this neighbourhood. We get paid to clean houses, he said, not play detective.

Alex, the pre-law student who in my estimation will never be able to drop the "pre" from his title, is cleaning the kitchen window again. This despite orders that we do the windows only when everything else is finished. His behaviour confirms my suspicions about the relationship between dirt and sex. His nose, chin and hands are smeared with grime, yet he's signalling out the window to his girlfriend Irene. He sprays the vinegar bottle once, then dabs at the glass with a clump of paper towel and smiles at her.

I can't see Irene, but I know she's hanging around in the back alley. She's in high school and gets a spare class at 2.30, so she's usually here before coffee. Then, when the rest of us go back to the shop for doughnuts, the two of them walk to her aunt's place and do whatever there's time for.

I chew my own fingernails, comb my own hair, pick my own nose, and dispose of the evidence without a grimace. You do it too, I suppose, and so did the Dixons. But you don't know what it's like to pry off a baseboard and find somebody *else's* fingernail, or blood-encrusted bandaid, or other bodily excretion, waiting there for you. It's not the same when it's not your own.

Alex and Irene are in the basement. Randy took the afternoon off and left Alex in charge. I can't hear anything right now, but a few minutes ago I heard a flurry of giggles. He's giving her the scenic tour, showing her the pile of dead beetles we found behind the furnace.

Benny and I are in the living-room trying to think of something to do besides clean the fridge. I offer him a cigarette and he takes it. We stare out the window and bounce our smoke off the glass in long breaths. Stacy's new boyfriend is out cutting his lawn. She'll likely be over to see him soon.

I tell Benny my thoughts about the confectionery woman, but I'm careful to leave out any mention of dirt.

"She's married," he says flatly. "Had twins last year."

Two oscillating cones of smoke extend from his nostrils.

"Nice body, considering," I say.

"Yeah."

"I just said I'd like to, anyway. Not that I'd be able to. Just imagining, you know."

"Yeah."

Benny squints across the street at Stacy's boyfriend, who's putting his lawn mower back in the shed. This new boyfriend is always arranging, cleaning, fixing. I, according to Stacy, am quite different: I am a disorderly person who thinks too much. This must mean the new boyfriend is an orderly person who thinks just the right amount.

It's quiet downstairs, too quiet to make it prudent to check what Alex and Irene are doing. I switch on the radio so we won't have to hear anything.

We're peeling tiles off the floor—me, Alex and Benny. I've got the tiger torch, which is really a flame thrower that's been brought into civilian usage. Yellow and blue flames shoot from the nozzle like from the throat of a dragon. The whole assembly is connected by a ten-foot rubber hose to a propane tank in the middle of the room.

I open the valve, and the tiger torch hisses fiendishly. I aim it at a tile in front of me and the flames spread out. Little pieces of paper, dead bugs and other small flammables ignite and disintegrate almost instantly. When the tile starts to bubble, I move on, and Alex pries it away with a flat-ended crowbar.

Under the tiles is a tar that's so black it looks clean. No dirt could be this dark. Our feet stick to the tar, and it sounds like we've got velcro on the bottoms of our shoes.

"Check it out!" Alex says, pointing at something outside the living-room window.

We look out and see Stacy stepping out of her newly painted white Chevette. She's wearing the bikini I bought her almost a year ago, a pink and purple one that's cut high on the thighs. She has a shirt on over the top, but we can see as much of her ass as decency would permit.

Alex walks to the master bedroom and yells out the window, "Nice ass!"

She's going up the front steps when she hears this, and she stops with one foot above the other. She turns around with half a smile on her lips and looks through the living-room window, directly at me. I'm standing here with tar on my face, flames snorting out in front of me and the torch hose curling like a tail behind me. A vision straight from hell.

She recognizes me. She's not as frightened as you'd expect, considering she already thinks of me as her own personal demon. Nor, though, is she amused. Her face crumples into disdain—a mass of creases and white lips. She turns away, pulls the shirt down over her ass, and opens the screendoor. It slams like a guillotine behind her.

"Hey, Jerkoff," Benny says to Alex. "That used to be Eldon's girlfriend."

"Really?" Alex comes out of the bedroom, ripping his shoes from the floor, and puts his hand on my shoulder. "Is she really as hot as she looks?"

I point the flames back at the floor, close to Alex's feet. "I don't remember," I say. I smile at the particles exploding like tiny fireworks on the tile.

Detritus is a word for dirt. It's what we get when our bodies wear down. The stuff that rubs off has to go somewhere. Did you know that seventy percent of household dust is composed of dead human skin? Right now you're inhaling someone else's body.

Dirt is death.

I go in to buy a pack of cigarettes and there she is, right where I expected her. She's sitting on a stool behind the counter, fenced in by a collage of multicoloured junk food packages. She's wearing a navy blue sweatshirt and baggy grey shorts. Her dark hair is pulled back in a barrette today, and this allows a better view of her pale green eyes.

"I'll have a pack of Viscount Kings," I say.

She doesn't reach for the cigarettes, she's busy picking at a piece of dry skin on her arm. She looks like the type that sunburns easily.

"You should use sunblock lotion," I say. She realizes I'm watching her, and she stops picking. She gets up from the stool. As she reaches above her head for the cigarettes, her sweatshirt hitches up, and I catch a glimpse of the loose, waxy skin around her navel.

She tosses the pack on the counter, and I flick a rolled-up ten toward her. She rings it in, unrolls the bill and tugs on it to keep it flat, then puts it in the cash register.

"So how come you're always around here?" she says, while handing back my change.

I point. "Working over in the rental units. Cleaning them out."

34

"Oh, yeah." She sounds almost interested. I hope she'll ask me about the dirt so I can have something intriguing to tell her about.

"Student?" she asks.

"Yep."

"What're you taking?"

I should lie. What's a good lie? Pre-law?

"Philosophy," I say.

She's looking at me like I said "cannibalism." I should have lied.

"Oh, yeah...." She moves a box of green liquorice shoelaces back into place, then pulls out one long strand and swings it around in front of herself. It whizzes by, almost grazing her lips.

"So what do you philosothize about?"

Philosothize. Philoso-thighs? Was that a hint? She's uncrossed her legs now, and I notice that her thighs are uncommonly thin.

"Oh, things-in-general," I say. "Sex. Dirt. You know. Theories about everything."

I roll my eyes and she smiles, skeptically.

"Sounds pretty weird to me," she says. "What're you gonna do when you're done?"

I take the time to pull out a cigarette and light it while I think about this.

"Clean rental units," I say.

She smiles and nods, but I can tell she feels like shaking her head. She makes herself busy again, shuffling and reshuffling the junk food like a Vegas dealer.

"Oh, shit, I'm late," I say, before I can even look at my watch. And I am late, it's after 3.30. "See you!"

"Yeah," she says.

I'm going down the steps, taking a final drag of my cigarette before I have to start running back to work. I've failed again. I still haven't got her name.

We've wiped out the Dixons. This house is completely renovated, just waiting for the next tenants to come in and wreck it. The only thing left to do is remove the tiles from one downstairs bedroom, which we forgot about because it was covered with the canvas drop sheets we use for painting. I, being the only volunteer, get to do the tiles all by myself.

When I've finally dragged all the equipment down to the bedroom, I spot a daddy-longlegs spider in the corner. I light the torch as quickly as I can. It's cruel, I know, but the way these little buggers ignite is fascinating. All eight legs burn from the outside in, then they curl into a tiny fist and poof! they explode like popcorn.

He's running along the side of the wall, and I think I can get him. Shit. I miss, and somehow I manage to scorch the wall. The new paint is blistered and smoked in a six-inch-long stripe. And now the spider disappears into a space between the wall and the floor. I go over there to see if I can flush him out, but he's long gone. There's a triangle of tile broken away where he escaped, and something circular is wedged into the black space. I aim the torch at the object for a few seconds, but it doesn't burn. I move the torch away and pry at the floor with a key. The object pops out and I see that it's a coin, a penny, with a hole stamped in the middle.

And I thought every last trace of the Dixons was gone. Here's a real treasure they left behind. I pick it up and try to wipe it off on my pants. It's almost too hot to touch. Most of the tar on the back comes off, but there's still too much junk on it to make the date visible. Around the hole I can see a profile view of George V. The drill, or punch, or whatever it was, brained him neatly.

I put the coin in my front pocket and get back to work on the tiles. The metal feels warm against my leg for a long time. I wonder what I'm going to do about that mark on the wall. To hell with it, I say. This house could use some character.

I knew my mother would come into this somewhere. I'm thinking of her when the coin touches my tongue, remembering the way she used to warn me about money. It's the filthiest thing, she used to say. You never know where it's been, who's been touching it. Diseases get transmitted on money.

I turn the coin over in my mouth, push the tip of my tongue through the hole. The taste is bitter, metallic of course, but with a smorgasbord of other elements too. Tar, dust, Mr. Clean. And something else—sweat? I must be imagining this. How could I possibly distinguish all these things?

Irene says she knew one of the girls who lived in the Dixon house: the eldest daughter. She was a tangled beauty with thick black hair and russet skin. Her eyes were the colour of tar. Irene can't remember the name but that's okay. I've smelled this woman for weeks, tasted her presence, inhaled her. I should be able to uncover any sign she's left, track her by odour if I have to.

She wore a perforated coin, tied around her neck with a leather cord. It nestled between her breasts, absorbed her body's warmth, wore itself smooth against her skin.

Her sisters believed the coin was the sign of a witch. Her peculiar beauty, which continued to increase even when she didn't wash herself or brush her hair, made them sure. They blamed her for every misfortune—their colds, stubbed toes, lost pencils. They plotted ways to get rid of that coin.

When their father told them one evening that they'd have to move away early the next morning, they knew the coin was responsible. That night, the second-oldest took a pair of scissors to bed. When her sister was asleep, she padded across the room and snipped the leather cord. But as she eased the coin away from her sister's throat, it slipped out of her fingers. It chimed on the tile and rattled into its place.

There must be other signs, and I'll find them. They'll lead to another basement room, littered with crumpled garments, papers, bits of food. Dusty light will stream through the window onto her bed. She's asleep, dreaming of her talisman.

A rust-coloured arm is sprawled outside the sheets. I place the coin in her palm, close the fingers around it. I brush my lips against her face. She wakes up, shifts her head to look at me. Black hair unravels on the pillow.

She's a darkness moving beneath me, around me, inside me. I purse my eyes nearly shut. Things dissolve.

MARILYN GEAR PILLING

Son of Night, Brother of Sleep

My sister says she was at death's door that afternoon, but I always think of Death as being separated from us not by a door but a river. I ask her if she really means door.

"Yes," she says. "I see Death living in a colourless house in the side of a hill. You can't tell there's a house there. Just the door, and not until you're right in front of it. There's no buzzer and no door handle and no peephole, but Death knows when you're there, and he opens the door and takes a deep breath. That sucks you in."

"I even know the hill," she continues.

"Where is it?" I ask.

"You know that gravel road at the east side of the farm. You know how the hill goes straight up and there's a bush on both sides? Down there, in the bush, in the side of that hill."

"I see. You could have told me this before, Rita. I've been up that hill alone many times at dusk. I even played in that bush when we were kids."

My sister Rita is a doctor. She's had three husbands, no children. I have three children, no husband; we always make a joke out of that. I'm happy about the way it turned out though; my three kids are what I'll give thanks for on my deathbed.

Rita's short hair has the burgundy shine of old French wine, and it clicks into place like a metronome when she moves her head. My sister went into medicine to defeat death. When she talks about the latest advances in medical science, she says "we." "We know now that cancer is many diseases." She practices up north, in the little town near the farm where we spent summer holidays and weekends as children.

Rita is not usually fanciful. At this moment, we are talking on the phone. I am wearing a housecoat that was dainty rose blush when I bought it, but now is plain faded puce. As Rita talks, I'm twisting my face under the light and plucking the

black hairs that are taking over my chin with the relentless-
ness of Leiningen's ants.

"Yes, well, as I say," Rita continues, "I was at death's door
when our mother came out with this. Trust her to do it then."

"What did she say?" I'm thinking of having electrolysis
done, but there's a satisfaction to the tweezer's thrust and tug.
Somehow it's more than hairs I'm rooting out.

"It was last Sunday afternoon," says my sister. "I've got this
fever of 104, maybe 105, I'm sitting there with three woollen
blankets around me coughing my guts out and wondering
whether I could have AIDS, and Mom says—'Oh, you know,
Rita, for the last six months or so I've had this funny sensation.
Especially when I walk any distance. This sort of pain, not
really pain, this feeling that goes right up my arm and into my
jaw. My throat burning too. I wonder if I should mention that
to the doctor sometime, do you think?'"

"What has she got?" I ask, putting down the tweezers. I
would be doing something like plucking my beard at a time
like this phone call seems it's about to turn into.

"Classical angina."

"What does that mean?"

"Given what is already wrong with her heart, it means she
won't be around more than two years at the very most."

I don't see Death as waiting for us behind a colourless door. I
see him in a ground mist on a far shore making scarecrows.
He's stuffing them with straw, dressing them in the clothes of
the new arrivals. Some of the scarecrow bodies are crosses,
crosses on which the clothes of the dead flitter in a little wind
that twists in and out of the ground mist from the four corners.
Some of the bodies are round—stuffed plump with straw. One
scarecrow is pregnant, a great straw belly hanging low over a
belt whose long dangling end makes her look as if she has a
penis. One is a small child, limbs of stuffed pink stockings, a
tinfoil-pie-plate face.

41

I see Death straighten and get into his hot tub. He is lolling there on the far shore of the wide river, scalding his bare white bones in the steam. Son of night, brother of sleep.

Bare white bones. Our skeleton. Hidden under the epidermis, gradually revealing itself as our bony prominences proclaim themselves to the world. Death slowly becoming visible as we age. The other day someone told me about a physiotherapist who can put her hand on a person's flesh and feel their skeleton. Know all its secret turns. Know death. I saved that anecdote for Rita. I think she went into medicine to know Death, as well as to defeat him.

Death lolls in his hot tub and sends his boatman across for us. Like in the myths.

I suppose these days the boatman might be hooked up to a Walkman that's blasting into his ears a Chili Pepper tune like "Suck my Kiss." He might be driving an outboard motor with a bumper sticker that says, "I don't date anyone who uses four letter words like Don't, Stop or Quit."

But I like to think he's a half-naked guy in an old row-boat. One of the seats is loose and you nearly tip the boat sitting down. It's night, of course, but there's enough moon for you to see his shoulders and arms, and you hunch behind him and watch his muscles get huge and then relax, watch his muscles breathe like the plastic cover of a Harley Davidson filled and deflated by one of those trickster winds. You start to smell his sweat about two-thirds of the way across. There's no deodorant where he comes from.

You smell his sweat and every now and then you feel a stone scrape the bottom of the boat. This river isn't so deep in spots. Some of the water from the oars comes into the boat and baptizes your scalp. I said he was half naked; I didn't say which half. All he's wearing is a grey muscle shirt. He stands up, and the boat goes back and forth like D.H. Lawrence's rocking-horse. His cock is bobbing like a teasel in an east wind. You shove the broken seat off to the side so it sticks out over the water like a ragged wing, and you have one last fuck down there in the tepid water in the bottom of the rowboat, rocking now like you did where you began, in the cradle of your mother's womb, drifting off course, cold water slurping in over the sides and biting at the edge of the mortal coil you're about to shuffle off. You come with an apocalyptic shudder.

Then you sit up, and there's the shore and Death way off to the left clattering out of the hot tub, rubbing his bones dry with a toddler's pink sleepers, shaking the creases out of his black cloak.

Saturday noon two weeks after my sister's call, I walk into our mother's apartment up north. She has my father out of the nursing-home for lunch. They sit across from one another, a loaded plate in front of each. "We commend this food to Thee and ourselves to Thy service, for Christ's sake, Amen," says my mother.

My father used to be the one to say that. Now his blue eyes stare straight from between the rigidified muscles of his face. He doesn't know me today, any more than do the vegetables that startle me with their technicolour clarity against the white plates. August tomatoes, red as the medieval hospitals for victims of St. Anthony's fire. Bright green lettuce. Half a roll, buttered yellow. Pork chops stewed in apples. My mother finds cooking difficult. She has worked all morning to prepare this food, then gone through the laborious process of bringing my father out of the nursing-home. She is sitting there with a hollow doll across from her, eating with it, pretending it's real. The TV on low to provide the talk.

"Come into the back bedroom," says my mother now, as she clears the table. Her voice is more animated than it has been in years. "Rita brought me two new outfits from her trip to the city last week. I don't know which one to keep." On her way into the hall, she bangs her toe on the doorstop. "Oh *ouch* that hurts!" she says. "If there's something to kick, I'll always kick it!"

A week ago, Rita phoned me and told me our mother had

been told her prognosis by the family doctor. "What do you think her reaction was?" Rita asked.

"I wouldn't venture a guess."

"Well," said Rita. "There's been a spring in her step ever since. I'd forgotten she could be so chipper."

Halfway down the hall to her bedroom, my mother turns around and faces me. "I've been thinking about my funeral. I know what you'll want, Vivian."

"What will I want?"

"You'll want me laid out in the coffin for everybody to gawk at."

"Actually, you're right. It'll be hard for me to believe you're dead if I don't see you."

"Oh I knew it. I *told* Rita that's what you'd want. I knew you'd want me up there on view. Well I'm not sure, Vivian. Your dad would want a normal funeral if he was able to say. But I might fool you all and get myself cremated." She turns and flounces into the bedroom.

On my mother's white bedspread is a cherry suit jacket with pleated skirt. The other outfit is navy and white. "I'm leaning toward the cherry," says my mother. "The skirt's a little short, though. I don't want to look like Barbara Bush."

"Who's that?" I say.

She wheels around with her mouth open, then realizes I'm joking. "Go sit with your father; I'll be out in a minute."

My mother has never worn cherry in her life. Inside her castle, a prosecutor. Out in the world, Jenny Wren. Beige blouses. Grey coats. I remember the time Rita and I were sitting on her patio, and Rita passed on to me the comment of a friend. "You mother is almost a saint, isn't she."

"Did you do a BM or the other when you were in that bathroom?" I answered Rita that day, in my mother's voice.

"The other," Rita said, hanging her head.

"I never saw anybody that could do either so fast. You must wait until the very last minute to go in," I replied. Rita and I have lots of scripts like that down pat. Our mother's choicer comments. "A saint," I howled that day. "Oh my God!" Rita and I rolled our eyes.

Rita is my baby sister. I was seven when she was born, and my parents let me choose her name. I love Rita as much as anyone on this earth.

My mother moved into an apartment up here two years ago so that my dad could go into the nursing-home in the town where he was born and where my sister is the doctor. Stripped of her little kingdom, the house she tended and rarely left in 40 years, my mother turned into Jenny Wren inside her new place as well as outside. Or maybe a tiny brown fieldmouse.

The first time I visited her in the apartment, she asked me to move away from the living-room window. "Why?" I asked.

"The neighbours might think you're staring at them." She got up and pulled the blind.

She put her piano on mute, used the TV only with the sound off, stood up and said, "Oh shush, please shush," if we laughed. A month later, she'd moved the phone from the living-room to the back bedroom. "I wanted to get it away from the front door," she said. "Mr. Hope can't hear what I'm saying back in there."

Mr. Hope is the superintendent for the four-unit building. I pictured him crouched outside my mother's door on his arthritic 60-year-old legs to hear her tell Rita and me over the phone what was on her grocery list.

"People up here go till they drop. I know what they're thinking. They're thinking I just shoved your father in the Home because I couldn't be bothered any more."

"Mom, they're not thinking that at all." My mother is 73. She kept my father at home until exhaustion altered the very contours of her face. She got up for him three or four times a night the last year.

"Oh yes they are. I know what they're thinking. I can't even go out to the fowl supper, among people I've known all my life, without getting, 'My, George was looking good when I saw him last week.'" My mother's face twists into a know-it-all leer as she relates this.

"Mom, they don't say it like that."

"Oh yes they do, I know what they're all thinking."

The farm is deserted now, but Rita and I go out every time I come up from the city. We'd never change a stick or a stone, and we'd never sell the place to strangers. Summers on the farm is where we had our happy times.

It's not just the memories from our childhood the place holds. I can never go up the gravel road at the east side of the farm—the hill Rita joked that Death lives under—without remembering the conversation Rita and I had there a couple of years ago. It was spring. There were a million dandelions in the ditches. We were near the top of the hill when Rita said it.

"My kid would have been grown up and away at University by now."

I stopped. My jaw must have been resting on my knees. I stared at her. I'll always remember exactly where I was when Rita said that. It's how everybody knows where they were when JFK was shot.

"I told you about that, didn't I?" she went on. "I was pregnant when you were. You were 27, I was twenty. My baby was due the same month. August 1973."

I still couldn't speak.

"I was in first-year medical school. I had an abortion. There was no way I could have a baby and become a doctor. Stop looking like that, Viv."

My daughter with a first cousin her age. My sister a mother. Me an aunt. The world swerving and crisscrossing.

"Rita, you never told me."

"I was sure I had. Stop looking like that. It was a long, long time ago."

46

This evening of my noon-hour visit to my mother and her cherry suit, Rita and I have been out to the farm. We're driving back into town along the ninth line as far as it goes before you have to turn right or end up in the river. On our left a huge red sun has just gone below the horizon, leaving behind the fire of a pure orange light in the west sky and fields. I like to think of orange as red somehow tempered by the yellow of understanding. The cattle in the fields to our left are humped black shapes. On our right, a full white moon and utter darkness.

"Stop the car, Rita."

Rita gives me a quick look, then pulls over into the long grass of the ditch, grey now with fine silk dust, and turns off the car. Both of us get out. Country smells of hay and wet wildflowers and gravel and grazing animals. A thousand crickets and one low cry from a cow to her calf. The orange light. The immense moon.

I stand for a moment in the middle of the gravel road, then move over and put one arm around my sister. "Rita, you're a doctor. Stop everything right here, right now, just like this." Rita doesn't answer. I hear the cattle methodically pulling up the grass and chewing away at it.

I lay my head on my sister's shoulder, "Rita, I don't want her to die." Again, Rita says nothing. I wonder if she's about to cry. I wonder if I am. Then for some reason I remember the day Rita cut her hair.

Rita's hair wasn't always smooth and burgundy. It was blond and unruly and down to her waist until one day a few years after she started up her family practice. Rita went out in the morning and had her hair cut short and dyed. Then she came home and went to bed with a bottle of wine. She drank all the wine and she cried all that day and most of the night. She wouldn't speak. Her second husband told me that. He said he didn't know what to do. He phoned all their friends to see

47

if anyone knew what was wrong with Rita.

The ditch beside this road is full of wild carrot. Rita still hasn't spoken. Silently I remember a day when I was around five years old, my mother telling me the fancy name for this weed—Queen Anne's lace—and helping me and my cousin make a bride's garland for our hair. The ants crawled out of the white petals onto our faces. Like those black beard hairs even now emerging onto my chin.

"Smell the river," says Rita.

"Yeah," I shout, whirling her around by her arm. "Want to go down and have a threesome with the boatman?" Rita knows my death fantasy. She laughs, and the two of us dance a jig, right there on the deserted country road. "Come in your muscle shirt and catch us if you ca-a-a-n!" I holler, as we get back into the car. "You'll find we two are a h-a-a-andful!"

The cattle are all stirred up as we pull away. Bawling and sticking their heads through the rail fence.

In her fifteen years of family practice, my sister has encountered Death only once outside the walls of the hospital, and that was earlier this summer. She tells me about it when we get back to her place after dancing our jig, and the way she tells it, I feel as if I'm there.

"Remember how the first two weeks of July were this summer?" she says. "Remember how beautiful? Just the way I remember those long ago summer days on the farm. No clouds, that huge blue sky, the red sunsets every evening, and the strangest thing of all—no bugs. Everybody was talking about the weather. So perfect it was unnatural. Like a dream almost. Day after day. Like living in a never-never land.

"On the Thursday of the second week, the ambulance went out Code Four. Code Four means you expect the worst. We got everything ready in Emerg. We waited and waited. Then we got the signal that means whoever they went for is beyond help. A few minutes later comes the call that the mother wants her own doctor. That turns out to be me.

"The mother is Jenny Malone. Forty years old. I delivered her twins three years ago after years of fertility drugs and failure. She was the best, most careful mother you could imagine, Viv. Everything you could do to make a farm safe for children, Jenny and Doug did it. Jenny never took her eyes off those twins. That's the first thing she said to me when I got out there to that beautiful, prosperous farm of theirs on the fourth concession. The fire trucks and the police cars and the ambulance were all lined up down the side of the lane and along the gravel road. The neighbours had her on the couch, in the kitchen. 'I never took my eyes off him, Dr. Rita. I was looking right at him when it happened.'"

My sister is drinking wine the colour of her hair as she speaks. She sets down the glass and leans forward. "They were such good parents, Vivian," she repeats. "They couldn't have been more careful of those twins. They went to extremes."

Extremes. Into my head comes the old Arab tale about the last act of evasion being the final twist that delivers you into the hands of Fate. I've always been fascinated by that story. *There was a merchant in Baghdad who sent his servant to market. The servant returned, frightened, and told his master he had seen Death in the marketplace and Death had looked at him in a threatening way. He begged his master to lend him a horse so he could ride to Samarra and avoid his fate. After he was gone, the master went to the marketplace. He saw Death there and asked why Death had threatened his servant. "I did not threaten him," Death answered. "I was merely expressing my surprise. I was astonished to see him in Baghdad, for I had an appointment with him tonight in Samarra."*

I don't interrupt Rita's story. "They'd rented a machine that digs postholes, Viv. It was standing in the corner of the barnyard. Craig went up to it and climbed on it and it fell over and crushed him. Doug had to use the tractor to get it off him. There was no way that machine should have moved, Vivian. It was solid as a silo. The police and the firemen were hanging from it when I got there, and they couldn't make it budge. Craig weighed thirty pounds. He was three years old."

"What did you do, Rita?"

"I sat with Jenny for a while and then I went out to the barn-yard to see Craig. Craig's corpse. Somebody'd brought a blue towel from the house to cover him. That was all it took, he was such a little gaffer." Rita pours herself another glass of wine. Her third.

"The thing is, Viv, no-one is with him. Jenny's in the house, Doug's with the police, somebody's taken Donny to the neighbour. I go and sit by Craig until the undertaker gets there. It doesn't seem right, leaving him all alone. It seems like something of him is still there."

I'm picturing it as if I'm God. The cloudless sky and the bug-free barnyard. No boatman this time. Death himself over by the tractor wearing the helmet that makes him invisible. My sister beside the small patch of blue, her head bowed, the July sun creating an arc of burgundy flame across her hair. And there, circling overhead like birds in waiting, two forms I can't make out at first, even though I'm God. Circling round and round and round in that never-neverland blue, like something out of Chagall. My eyes follow the forms until at last they come into focus. Rita's long blond hair and the child that would have been twenty this month.

Mid-September, I'm up from the city for another visit. Our mother has moved her phone back into the living-room. When I tell her I'm going with her to church, she says we'll have to leave a bit early—she's shaking hands at the church door before the service. Friday evening she washed dishes with the other ladies after the church social, she says. That cherry outfit has been seen at the hairdresser's, at the post office, at church, at the nursing-home and at her cousin's, all in the same week. My mother's got a definite date with the Son of Night, Brother of Sleep, and she's finally free to live.

"I can't believe it!" I say to Rita, as we drive out to the farm Sunday afternoon, goldenrod high in the ditches, the trees already beginning to turn.

"Don't forget perversity's always been her presenting characteristic," says Dr. Rita.

When the boatman comes for *our mother*, there'll be no shenanigans, I tell my sister. He'll have his pants on, a clean white shirt, maybe even suspenders. The rowboat seat nailed down solid. Death'll be standing tall at his gate with his black cloak pressed and fastened all the way down with sprigs of wolfsbane from his garden.

His garden. I describe it to Rita. Elephant garlic and dead nettle and wormwood along the fence. Rue, its blue-green leaves giving off that strange, acrid scent. Hyssop with its sharp, bitter taste. Horehound and wolfsbane and creeping thyme. Our mother'll be weeding Death's garden before she's ten minutes off the rowboat, and it won't be weeds she's pulling. It'll be sloth, ungodliness, gluttony, unrighteousness. Her angina gone, she'll root them all out in jig time, as she would put it.

Then she'll set to work ironing the clothes off the scarecrows' backs. She'll get at them one by one—the pink blouse of the child with the pie-plate face, the emerald maternity top of the pregnant lady with the penis, the red plaid shirt on the chubby one nearest the gate. She'll set the iron on high, deftly turn the garments this way and that, press them perfect till the humid, beneficent billows of steam rise up to rival the ground mist and finally overcome it, till the horehound lies down with the wolfsbane and both slowly raise their withered limbs in a gesture our mother will see as defeat.

Like Her Sole

When Lizzy was fifteen years old, she was still galloping down a country road on a stick; even so, Mr. Erb was in love with her. Though its bark was long gone, the stick gleamed like blond flank of a palomino. A fork in the stick just where a saddle horn might be was what Lizzy gripped in her right hand as she rode down the gravel road past the cat-tails and the wild carrot and the cedar saplings. A polished knot in the wood below the fork rubbed her in just the right place between her legs. The binder twine reins were solely for the purpose of tethering her horse whenever she went indoors.

Summers and weekends on her cousin's farm was when Lizzy rode her stick. Home in the city the rest of the time, she dressed in long-sleeved blouses and checked wool skirts, white ankle socks and saddle shoes. Days she sat through a series of high-school classes, one unfolding after the other like the seasons—French, English, Latin, History, Geography, Gym, Math, then finally, last period of the day, Science.

On Friday, 26 October, 1962, Lizzy reached into her middle drawer and took out a garment wrapped in tissue paper. It was a Dalkeith sweater of dark periwinkle blue. Lizzy had babysat for almost a year to earn the money to buy this sweater. She put it on. This might be her first and her last chance to wear it. The evening before, she'd sat with her brother and her father listening to the radio as the Russian ship came closer and closer to the American blockade. The radio announcer said President Kennedy had alerted both the conventional and the nuclear forces of the United States, world-wide. The announcer said the world was on the verge of nuclear war. Lizzy's father confirmed it.

Lots of people had bomb shelters and stacks of dried food in their basements. Not Lizzy's family though. Lizzy's family had no bomb shelter, no television set, and no mother. They never had folks over. They never ate in a restaurant. They never went any place, except to Lizzy's aunt's farm.

Krushchev backed down and promised to withdraw the Soviet missiles from Cuba. The atmosphere of crisis disappeared and Lizzy entered her sixteenth winter. She did three hours of homework every evening, studied her textbooks and got As on all the tests and exams. She stood on the fringes of the groups of girls who gathered in the washrooms and halls and cafeteria to talk about boys and clothes and dates. Lizzy tried to look to anyone walking by as if she were part of the group. She tried to look to the girls in the group as if she were just standing there waiting for someone else, not presuming to be part of them.

Years later a psychiatrist will ask Lizzy if she would describe herself as shy. I used to be, Lizzy will answer, feeling the hot red rise from her chest to her neck to her face like tomato paste rolling up the sides of a measuring cup in defiance of gravity. Did you used to feel as if everyone was looking at you? he will persist. Yes, says Lizzy. Did you ever stay home from parties? Did you ever not answer your door? Did you ever not answer your phone? Yes, yes, yes, says Lizzy. The psychiatrist lays down his pencil and regards her as if she is the prize orchid at the annual show of the garden club. That is about as shy as a human being gets, Elizabeth, he says, gently.

These mornings of her sixteenth summer, her stick scraping along the gravel stirs up a billowy puff of white that follows Lizzy as a nimbus follows a goddess. Field daisies and wild phlox and chicory crowd the ditch; the summer morning air is flavoured with dew-soaked cedar and black muck from the edge of the pond that is hidden from the road. Across the ditch and down the slope to her right, large frogs emit the sharp thrum of their single notes from the borders of the hidden pond.

The person watching Lizzy these mornings on this deserted

country road is Mr. Erb. Mr. Erb was Lizzy's science teacher last winter. In the summer sunlight, Lizzy's hair is a shimmering, beckoning gold; it holds lights undreamed of in the fluorescent classroom. Mr. Erb is always present, watching Lizzy, marvelling at her activities, longing for her. There is always the possibility that Lizzy will come upon him suddenly—that he will rise from a stone beside the frog pond or step from behind a bull thistle or a tree.

Lizzy always knows when Mr. Erb is coming to her bed, the bed she shares with her cousin Em. There is the faint odour of a bunsen burner, a whiff of partly dissected cadaver, then Mr. Erb is standing there, his familiar white lab coat open over his short-sleeved, grey-checked shirt. Lizzy moves over so Mr. Erb can sit on her pillow, swing his feet up on the bed and rest his back against the wooden headboard. Then Lizzy gets on his lap.

Sometimes Mr. Erb appears before Em is asleep, and Lizzy has to sit very still on his lap, her finger against his lips, until Em gives those long snuffling sighs that tell Lizzy she's finally gone to sleep. Then Lizzy can put her face up to Mr. Erb's and move her body until they are as close as kernels of corn before shucking. She can snuggle against Mr. Erb's hands, which are now in her hair, now on her cheeks and neck. She can undo the three buttons on the front of her yellow nightgown and twist hard against Mr. Erb while his fingers touch her nipples till they stand firm and straight like crokinole pegs.

Lizzy's thirteen-year-old brother Peter and her fourteen-year-old cousin Emma also ride sticks, but their sticks are not blond, their sticks do not have saddle horns or knots. Nor is anyone interested in watching Em and Petey as they ride down a sunny country road. Lizzy's brother and her cousin change their mounts every few weeks or so. Lizzy has had hers since she found it shedding its bark on the forest floor when she was nine years old. Her horse's name is Mino. Nights, Lizzy stables Mino in her cousin's bedroom in case of horse thieves. Aunt Gwen doesn't mind. Winters, when they don't come to the farm, Lizzy wraps Mino in a blanket and lays him at the back of her cousin's cold upstairs storage room to hibernate.

At an age when some human beings are raising the babies they have conceived in parked cars or fighting in the wars their countries are torn by, Lizzy is robbing banks, watched admiringly by Mr. Erb. Every other morning, she and Petey and Em thunder on their mounts to the peeling red gate in the side yard. There they strip Aunt Gwen's lilac tree of more leaves, counting and stuffing the thick wilting stacks of forest green hearts into ancient billfolds they carry in their back pockets. Later, they pillage their Aunt's garden, pulling dozens of carrots and beets and onions from the long straight rows while she hangs out wash on the other side of the house. They stash the vegetables in piles in their fort among the bushes at the edge of the orchard.

Lizzy and Peter and Em do this morning after morning, until the mounds of dying vegetables encroach on the centre space in the fort where they crouch to make plans. The carrots are the first to die. The speed with which they curl into flaccid, grey corpses is amazing. Their grey is the grey of Lizzy's mother's skin when she couldn't wear her wig anymore and walked with a cane, before she went into hospital for the last time.

Lizzy's cousin Emma goes all summer in her bare feet. Not just in the house carrying the preserves and pickles from the kitchen to the swing shelf above the earth floor of the cellar. Not just through the burdock and across the dandelions to stand on tiptoe at the clothesline and wrench the wooden pegs from the stiff towels. Em goes in her bare feet to do the barn chores, to gallop along the gravel road on her stick, to wade through the creek, to run through the back field over the thistles and stones and cow pats.

Both Lizzy and Petey have had their hands against the bottom of Em's feet and both have granted it was nothing like touching skin. The bottom of Em's feet feels like the tanned hide of an old steer or like the tar-paper walls of the empty shack at the juncture of the sixth and the ninth concessions. Lizzy sometimes turns her own foot up and compares her pink and white and tender sole to Em's, so brown and leather-tough.

Afternoons, the three of them light fires. On this, Lizzy's sixteenth summer, fire-setting takes the place of afternoons at the creek. Em questions the substitution of this hot activity for the hours of swimming in the warm, dappled brown creek water. Lizzy tells her she doesn't like swimming any more. Em and Petey make a small fuss. Lizzy draws herself up the way Aunt Gwen does when Em goes outside without clearing the table.

Emma Gwendolyn McDowell Baxter, says Lizzy, I am telling you I am sick of lolling around in two feet of leech-infested bog. Now are you coming with me or not! Ever since their mother's death three years ago, Petey has been so anxious to stay on Lizzy's good side that Lizzy can subdue *him* with a look.

Lizzy has something she pronounces "ain" in her head, "ain" to rhyme with pain. She has seen this word in books. The books say there is no cure but cleanliness, and chocolate makes some people worse. Lizzy has washed until her face puckers like the waistband of the skirt she learned to gather in home economics, and she hasn't touched chocolate since the ain started. No-one Lizzy knows has ever spoken this word aloud and no-one has ever referred to her face. The ain is on her back and her upper arms too; these she can keep hidden. No more bathing-suits, no more scooped necks, no more sleeveless shirts in summer, no more blouses that will not button right to the neck. Ain means long bangs and long hair that swings forward over her neck and cheeks. Ain means swimming is a thing of the past. One of the best things about Mr. Erb is he never notices Lizzy's ain. He puts his hands in her long hair and tells her it is gold. Spun gold, he calls it.

Some nights Lizzy is wearing her two-piece, blue, shorty pyjamas. The second time Lizzy wore these pyjamas, Mr. Erb asked her to take her top right off. Then he asked her to get on her knees and hold onto the corner of the bed post, high over her head. She can just reach if she stretches. Her pyjama bottoms slide down to her belly button. Mr. Erb moves around in front of Lizzy and sucks roughly on her nipples, exactly the way it happened in the book Lizzy read in the public library last winter. This time, the fire that by day is in Aunt Gwen's pastures and by night is under the blue pyjama bottoms between Lizzy's legs, breaks into long shudders that start between her legs and move through her belly and over the rest of her body. After that, Lizzy curls into a satisfied circle and does not even feel Mr. Erb's goodbye kiss on her hair.

The matches are kept in a tin box affixed to the wall of Aunt Gwen's kitchen. The wood of the matches is blond like Mino's hide, thick and soft like the best kindling, the match head red and blue like the face of a turkey. Lizzy and Em and Petey light fires near the worn dirt path the white cattle follow to pass from their pasture to the creek. They light fires at the other end of the farm, where the ground is swampy and poison ivy is thick among the stumps and the thistles. They light fires in the dense bush that borders the hill in the east field. Lizzy and Petey and Em crouch around these fires; they count their stolen money, plan their holdups and wait to be caught.

They never are. Finally, Lizzy lights a match in her bedroom at home in the city. Labour Day Monday, the evening she and Petey return home from summer at the farm, the evening before Lizzy starts Grade 12. She lets the match burn to the place where it stings her finger and thumb, then uses it to light a cigarette from the package Em found beside a car at the farm auction a week ago. Lizzy inhales the smoke and her room swirls and lurches like a car on a hairpin turn.

Lizzy steps on the cigarette, wraps it in a kleenex and puts it in the toe of her saddle shoes on the closet floor. Then she runs the two inches of water she is allowed into the bathtub, and hurries downstairs for the iron. The bathroom door will not lock or even close unless the iron is shoved tight against it. Lizzy is no sooner settled in the water than her father is hollering on the stairs. Is somebody *smoking?* he shouts. His tone is just what Lizzy has imagined if he ever came upon her in bed with Mr. Erb.

Lizzy bends her knees and curls her arms around her bare self as her father bursts into the bathroom, knocking the iron across the floor to clang against the toilet. She puts her head on her knees and hunches around her shameful parts, feels her arms turn into the eight muscular tentacles of an octopus winding round and round and round until, like a mummy in its linen bandages, she is encased in a space where she is deaf and unreachable.

That night, in her unfamiliar city bed, the streetlight making the room bright as Aunt Gwen's kitchen, Lizzy gives herself to Mr. Erb. Take me, she says, lying on her back, pulling her yellow nightgown right off and opening her legs. I'm ready to go all the way. I'm yours.

What Lizzy is offering up is white and pink and tender, like her sole. It is round like the nimbus of dust that crowns her spun gold hair. It quivers like the belly of the frog in the hidden pond. It shines like Mino's flank after a long, hard gallop down a gravel road, and Elizabeth Bernadette McDowell doesn't want it anymore.

Tib

On the morning of her baby's first birthday, Tib awakens thinking about Ralph's belly button. How it was always lined with lint. How her first act on having sex with Ralph was always to remove the lint from his belly button. How if she'd known what was going to happen, maybe she would have kept all that lint. Used it to stuff a frog for the baby, Goosey. Just as she, Tib, still has one beer bottle of her daddy's. Her daddy, whose name had been The Belly.

From thinking about Ralph's belly button, Tib goes on to thinking about Ralph, and the events of one year ago. Later that morning a white convertible with the top down will stop outside the office in Fort Myers Beach, Florida, where Tib is talking on the phone. Ralph will be in the front passenger seat, and Tib will think that she has produced him with her thoughts.

The office is across the road from the beachfront apartments it serves. The office is square and dark, only a thin strip of ocean visible from its small front window. A ceiling fan clicks and sighs as it pushes the humid March air before it. Tib and her baby Goosey live above this office in a tiny apartment.

Tib is standing to talk on the phone. Her body is so strong and so flat you could turn it sideways and scrub clothes on it. Her orange hair is cut in bangs across her forehead and drops to her waist; her green eyes hold the light of a child who is at home in a tree. Tib's eyebrows and eyelashes too are an orange that is not quite of this world, the fringe of hair on a clown's wig. Goosey is crawling around the office floor. When the baby grasps the side of the counter and pulls herself to her feet, her orange hair sways and explores like the tendrils of seaweed at the ocean's edge across the way. She bounces and says, "Ma, ma, ma, ma."

At the wheel of the white convertible is a woman. The woman and Ralph get out of the car. Tib has not seen Ralph since he left her almost a year ago. He looks exactly the same. When the door to the office opens, Goosey crawls behind the desk out of sight.

"Hello Tib. I'd like you to meet Edi," says Ralph.

"Spelled with an 'i'," says Edi, shaking Tib's hand.

Edi is wearing a short, shiny raincoat fastened shut with sequined buttons. Edi's silver blond hair is held into a high ponytail by a wide black ribbon. The heels of her sandals are as tall and as thin as the legs of the white egret that hangs around with the pelicans across the road.

"We've come to see the baby," says Ralph.

"You never asked to see her before," says Tib. "Why are you here now?"

"Edi and I have a nice place all fixed up. I want the baby there half the time. She's my daughter too," says Ralph.

"You can't have her," says Tib. "She has a father already."

Edi puts her hand over her mouth and looks at Ralph. "Oh, sugar," she says. Tib notices that Edi's nails are painted silver and filed square across the ends. She imagines those nails next to Goosey's pudding cheeks.

"What are you talking about?" says Ralph.

"The baby has a father already. He has blue eyes, and he sits in this doorway every evening and guards the apartment. I feel sorry for anyone who tries to get by him," says Tib.

Ralph looks at Edi, who puts her hand over her mouth and giggles.

"I warn you," says Tib. "Goosey's father is not here right not, but if he was, you would see that he looks like a man who has sharpened five pencils to hard points, and is about to sit down and do his income tax."

"What?" says Ralph. Again, he looks over at Edi.

"Ralph," says Tib, "can I see your belly button?"

Ralph jumps backwards, clutching his front. He knocks into Edi, who teeters on her egret heels. He grasps Edi's hand and hurries her to the convertible. "I told you she's crazy," Tib hears him say, as Edi starts the car and pulls away.

"Ma, ma, ma," says Goosey, crawling out and pulling herself to her feet. Pieces of cobweb festoon her questing orange hair. "Ma, ma," she says, opening her arms to Tib. Tib sits on the floor beside the child. "Daddy," says Tib. "That was your daddy, Goosey. Your daddy. He wants to take you away from me." Tib picks up the phone with the long cord in case there are calls from tourists inquiring about the beach front apartments across the way. She carries the phone and the baby outside to the hammock in back. Tib and Goosey swing and sway, swing and sway. Tib is silent, for she is remembering her own daddy.

Tib's daddy had a belly like a table mountain. When he lay on the couch after supper, the belly rose straight in the air from his lowest rib, travelled flat for endless miles, then dropped off suddenly at his pubic bone. The belly button was a crater halfway along, a seeming haven for travellers weary of crossing this slithery, hairy, no-man's-land. But the traveller who rested there must be alert or be crushed beneath cold glass, for Tib's daddy was in the habit of sticking his beer bottle into his crater of a belly button. The bottle just fit. It made a pop each time Tib's daddy wrested it from its hole for a swig.

Evenings, Tib lived in a cave in a corner of the living-room. The cave was made from a moth-eaten wool blanket Tib had hung between two chairs that oozed stuffing along their arms. Tib could not remember her mama. She had the feeling she'd been born from her daddy's miraculous belly, maybe crept out of the crater some evening in between the pop and the swig, cleverly fending for herself even in the timing of her emergence into the world. Evenings, the tv flickered black and white, the beer bottle popped, and late at night Tib washed to sleep on the ebb and flow of her daddy's snore.

The belly was impervious to cold. Where Tib and her daddy lived, there were two seasons—winter and summer. Winters were the long season. Winters could burn you or bite you or kill you. Tib's daddy wore work boots, wool socks and shorts.

Nothing else. On winter days with a wind chill of twenty below zero, Tib's daddy pumped gas in his bare belly. He stood with the gas pump leaking its last few drops onto the ice, and talked with the farmer in the pickup truck for as long as the farmer could stand to have his window open. On all sides, the fields glittered white.

Tib's daddy was known for miles round as The Belly. Kids asked to come along when their daddies went to get gas from the pumps in front of the shack where Tib and her daddy lived. The fields glittered in the summers too, white with a light you couldn't face, the heat shimmering in a way that made visible the swimming, dancing world above the yellow grass and the hard soil. Summers could kill you too. People got prickly heat, they got sunburn, they got sunstroke. Occasionally they keeled over dead between the henbane and the chickweed.

Tib watched the kids from her summer cave—the same blanket now nailed to the trunk of the scrub willow at the north of the shack, and the wreck of a waggon beside it. She observed the kids looking at The Belly. She saw the fear and the scorn and the awe on their faces. Tib knew that she had special powers, she who had emerged from this magic belly that had the power to repel winter, the power to draw folk from miles around.

When the kids were gone, Tib swooned into the swimming, dancing world above the yellow fields and with her special powers looked into the future. She saw a man who was the opposite of The Belly. She saw a little girl of her own. She saw herself leaving this world of the killer summers and the killer winters.

Tib was nine years old when she awoke one morning in her winter cave to a silence that did not breathe. She tiptoed over to her daddy's side. The last beer bottle was erect on a belly that was now like the boulder beside the broken waggon. The streamlets that had flowed summer and winter across and down this table mountain had turned to icicles. Not breathing, Tib reached out and touched one of these rivulets of ice.

For an instant the room wavered like the mermaid's hand Tib had seen in the flickering evenings, and again came that feeling of swooning into the other world. She lifted the upright bottle from her daddy's navel, and returned to her cave. When a lady finally came to take her away, Tib hid the bottle in the sleeve of her winter jacket.

By the time Tib awakens from these memories, Goosey has fallen asleep on top of her. Tib carries the baby inside. Slip, slop, gobble, slop go Tib's feet on the bare floor. Yesterday, she wore these same slippers with the loose sole to the Mini Mart one block down the beach strip. "Slip, slop, *gobble*, slop," Tib said aloud in a friendly tone, as she passed a woman in the frozen foods aisle. The woman wheeled her cart around and hurried away.

Tib climbs the stairs and settles Goosey on the mattress in the corner of the one-room apartment. Then she takes from the cupboard a chocolate cake mix and slides the contents into a bowl. The buzzer downstairs rings twice while she does this, and twice Tib runs down the stairs to answer the requests of the tourists from across the road. One wants to know where to get ice; the other wants to stay on an extra week.

Several minutes later, Tib has the cake in the oven and is making chocolate icing. "You weren't any too anxious to show me your belly button this morning," Tib says aloud to the absent Ralph, as she stirs. "You *used* to like it when I asked to see it."

Up there in the land of the killer winters and the killer summers, Ralph had made his living travelling from farm to farm in a three-piece suit and glittering glasses, knocking on doors and showing the contents of his black case. Inside were tins of ointments—unguents for all conditions, even those bordering on the unsavoury. An ointment to moisten the lining of the nose, for instance. Weekends, Ralph came back to his mother's place in town. He knew Tib as the slim, freckled redhead who worked in the Five-and-Dime. He knew nothing about The Belly. He andTib kept company for a lot of evenings before Tib decided Ralph was the one she'd imagined in her summer cave.

On that evening, Ralph's mother was helping to serve the annual fowl supper in the church basement. It was winter. The window of Ralph's bedroom was a fantastic, teeming landscape of fairyland vegetation. Ralph and Tib got under the blankets because it seemed suddenly too cold to be anywhere else.

Ralph's shoulders were tiny and sloping without the padded jacket. His torso was narrow and round like a silo, his ribs like the silo ladder that started in the pungent black dirt and rose neat and unyielding to the top. Tib held her breath as she approached the belly button. She lifted the blankets so that the silver light could scintillate through the fairytale fronds full upon Ralph's body. There it was! Ralph's belly button was the size of a thimble. Then she saw that the belly button was lined with lint. She stared, feeling the same wonder that enveloped her whenever she stumbled across a nest in a bush or a tree. Who would have thought that Ralph harboured this cosy, round refuge only inches above the fierce bristles under which at this very moment such a commotion was in progress? At this moment, Tib knew that she would marry this man with the silo chest and the tiny, lined refuge. She hovered above the sweet nest, wondering whether to climb the ladder to Ralph's face or work her way in the direction of the commotion. She knew that together she and Ralph would leave this world of the two harsh seasons. They would start a new life in a milder land.

Goosey wakes up just as Tib finishes icing the chocolate cake. Tib changes Goosey's diaper and sets her in the middle of the kitchen floor. She lifts down the cake with its one candle and sings the birthday song to Goosey, who claps her hands and grins. One side of Goosey's face is red and mottled with the pattern of the mattress button. Tib blows out the candle and makes a wish for her baby. The wish is that Goosey's daddy will not take her away from Goosey's mama. Tib shoves the cake closer to the baby. "Here, Goosey, today is your birthday. Do whatever you want with this cake! I'm not having any. My stomach is too full of glittering glasses and silver nails filed square." Tib wraps her arms tightly around her body and crouches in the corner of the kitchen. She rocks back and forth, and watches her baby.

Again and again Goosey brings her hands down flat on the cake, spattering icing onto her belly, her orange hair and the kitchen floor. From the corner, Tib watches, reliving as she does so Goosey's birth one year ago in the Fort Myers Beach hospital.

On the white bed in the labour-room, Tib had lain alone on her back, and suddenly had seen her reflection in a shiny machine that stood beside the window. To her amazement, it was not she, Tib, on the bed, but her daddy. The same monstrous, magic belly. The same capacious belly button, this time thrusting outward into the world rather than collapsing into a crater. The same streaming rivulets flowing and rippling from the very centre of this magic table mountain to sprinkle and trickle upon all who approached. Tib stares into the machine, seeing her daddy-self contract and expand, approach and recede, almost expecting to see the child within emerge from her thrusting navel, or is it she herself about to slip cleverly into this world between the pop and the swig? She is crashing close in and grinding back out on the waves of her daddy's snores. Then a new force has her, and Tib hears herself growling like an animal whose name she does not know.

Moments after birth, Tib looks into the tiny heart-shaped face of her daughter and sees her own. "I know you," she says aloud. "I recognize you."

The baby contorts her face and opens her mouth in a jagged yawn. "You goose," whispers Tib. "You goosey, goosey, goose."

On the floor of the small kitchen of the Fort Myer's beach apartment is now a chocolate polka-dotted Goose. Tib is standing at the counter eating a piece of cake. For Tib has a plan. A plan that involves a cat. The same cat with whom Tib drove Ralph away one year ago.

On the third day after Goosey's birth, a baby with dark brown hair had been brought to Tib's bed. It had nursed eagerly, and grasped her fingers firmly in its tiny hand. My goodness, thought Tib, what an improvement in one day. Only yesterday, her baby had been almost bald, choking on mucus as she attempted to suck. This newly vigorous creature was doing a fine job of draining Tib's right breast when two nurses came hurrying into the room. They had the look of those rabbits that hung skinless and upside down in the Fort Myers butcher shop as they stammered that this baby on Tib's breast was Mario Di Pietro. Tib opened her arms for the wheezing pink bundle they now proffered. The nurses snatched the hairy, robust stranger and hurried off with him. This incident gave Tib her idea for surprising Ralph.

Ralph was away when Goosey was born. He had graduated from selling unsavoury ointments to selling real estate. Ralph had taken a course. He had done well, and now spent his time travelling around southern Florida with his boss making profits by selling untouched acreage for development. Ralph was due home a week before Goose was due on earth. Goose arrived on earth a week before Ralph was due home. Tib had one week to plan her surprise.

Tib's friend four doors down the beach strip was a breeder of purebred Persians. One of her cats was named Zara. On the day Ralph arrived home to see his new daughter, Tib asked to borrow Zara the cat. She dressed Zara in an assortment of gifts from her beach-strip neighbours: a frilly white nightgown with eyelet trim and silver ribbons, knitted pink baby boots, a flowered pink sweater and bonnet. Zara was utterly complacent. Even to Tib, Zara's flat white face and round blue eyes looking out from the pink bonnet seemed strangely human.

Tib's friend was happy to be an accomplice, and babysat the real Goosey on the afternoon Ralph was expected home.

Ralph entered the apartment. Squeaking and cooing, he tiptoed over to the couch where Tib cuddled the pink bundle. He bent down for his first look at his new daughter. The creature stared up at him, her blue eyes pure and steady, her whiskers long and wise.

Three days later, Ralph sat Tib down on the chipped brown kitchen stool. He stood across from her at the end of the counter. Ralph told Tib that when he looked into the creature's face, he felt like a bingo card—jolted so sharply that all the chips were dislocated from their squares. He said that he felt like that for a week. Then he paused and said that there was a part of him that would always feel like that. He moved so quickly that he zinged his funny bone on the fridge. He told Tib that he was leaving her for the woman who wrote the gossip column in the Fort Myers Beach newspaper. He'd been having an affair with her for nine months.

Tib bathes Goosey in the kitchen sink, where the water quickly turns chocolate. She dries the baby and puts on a clean diaper. Holding Goosey on her hip, Tib phones her friend four doors down. She asks her friend to allow Zara to live with Tib and Goosey. She explains her need to replace Ralph with a new daddy. Zara will be this new daddy. Tib will trim Zara's wandering antennae to short, pert bristles so that Zara looks like a man who is ready to do his income tax. Tib will set Zara in the door of the office to guard the entrance with her blue eyes.

Sure, why not, says Tib's friend. Zara can live there just as well as here. In ten minutes, Tib's friend is at the door of Tib's apartment with Zara in her arms. She hands the cat over to her new family.

Zara has been living in a basement with the other purebred Persians, where she pees on folded newspapers. Her fur smells of urine. Again, Tib fills the kitchen sink with water, and this time gives Zara a bath. She sets Goosey in the other half of the double sink, so she can watch. This is your new daddy, she tells the baby.

The water reveals Zara's body. Tib is surprised. The cat is no bigger than a baby squirrel. It is that long, white coat standing out around her face and body that give her her size and her presence. Like Ralph in his padded suit and his glittering glasses.

When the cat is released, she leaps from the counter. Followed by Goosey, she walks into every corner of her new home, ending by taking up her post in the office doorway. Tib watches the wisdom in Zara's long whiskers, and understands that she may not cut them down to bristles.

Late that night, Tib folds the last of a pile of towels and sheets from the beach front apartments across the way, and prepares for bed. She puts on her sleeveless nightdress, tucks her daddy's beer bottle into the warm nest underneath her arm, then slip-slops over to the corner where the mattress lies by the window. Zara's furry white body is stretched full-length against Goosey's; her paws are on the baby's cheeks, her claws folded away. Goosey's belly button is a crinkly white bud, swelling and twinkling in the Florida night above the edge of her diaper.

Goosey and her new daddy are breathing in tandem, daddy's rich round purr ebbing and flowing like the nearby ocean. Tib curls like a fetus at the end of the mattress, and through the night on their small barque, these three drift across the vast, midnight-blue underside of the world.

FRANCOIS BONNEVILLE

Reach

Kassee kooee, we Iroquois shout. Kassee kooee! Kassee kooee!
But the hairface in black will not do what he's told. He will not
go away. He steps out of his canoe to stand with his Huron friends.
The Hurons will die. Does this young hairface want to die too?
Those Hurons... One or two pump courage. The rest hurt the eyes
to watch them. What did they think? Did they think their birch
canoes didn't sit higher in the water than ours? Were we not supposed
to notice them? The ups and downs of their paddle arms in the pink
night sun?

The hairface holds black crosswood in one hand and a black book
in the other. We've seen these before. They are nothing. They are no
harquebus. When a soldier comes with a harquebus, he holds death in
a finger. No bravery in that. No feel of the enemy's skull cracking at
the end of your stick-strung rock. This hairface might only be simple.
Eating his heart might not give courage but some same stupidity.

It could be too that every hairface is stupid. They have all that
hair. Even the fur-traders aren't very smart. They might take off their
stupid wooden shoes and put on ours of skin, but they never know
enough not to let their tongues wander in the summertime. They should
wait until winter when the gods are frozen. Who knows what could
insult the Manitou?

Some things confuse, and other things don't. What to do with the
robed prisoner will call for much talk. We, the men who surpass all
others, will kill the Hurons the usual way.

—We will sleep here tonight. Tie the prisoners to that row of trees.
We will eat their foodstuffs now.

Two Hurons have hurt quietly all night. They will have their
hearts cooked apart, to feed their courage to Iroquois young. They die
alongside the others now, all of them their fingernails torn out, their
limbs broken, the mark of the hot stones on their sex. Those others all
whined at some time tonight. Their hearts might go to the dogs.

But the hairface. What to do? He showed no fear for himself while
watching the Hurons die. We teased him. We put hot stones on him.

But he looked like he was having sex with the sky. He confuses. Maybe he is stupid. He doesn't come to kill us, to steal from us. He doesn't want to trade with us. He only wants to show us his book, he says. As if the Manitou were kept in there.

—Ha-ha-ha-ha-ha.

We could kill him. But the hairfaces in black keep coming back the way dogs do. Maybe they don't know how much we hate them. They are ugly. We hate them.

—Somebody bite a finger off him. One from each hand. He will know not to come back. He will tell his brothers about the men who surpass all others.

The Iroquois sleep well all night. The moon is up. The nightwind warm.

This morning all corpses are slashed. On bellies. On buttocks. They are tied to rocks and dropped in deep waters. Ropes are left on them to pull them out much later in the season. For us to collect the shells in the gouges. The colourful shells. To make history bands. Trading bands. We must mark these waters.

The hairface sits in his canoe. We leave him here. He can do what he wants. He cannot keep up with us. His hands have stopped bleeding, but for now he is only downstream strong.

Maybe we should have killed him. We hate him. We spat out his fingers. They're around here somewhere.

In his bed back in Québec, Father Boudreau mused: This is truly the pristine land, and I was right to come. Forests here burgeon with rough-hewn souls. This is more than just the test of dreams.

He told Father Lalande: "I could have died. I would have died. I would have perished in such ecstasy if the sight of me invoking God's glory in my death could have bloomed one yearning in one red soul. If it could have caused one doubt about that Manitou."

At the supper table he mentioned to one of the lay brothers: "Each was like a cruel child, yet of as perfect a human form as I could have conceived. What men! What heathen! I will go back. Their paining was not pain but drink for my faith. Father Jogues says that he will go back, and he was their captive the winter long. The *Ongue Honwe.* The men who surpass all others. The test of them surpasses all tests. More than the Hurons who are not so tall. Not so haughty. Not so splendidly thewed as these."

When the lay brother had left, Father Jogues invited Father Boudreau to come sit next to him. He apologized for having overheard. He said that, yes, he would go back to the people of the long house, and yes, it would test his vocation to take on such a journey again. He agreed, yes, that Father Boudreau's avowed lack of fear would testify to great faith. But he wondered privately to him two things. He asked first, "Does your need to tell so much to every ear mean that you do own fear somewhere?" And then he asked also: "Could it be that Iroquois arrogance is bringing out your own in you? Is pride pulling you to them alone when a Huron soul would stand as tall in the only eyes that count?"

Father Boudreau thanked Father Jogues. He said he would supplicate wisdom to find out.

For three days Father Boudreau prayed—under the leaking roof by rain and under the walnut tree by light. He fished for smelt at the base of the cliff. He helped lame-handed with the weeding of the corn. The leeks. The beans. The peas.

Then when after Vespers he saw Father Jogues alone, he offered to him: "You were both wrong and right, Father. I did put faith above fear when tied to that tree; I worked the work to which I'm wed. But I'm just twenty years this season. If at the remembrance of that night, my blood chills such that I can't help but talk, I find no fault in that. About the *Ongue Honwe,* though, your words were sage. All souls are souls— none above the other. To right myself, as soon as possible and with permission, I would canoe instead up the Ottawa this time and west to Huronia before winter comes. I would guide Huron souls and force myself to forget for now the people of the long house and the elm-bark canoe."

The two priests knelt. Each prayed from his book. The river lapped its banks.

That night, between fitful sheets, Father Boudreau woke up to the orgasm of his dreams. This had not happened to him since he'd left Québec last time last month, yet here he found himself again, a pool of semen all over his thigh. And not from any throw of the hip but from the slightest of dreamtouch (palm to palm would do) onto any of these birdwomen, cloud-women, angels neither women nor men, whose close-pored skin glistened. Could these be tests from heaven's images? And if so, how could he do right by them? Wherefrom volition, he would wonder, daubing at his leg—If I'm not awake to weigh my choices out?

In Huronia at last, Father Boudreau learned that he stood no chance of guiding anyone's soul to everlasting life if he couldn't first keep his own self in shape. He could not eat. He could hardly walk. His robe seemed more of burdock than cloth. To the close-up smell of the dried fish-and-corn, he could only retch at first. But over the weeks he worked at it. He soon managed to keep some down. From his trip his feet were rubbed raw and bloody, but he traded a looking-glass for two pairs of moccasins. They felt too nice, almost. Too civilized. Strangely more refined than anything he'd ever worn before. As for his robe, he cut its hem at the knees. He saved the cloth for leg-wrappings.

More and more he wondered to himself, How will I ever learn this tongue? These heathen spin such a taciturn phrase. But Father Lacorne, the other priest in that village, did teach him as much as he could. Plus as winter came on and he left the rooms of his unheated church for the warmth of a village lodge, he saw these red men change entirely. Into actors all. Still too treacherous to seriously ignore, yet now gabby and clownish and wide-armed eloquent. But the lodges stank. The smoke worked at his eyes. On very cold days, the smoke hovered so caustic and thick that everyone burrowed his face into the ground. Each gathered sand to the sides of his cheeks and held it there with his hands. Breath could be possible then, but with no-one to kick them the dogs ruled the lodge. They soiled the prone at will.

At the church he watched what Father Lacorne did, but he couldn't abide by half his acts. The way this priest used the chime of a clock or shiny clothes to get the Indians to church. Why lie? Why call a magnet the Manitou? Or a magnifying-glass the firemaker of God?

No, he couldn't approve of such trick means, no matter how proper their end might be. So after celebrating his usual Mass to a practically empty church, he would enter the chaos of a lodge. The stench. The smoke. The young girls always reaching for his groin. (They would have gladly put their mouths on him. Opened up their legs for him. They did it for others all year long.) But Father Boudreau had no need of that. In his dreams he lusted after forms so angelic that by comparison a lodge full of Hurons without faith looked, sounded and smelled to him more like the barnyards of his youth. At all waking times his mind dwelled rather on the problem of how to teach what he knew. How to frighten these people with the torments of hell. Entice them with the joys of paradise. Render them such that their faith should pull them far more doggedly than their carnal sides pushed them now.

He would use no tricks, so he studied instead. He studied these thievish, lazy, inefficient men. How mean they could be, yet unpredictably considerate too, one time up and singing to him when they sensed his sadness so far away from home. He studied these women who burned up their pubescent years in rabid wantonness until, several fast marriages later, they sank ever-so-quickly into plodding tasks, hopeless, barrel-hipped drudges, crueller than the men, until death should find them too hardened to sigh.

But most of all he studied the tongue. He had to know exactly what meant exactly what, because, as he thought: How can I speak this phrase or that to teach of Jesus Christ?

These people don't use half my words. Their words are born of the forest. The cold. Sounds fix themselves first to what the senses detect. Only then can they fit to the mind's conceivings. Or is it only then that the mind can conceive? *Agnus dei.* Lamb of God. What use is this picture with no sheep hereabouts? Would a Huron rather say "Fish of God?" But fish are not tended but caught from the wild. Would the Huron rather say "Corn of God?" For corn is tended. But it does not breathe. It bears no young to noise and suck.

The hairfaces in black give us things. For that they smoke with us. They eat our food. We ask for soldiers and these come instead. Six soldiers in all of Huron country. In all Ouendake. *Of Iroquois warriors across the lake: two thousand or more. The forests are scarce of game.*

In all Ouendake, *six soldiers and twenty priests. Fine allies. They should defend us. They're the ones who made the* Ongue Honwe *mad. Without them we would never have attacked.*

The new priest. The one who calls himself Serge. At least he doesn't push himself on us. He has survived the Ongue Honwe *with only two fingers gone. He is stupid, of course, but he wants to know things. He asks. He asks. He is like a little boy.*

—So, if as you say, a woman cannot go anywhere when she dies, then is a woman more like a dog than a man?

—Ho, ho, Serge. A woman is not a dog. A favourite dog can go with a man. Hunt after a proud death.

—And the part of the dog that can go is the spirit?

—The spirit, yes. A good dog, we speak of.

—And a woman's spirit. Where can it go?

—Are you really that stupid? A woman doesn't hunt when she is alive. Why would she want to hunt when she is dead?

—Does the Manitou like dogs better than women?

—Manitou does not like. Does not hate.

—Can you see the Manitou when you die?

—Enough, little boy. Try another lodge.

The one who calls himself Serge. He doesn't hunt. He works with the women sometimes. He talks to them, but they laugh at him. Maybe he thinks he is a woman.

    —So, if a woman can choose who her man will be, does she wife more than one before she chooses?

    —Many. She wifes as many as she can.

    —Is Manitou a man or a woman?

    —Manitou is both woman and man. Manitou is all around you. Above you. Underneath you. Inside you.

    —And is Manitou good?

    —What do you mean?

    —Mee-hee. Mee-hee. Is the Manitou mee-hee?

    —We don't know what you mean.

Father Boudreau asked Father Lacorne: "I thought you said that *mee-hee* meant *that is good.*"

"So I've always thought."

"But could it just as well mean *I like that?*"

"It could."

"Then neither the *mee* nor the *hee* necessarily means *good.*"

"It could be not. Except that one likes what is good."

"But whichever word means *like* or *good*—Is it a verb or an adjective? And more importantly—Can one make a noun out of it? *Goodness* out of *good. Love* out of *liking.* Because that noun would mean God. Much more than Manitou or sky."

Father Lacorne was not a severe man. Balding. Thirty-five. He rested a kind arm on Father Boudreau's shoulder.

"It could also mean *This pleases me.* Which would bring us to *pleasure* for a noun (if nouns do avail). Heaven knows, pleasure is a dominant pursuit hereabouts."

"And we don't want the heathen to think..."

"...that the God of whom we preach..."

"...is one of pleasure only."

"Such is my thought."

"Still, there must be a way."

"Maybe there is," Father Lacorne mused. "Maybe you will find one for us."

"I pray that I may."

"Let us pray, then."

Father Lacorne made to kneel, but he stopped instead and stood back up: "Let me only add, Father, that after a few more years in the woods, you may conclude that *manitou* is in fact the proper word. Manitou is the spirit of everything. The mystery in it. All we need do is convince these heathen that the spirit that is in everything was once all in one man. A man so true that he died for us all. And that that man once taught us what we are now telling them."

"But don't such thoughts ring heretical, Father? You speak of pantheism, no?"

"Call it what you will. When spring comes, Serge, lose yourself in the forest and pray. Try it tomorrow, if you wear enough fur.—No. Don't. You'd better wait until spring."

Hunter of God? Rabbit of hawk? Rabbit of benevolent hawk? *Mee-kee tiang.* We will do that. Then *mee* must mean *that.* And *kee?*

Come spring, once the cherry trees had opened buds and the hepaticas had issued from the soil, Father Boudreau packed a meal for himself and proceeded to march perpendicularly away from any path he came across. He started before sunup, yet by dusk he could still tell where he was. Each time he thought he might be lost at last, he would either fall, surprised, upon some second path, or he would hear the voices of women gathering wood, or clawing one another, or maybe planting corn. All day the crows passed overhead, one bird advancing then calling for the mate: then jointly they rode the uppermost branches until one moved off again. The sole time Father Boudreau did lose his sense of track, he found himself all too soon mucking through reeds, and then right onto the shore of the bay. From a canoe smoothing by, Hurons bass-fishing laughed at him. He laughed along. He was busy with thought. But he registered their scorn.

As far as he knew, he couldn't lose himself. As far as he knew, this flank of the world had been too stamped already for such counter-design. Those crows overhead, their wing-thrusts insistent in the off-lake winds—No doubt they'd known about this mesh of trails. Hoofworn. Footworn. Between beach and glade. Past thicket. Through timber-stand. The crows' black laughter rasped cruel to him. No less cruel than the fishermen's guffaw. No less cruel than the long of winter. The cold of the bay on his now-drenched feet. What could Father Lacorne have meant?

"It comes to me," Father Lacorne said, as he heated more water to soak his friend's feet, "that by taking the right angle of established paths, you never really forget that they exist. This could or could not be a problem. Should you want to try again sometime, you might just head in one direction (other than south toward the Iroquois, of course (or west, what with the bay (or east, since that's the traders' route))). So, it's north, my good Serge. Head north, and for more than a day; and try to lose, not your faith, but all that is trapping to your faith—

"Oh, I'm probably wrong," Father Lacorner went on. "It just happened to me one time. A mystic visit, as other priests have mentioned having had hereabouts. Such a thing clears one's head of much that is decor. But there is nothing to say that it would come to you. I was speaking partly in metaphor, I guess. More water?"

"Pardon?"

"Is your pan getting cold?"

"Oh. Yes," Father Boudreau said.

He would have nodded assent to most questions right then. On its own, his mind had begun a slow rotation around two words: trapping and decor. For Father Lacorne had sounded just now like a more sedate, more mature version of what a younger Serge had been. How Serge had once ranted at his mother's trims. The churchly trapping of her. Hadn't Serge's vocation called him here (rather than in more comfortable France) because he'd thought that here souls would be waiting on his word with none of the ornament he'd found so encrusted everywhere back there? The decor?

How he had yearned to blow Christ's truth (softly, perfectly) into lungs that had never breathed before. Yet— irony of ironies—Father Lacorne was suggesting to him that somewhere undetected in his religious clothes, some Old World embroidery had followed him here. And not only that, but among the Hurons, and certainly among the *Ongue Honwe,* no lung had waited for his arrival before drawing breath.

Hereabouts paths had been fashioned long ago, where the land and the needs of the human had met. Paths fashioned throughout the common brainscape as well. Paths so tongue-worn into the language by now that only an outsider stood a chance to tell.

But which of the vestments in his baggage came trimmed? And which path was which? And what of the universe was what?

Any reaction right now would have been as into an airless room for him, so, rather than outright challenge his approach, what Father Boudreau did was drug himself with work. He began compiling his own Huron lexicon. He devised proba-ble grammatical rules. With Father Lacorne's blessing, he travelled to other villages in *Ouendake.* (Most like his own on high ground near a creek or spring; most surrounded by the same spiked, wooden palisades.) He visited the Huron tribes of the Bear, the Cord, the Deer, the Rock, and compared the little shiftings of speech. He met with a dozen other mission-ary priests: Brébeuf, Arbrevert, Lalemant, Bongagné. He traded notes and observed their methods.

Theirs were more like Father Lacorne's than his. Much of their rituals ran like mummer-show acts. Father Boudreau's own, by comparison, had stiffened if anything, so that what sparse attendance he'd been able to draw even shrank as he returned each time to the paces of his Latin Mass. But what to do? He felt he could never be an actor such as these. Or if he could, that he had no script other than the one he'd grown up watching once a week, and then studied so long to marry this, his bride, the church.

Ritual to him was something one did so the flock wouldn't drift. So that youth would learn the selfsame truths of spirit that old age prepared to attend. Up till now, he'd seldom paid more than abstract attention to the baptismal act, the Confirmation, the Mass. He'd seen these as actions repeated in a flow of time. Prescribed by earlier, more sentient types. Approved by prelates whose ears touched God.

He may not have understood every detail of them, but he'd always thought that he would in time. Or that if he didn't, it didn't matter so much. The fervour of his love was for the glory of God and not for earthly codings of it. What need had he to contest anything? He'd had no questions as he did now. His heart for it shrinking. The rote of it weakening him.

Winter returned, and with it the narrowed movements of all but the pike, the deep water muskellunge. Father Boudreau's lexicon was gathering form. Genera. Specific differences. Synonym lists spilling into the margins. But still! So few converted! He couldn't help but wonder what good he was doing here.

Father Lacorne and a few French *donnés* had built a rock fireplace in the living quarters, so with heat no longer a driving motive, it became harder for Father Boudreau to leave for the lodges with his ink, his birchbark and his tender quills. So little had changed from last year at this time. The bickering. The smoke. The same old pranks. His prayers would lapse for minutes sometimes, into reveries so mundane that he would double his sessions on his knees.

And then, at that time when the elder bushes showed their leaves once more, the raspberries budded, the violets flowered and the chervil stood out ready to cut: what should arrive to Father Boudreau but the very mystic visit that he'd tried to lose himself to before. It came unexpected. He hadn't sought it out. He'd been dragging a crude rake under bushes by the church, and one time like any other that he'd reached in deep to draw last year's leaves from where many stems tangled, it only took an instant, but for that instant it was as if a pane of the clearest glass had come unbroken before him. A pane that he couldn't recall ever having noticed break before. And then just as quickly as it had come together, it shattered back apart. But for that timelessness when the glass held itself sheer— What contentment. What delight. The bush itself looked no different at all, yet his understanding of it came from beyond all science, because, as he now knew, all that he had called truth before had been no more than a shard of it. One piece the most that his mind could have conceived at any one time, without beauty's own logic to broaden the plane. And now, though once again he couldn't hold it all in mind, at least he had seen what before he had only faithed. That a moment of grace could come to a person and draw all of the truths that lay scattered in his soul together. Humankind the slow-ripening image of this selfsame wonderment.

Father Boudreau rose from his underbrush stoop. He looked dazedly about. Had anyone else witnessed the same? It didn't seem so. People came, and people went. Dogs snarled over scraps. Father Lacorne's carnival voice kept up from inside the church.

Where he stood, on spring's blond tufts of grasses between the bush and the alleyway, Father Boudreau kneeled and prayed. He thanked God and let out a laugh.

He looked about once more, yet he soon withdrew into sheepishness this time when he saw that here in his corner of the *Ouendake* village, his laugh had sounded out louder than he'd thought. Louder than he'd heard it within himself. Because several women across the way were looking at him now with that blend of mistrust and amused disdain that they always reserved for the fool. And a boy of thirteen walked up to ask:

"Were you thinking of a funny thing, Serge?"

"Yes and no, I think. More a beautiful thing."

"Like a beautiful girl?"

"Something like that."

"Did she have a tight cunt?" the boy then asked, surprised as usual at how the simplest comments could bring on such looks from this man. All that hair on his face... Maybe the women were right.

There is less difference than one might think, between a life based on the belief that perfection exists beyond close reach, and one based on having reached it once. Though the memory might grant relief from doubts, it can also torment a person that any bringing back of perfection's raw joy is more a matter of chance than of will or work.

For all Father Boudreau could tell, so glad a sight might not return to him again until the moment of his death. And so, if he went back to his labours with greater resolve, it was not only because his vision had given him direction, but also because he still needed work's narcotic—this time to ignore his regret.

Either way too, he still had to believe. He might now have gotten what he knew from witnessing rather than from faith, but he still had to believe that glory so pure, although only now visible to few people for maybe one or two seconds of their lives, would one day be probable, and the next day commonplace—until that morning should come when all souls everywhere would slip their earthly coils and laugh into perfect light.

He had to believe that however he ordered the labours of his life, at least some tiny portion of them would shrink time waiting for humankind to produce characters more perfect than now. A common spirit more perfectly seen than now. This he always had, and always would have, to believe.

He still had to eat. He still had to sleep. He still had to squat once a day in the woods all summer and in winter over cracks in a lodge's planks. To the rhythms of no known moon or clock, he could still wake up to semen on his leg and the immediate recall of nebular dances, coy pursuits, glimmerin-the-dark attendants of God prancing slowly up to touch. He would always have these. Off and on. His whole, long, earthly life.

Which was not to say that this mystic visit made no difference to him at all. What it did, more than anything else, was reshape his intent. That is: although he kept up the same studies, the same painstaking recordings that he'd done before, now, rather than seeking a way to best fit the Indian tongue to the rites of Rome, what he did was reach one hand into the sky and drive the other into the soil. For his next seasons here, his only work would be to fit the celebrations of his church to the people and land of *Ouendake*. To marry the two. To create for all souls, whether red or white, the perfect ritual for the New World.

Yes, he swept away all doubts. He, Father Serge Boudreau, missionary of the land beyond the River of Cod, was himself one of those sentient types who could prescribe actions for all to repeat. Come each morning's rise, he prayed first for guidance, and next for humility, so as never to think of himself as anything more than God's hand here on earth. Because, as he thought, my work will announce itself so true to my vision, so good and beautiful, that the Pope will only have to see it once, and then ask God about it once, to approve.

"I don't know," was all Father Brébeuf would say. He was a huge man with the smile of a child. Everybody liked him so.

Father Lalemant was more known as a thinker. He mentioned, "You may be wasting your time."

Father Lacorne served his venison to all. He sat down and told Serge: "I am heartily glad that you were able to witness something of what I spoke. But to rewrite the Mass so that you can send it to Rome—That's so much more than what we're doing here."

To which Father Lalemant added: "All we've ever felt was that if a little theatre is required to keep the heathen in church, then so be it. You have to keep their attention before you can sow the seeds of faith. Once we have enough souls to form self-sufficient parishes though, we all intend to return to the entire Roman Mass."

"It's really not that complicated," Father Brébeuf put in, Father Lalemant continuing for him: "You see, civilization is working its way west through us, as it will through our successors. Soon all souls here will speak nothing but French. One man's actions can't change the flow of all of history, Serge."

"Would you have said that to Jesus Christ?"

"That's hardly fair."

"Yes. You're right. I'm not the Christ. But I am *a* Christ. As you are too. This is what I've seen."

Father Lacorne swallowed his food. "Go with God, then, Serge. And get plenty of rest. If you want to take on Rome with no family there—No friends—You'll need a long life, that's for sure."

"If they don't burn you first," said Father Lalemant.

"To the glory of God," said Father Brébeuf.

"To the glory of God."

All four drank water. They ate their venison, and then father Brébeuf and Father Lalemant left for *Ossossané,* the town the French called *La Conception.*

The one who calls himself Serge. he is more of an idiot than all the others together. He speaks better Huron than them, but what he says is stupid, stupid. He should stay with asking questions. He shouldn't throw firebrands into the air or the whole village might burn. He shouldn't wake the lodge up in the hard of the night by walking around and waving his see-through cup everywhere, filled with fireflies. He shouldn't heave fish into the morning embers if he doesn't want to eat them. Just to watch them crust all black.

He shouldn't shout out things like Ouendake *drowns in blood of Christ, or* Manitou *cooks his own heart for you.*

He scares the children. He is more like a bad shaman than a Frenchman priest. He has no hair on his face anymore. He plucked it

all. His face looked like a catfish's belly before the sun gave it brown.
Sick. Stupid. Dangerous priest.
Last week he put a handful of corn in a basket, and then he prayed
foolish around it. He said the handful should become seven handfuls.
It didn't. He tried it again yesterday. He kept saying, Drink the
sky! Eat the sun! *It didn't work. Today he smeared his face with*
entrails of trout. He dripped over the corn. He scared the children. He
is crazy, we think. Father Lacorne does not say yes say no.

"I mean just look at you!"

Father Lacorne turned to dismiss Father Boudreau's catechism class. He waved his arm in the erratic air until every last
Huron had left. Then he turned back, still waving, now in his
supposed partner's direction:

"Are you no longer a Catholic, or what?"

Father Boudreau looked hurt. He said, "Of course I am. I've
never been closer to God's work in my life."

"Then what in heaven—I mean, just look at you. First you
pluck your face, and now you trade in your robe for a breech-
cloth and furs—"

"My robe was torn," Father Boudreau said. He breathed out
of his nose, tiny tremblings within each push. "My robe was
tattered. It's getting cold. Furs are this season's cloth around
here. Why? Do you think Jesus minds?"

"Do I think Jesus minds... Do I think Jesus minds... What
am I supposed to think about you, Serge?"

Father Lacorne leaned against the wall. He calmed somewhat, then went on: "For years, you and I have been working
with these people. Cajoling them. Abiding by their every
hesitation as though they were does in the forest. And now. I
walk past your catechism class, and you're no longer teaching
the same as we others."

"I teach the love of God. I teach compassion in the face of
misery—"

"You teach a hierarchy of Gods, Serge Boudreau. The chief's

brother asked me yesterday why Christ, God's son, kept his foot on the god of cold for only half the year."

"He was confused."

"And today I overhear you promising something about a longer life on earth—"

"I promised no such thing. Someone was asking me what it was I could be talking to God about, everyday on my knees. I told him I prayed for the salvation of the Indian. For guidance in my labours. For the strength to see my vocation through. I was explaining that I can be weak, like everyone else, but that the only time I ask for something for myself, it's that I can live as long as it takes to witness perfection start to bloom here in the New World. Obviously it was too much for them. If I made a mistake, forgive me."

In 1646 word made its way to all French in Huronia that Father Jogues and Father Lalande, on their way from Québec into Iroquois country, were captured south of the big waters and killed. Their tortures, no-one doubted, had been long.

One summer afternoon when Father Brébeuf looked into the sky, he saw a great cross there. "Far away," he said. "Above the land where the men of the long house live." "How large?" asked a friend who didn't see a thing. "It's large enough," said Brébeuf, "to crucify us all."

In 1648 *Taenantaye,* called Saint Joseph, was overrun and destroyed by Iroquois Senecas. All inside the palisades were dismantled.

In the summer of the next year, while fishing for bass with two Huron boys, Father Boudreau saw fifteen deep canoes clear a point on the horizon of the bay. He and the boys quickly pulled theirs into the brush and watched from their cover as the *Ongue Honwe* skimmed by.

The boys couldn't wait to get word to their village, and Father Boudreau's excitement burned too, but his was for his own concerns.

He had heard no voices from these elm-bark canoes. They

hadn't come that close to the land. Yet he could tell. He could tell, just from their posture, that these were the men who surpassed all others.

Oh. Over the years. How hard he had tried to forget. But he hadn't. They hadn't let him. The *Ongue Honwe.* Only mention their name anywhere in *Ouendake* and all idle talk stopped. Plus now and then a captive brought to Father Boudreau's village for communal sport...

These times had been the hardest on the French. The torture times. The rabid crowds. At first priests had tried to save the Iroquois. But the hot veil of lust in each Huron's eyes, down to the smallest child's, had warned all whites not to spoil revenge. Even arguing for a fast execution drew a mix of scornful taunts, disbelieving laughs and snorts. In one of the Rock tribe villages to the east, one Father Chanceguy had tried to stand between the villagers and their thing of play. Before night was done, he himself had been laced to the stake, kept alive but then thrown beyond the palisades with no more than scars for clothes—his crude church bashed to the earth.

"We're only tolerated here," Father Lacorne had told Serge when first he'd witnessed such a prisoner brought in. "We don't have the soldiers that Québec enjoys."

Then, steering his partner aside, he'd gone on:

"It's not yet noon. The children will poke at the Iroquois for a while, and then they'll tire. The women will bring bonfire wood. Some will spit at him. Some will play with his sex. And then they'll prepare the evening's food. That's when you and I approach the chief. We give him a trinket, then we smoke from his calumet, then we ask for permission to baptize the Iroquois. Half the time he says yes, half the time he asks why we should do that, since the Iroquois hasn't studied Christ. We say that God will respect the chief if he lets all dead men have a chance to visit if they've proven themselves on earth. Half the time the chief laughs yes, that this soon-to-be-dead man will get a great chance to prove himself. Half the time he says no."

Over the years, then, every similar instance since, this is what the priests had done. Either they'd baptized the man. Or they hadn't. And then, either way, they'd withdrawn to kneel and pray outside the circle of the orgy of pain. This is what they'd done, Father Lacorne soon retiring to a tearful bed, but Father Boudreau remaining the whole night of Killing's drunkenness, most of him entreating God to take this soul as soon as he could, but some of him in constant awe of the *Ongue Honwe*'s mute pride until death. Such will, Father Boudreau would wonder. Here the man's tendons hang exposed from the frolicked ripping of strips in his flesh. And still he faces the hundreds with scorn.

Yes, then, this is what they'd done. The two priests. At first.

But then later on in his stay, after the reforming of his intent next to an everyday bush by the church, after having attempted so many actions and words, recording them, regrouping them: it came to Serge that when Father Jogues had suggested to him some five years back that it was his own arrogance drawing him to the *Ongue Honwe* instead of to the tribes of the *Ouendake*, maybe, just maybe, Father Jogues had been wrong. Maybe, instead, since God had known that Father Boudreau would be struggling in his quest for the New World's perfect rites, God had been guiding him for his test: not to these Hurons whose own sag-shouldered laziness could soon drain them from the earth, but rather to these other men, the ones above whom there stood no greater—no closer to corporal perfection.

"Thank you, oh, Lord," Father Boudreau prayed. Every conceiving had to be tried. He pondered, and he planned, and the next time a captive was tied to the stake, he knelt in front of him all afternoon. The Iroquois kept barking, spitting at him, but still Serge prayed that the man might not suffer, that something of his ritual might help. And then, when he and Father Lacorne were allowed to step up and celebrate their sacrament, Father Lacorne did so with water, but Father Boudreau did so with blood. He had filled his small wooden bowl with drainings from rabbits and a drop of his own. Now he tipped it over the Iroquois's brow. A sharp, red river split to make an island of an eye, to meld again and accent the cheek then stain the Iroquois's chest. Father Boudreau started out, "In the name of the Sky and of the cleansings of Grace—" but just then Father Lacorne turned to him and slapped the blood-cup out of his hand.

Serge had never seen Father Lacorne so angry, his balding brow so blue. Which was probably why he submitted so readily to him, letting him pull him by the arm, directly away and into the church. Neither priest looked back. Neither could have told, one hour later, exactly when the Iroquois had slumped. Exactly how or why.

All they would know was that once in the church, Father Lacorne had shouted and stomped and accused his partner of satanic intent. "What did you make? Some kind of a pact?"

Serge replied, "I'm saddened, Father. You know my devotion," and argument went on from there. One hour later they were arguing still. That was when the chief came in. He had many men with him—some young, some old—and every last one wanted to know right now how their *Ongue Honwe* had died.

The priests looked to each other.

They looked back to the chief.

Father Lacorne opened his mouth first. He bagan to insist that neither he nor his partner had harmed that Iroquois. But then Serge stood forward: "This is the work of the sky, all you men. I begged the sky, and the sky took the warrior. It was blood that cleansed the Iroquois for his journey. Yes. Here in the New World. Real blood is the drink of rite."

Father Lacorne's last words to him were: "I'm praying for you, Serge. Be quiet, please."

And then the chief had Serge stripped. They took off his moccasins. His cloth. The women blocked the village gate with a quickfire of the driest pine, while the children collected rocks to throw, and still others made switches from boughs. Then from the square the chief told Serge:

"You will run past the crowd. Through the fires. Beyond. You will do it as fast as you can. If not, we will cinch you to your Iroquois friend. Belly to belly. Very tight. To see which one of you will rot first."

When Father Boudreau, all blistered and bruised, showed up at the village of Saint Louis, Fathers Brébeuf and Lalemant took him in. They fed him. They washed the welts on him. They made up a careful bed for him. Yet not two months later, they had to sit him down:

"Listen, Serge," they said. "(We can't call you *Father* anymore.) Listen. We've watched you, and we think you're ill. We want you escorted to Montréal, but the Iroquois have the trade routes cut."

"Listen, Serge. The Hurons don't want you. They say you confuse their brains too much."

"Serge. Here's you choice. If you promise to stop preaching blood everywhere, then you can live with us, and we will care for you."

"You have to promise."

"We can't tie you up."

"If not, you'll have to go."

And so Serge went.

At Sainte Marie he lasted three weeks, and that because he spent much of his time outside the settlement, trapping small mammals for their hearts and blood.

Saint Ignace came next. He built himself an altar there, to the side of the village square. He carved vessels of wood for it. (By then he had pinpricks in all eight of his fingers. He gave one drop per day to the communal cup.)

It was in Saint Ignace that he hired those two boys to take him out to fish. None of the men wanted to go with him. Only the boys would accept his baubles.

In return they paddled for him. They reminded him more than once that the first rule of spearing called for no sound at all. Because he couldn't keep it up. He would either have to ask something, or try to explain, or else, without knowing he would talk to himself. He let his mind go where it would, as he did his gaze into the shadowbitten shallows.

And then that morning when he and the boys spied all those canoes—They spotted fifteen of them at first. But soon came twenty more. And then such a stain across the waters of the bay—All those pulsing little needles in the distance, dark yet glistening between the ripples and the sun, as if some mammoth rodent were swimming underneath, only the hairs of its pelt to see.

Serge and the Huron boys waited for dusk. Under the moon's tense light, they edged the shore until at last they passed a tall stand of pine, and beyond the next clearing they couldn't fail but see that awful aura in the sky.

"Saint Ignace," Serge said.

The boys could only stare.

"Let's get closer," Serge said.

Neither of the boys had any need to consult. In chorus they answered, "No."

To which Serge came back: "Then let me off at the shore."

The boys let him off, and after he'd watched them glide into the darkness, he turned back toward where the sky shone bright. This is it, he thought. Now I shall know how these *Ongue Honwe* will take to the rites. These perfect bodies. This New World.

For two days Father Boudreau stalked Saint Ignace.

The first night he approached as far as he could until the noises of slaughter grew too loud for him. Too rude for him. Too sad. Under a thicket he prayed for them all—both those killing and those being killed—and then sometime before morning, he slept.

Ongue Honwe woke him up. The sounds of them. Their easy talk. They must have been on patrol to secure the countryside, but they didn't seem to care whether or not they could be heard. They were so many. They bantered and they poked. Some gruntish. Some giddy.

Only after darkness did he hazard to roll sideways out of his thicket and rub the cold out of his limbs. He inched his way to the skirt of the woods. He climbed a spruce. He parted the boughs.

Some of Saint Ignace's palisades were down. Smoke still coiled from some of the buildings, and judging from what other roofs he could see, every lodge had met with the torch. He couldn't tell anymore. It was dark. The village stood high on its hill.

Back in his thicket, he thought it all out. Come next night he would crawl to those walls, make his way inside through one of the breaks, and then hide himself as best as he could. He'd wait until he was certain that all were asleep, then he would steal to his altar and commence his rite. After that, he didn't know. He'd have to see if his vessels were still there. His mammal hearts. His bladders of blood. He wanted to be able to bless those hearts in the name of Christ's own, and then feed them to the Iroquois, to be swallowed with the blood. How this could happen, he had no idea. When he thought about it at all, it was with a quick, reckless hope. Hope that if his sacrament could only reach that point when he could stand, feet apart, and offer Communion's chalice to the sky, then every *Ongue Honwe* in Saint Ignace would wake up on his own, and then line calmly up to the altar, forever changed.

Still, Father Boudreau need not have concerned himself with these details of his sacrament. He need not have fretted more than the walls. The hiding place.

He crawled through grasses up the hill, to a breach in the palisades. He heard no breathing, no motion beyond, so he wedged himself through. Nobody there. On felted steps he made for a lodge. He worked his way along its side until he faced the village square. (His altar was still there. Would his containers still sit underneath? He had them wrapped in cloth. The stars gave miserly light.)

Of the *Ongue Honwe,* some sat talking close to their fires, though most others seemed to be sleeping already, curled on the village grass. Or rather, some were not curled but stretched. Or rather—

Only now did it occur to Serge that these could be something other than asleep. No. Not a single one stirred. Not one body touched ground in repose, but each instead in its own halted fright. Father Boudreau let out a breath. (In spite of himself, all he could think was how, in his youth, before any goose was slain it was harried by the children. Then it was killed mid-flurry. For the fear to make tender the meat.)

But if these were the slain, then where was the horde that had only just attacked? Serge spun his head quickly around. For one unreasonable instant he thought that he might have missed the mass of them on his way in. And then, just as quickly, his reckoning changed. They must have left, he thought. Of course. They must have moved on. All the better to make my way unseen.

He withdrew from the square. He searched around in the dark until he found, amid the chars of a lodge, a pile of plankings just right to slide into. To back into. So he could keep the Iroquois in his sight. He hid there, and while he waited, he ran the length of his ritual through his mind, so as not to forget a single step.

But he need not have concerned himself with details of his sacrament, because before the last of the Iroquois would surrender to sleep next to a fire in the village square, before Father Boudreau could even think of tiptoeing to where his altar stood: he heard, from beyond the palisades, the shoutings of hundreds of men. A Huron attack? No. These weren't of rancour but of joy. These were the *Ongue Honwe*. The whole remaining multitude of them. They spread into the shell of Saint Ignace and thickened.

They brought wood. They fuelled their fires. Nevertheless, for all this new light, Serge could make out no more of them than the silhouetted shiftings of limbs. Close-shaved heads.

Weapons waved. From where he lay prone among the planks, he could only guess what was happening. Why the men would pause, and then cheer, as if watching the staging of a play.

But dawn was not long in offering light of its own. And with it its warmth. So that soon the horde was outspreading from the fires, to sit or squat on the grass. And it was then that the scene came sharp to Serge. It was then that he saw what these cheers had been about. What these men had done, and were doing still.

He saw how they had removed the corpses that had still hung on the village stakes, and replaced them with two who breathed. Two black robes. Fathers Brébeuf and Lalemant. He saw his friends, their eyes uplifted and their torsos bared, the gouging already begun on their flesh. Yet he couldn't look away. He could neither help them nor avoid their dread. There was no question of his leaving his hovel, nor of letting them suffer an unwitnessed death. The morning long he watched.

He watched, and he cried, and then midway through the misery of it all, all of a sudden his crying stopped. He felt a strange, sick hollowness under his ribs, as if every last entrail had emptied from him. He was hungry, yes—he hadn't eaten in days—but this distress was born more of thought, because just then it had occurred to him what it was these red men were doing. Theirs was no torture like the others before. Something more.

It was as if they had staged it for Serge alone. To show, with each new detail of their tormenting, how unformed his sacrament had ever been. How, for all of his efforts to marry Rome's rites to the practices of the New World, it had only taken the Iroquois a few playful flips of their accepted methods to show, without a flaw, what the celebration would be.

He watched, he learned and he swallowed the truth. And the truth emptied him.

The *Ongue Honwe* knew their sphere; Serge Boudreau never really would. They knew their arrogance, their strength. They knew their ambition, their spite. They were a conquering race

that had no need of any half-crazed man with fingers chewn
and pricks in the others to show them what to do. They could
show him themselves.

And when they were through, they left. Come mid-after-
noon, only Serge Boudreau in Saint Ignace moved. He buried
what was left of his friends.

—*Ha-ha-ha-ha-ha!*
We pour boiling water on the hairface priests.
—*In the name of the Father and of the Son—*
We tear their cheeks:
—*Soldier of Christ.*
We carve deep crosses in their chests. We feed them stones, hot from
the fire.
—*Take this stone. It is my flesh*
Drink this hot drink. It is my blood.
—*Ha-ha-ha.*
We have no thorns, so we make their crowns of burning stones. We
make collars too. We have many stones.
Oh, we have to admit these priests have courage. No matter how
much they hurt, their eyes keep having sex with the sky.
We will cook their hearts. Yes. We will cook many parts of the
priests.
—*Bring dried pine. Bring birch too. Bring the wood from that*
silly table over there. Wrap it around their feet.
—*Ho-ho-ho. See the big one cook.*
He doesn't like it.

Voyeurism

She is a New England woman in a French summer coastal casino town, in sleeveless print dress and sandals. She hardly feels the dress, it's so loose with just a bikini-bottom underneath in case she might try the beach. There's a nice beach here. Not Riviera but west Normandy. Hot with dulcifying winds. Space between blankets. Some British, some German families. Americans rare. She's alone and in no hurry for anything.

She buys new sunglasses. They cost twice any workaday price, she's sure, but it's worth leaving her old chafed lenses in the cashier's hands. He professionally trashes these for her somewhere under his counter. His moustache is seagull coloured and also seagull shaped. The wings flap as he sings his *Au revoir, Madame, merci* to her, then they return to hovering over business. Our woman has nodded her thanks to him. She's moving away. She's got the glasses' tag removed, her hand sweeps up, and now behind cool tincture, she's a flinger of small glances.

It's too obscure inside, really: blue-green stationery sets, hardbound comicbooks the selfsame colour, a map beside the door the same again though striped somewhat brighter from slim jalousies. An aged couple assist each other indoors (sister-husband-brother-wife?) and she defers to the shuffling of their profiles.

Then she's out. At the sidewalk. In blanching heat with a blue-green breeze. She turns to the postcard rack and lifts some out, but more she's studying herself in the glass behind. A blue-amber thirty-year-old with novel eyewear and novel hair. Hair black and newly quite brief, from a coif-stop in Paris not three days after she corrected her last exam. History of Europe. Whims. Resolves. No more buns, no more ponytails for her. New cheek-hollow punctuation. Pretty. She decides tomorrow she'll buy a hat as well.

She's dawdling near a creperie to inhale the vanilla, when she notices seated in there a man. He has never introduced himself to our woman, but there's a good chance this is the same man who addressed her at this same beach the last time she was here, two years ago.

Sand dusts all corners, all crevices. Her sandals' soles grit to it, and if she pictured a careless spinaway for herself, what she senses instead is a lingering, a stuttered half-pirouette. So... Tourist persona is now invoked. It is insisted upon. Time to appreciate the village oval.

Under the slate of a mansard roof, crates of endives, oranges and grapes spread from a grocer's entranceway like cubist, hued lava. The pharmacy's plateglass glows all chrome and sapphire—white stucco packaged. Across the street, parking-spaces radiate from out of the grass and pebble, well-benched island, their intervals no longer governed by painted lines but by the dark, regular stains of motors' lost oils. There's no statue at the island park, nor a fountain, but a stone. It's a menhir miniature with, as our woman recalls, a bronze plaque somewhere on its opposite side. With words of the Napoleonic wars, she thinks. A naval almost-a-victory, but glorious enough. "Prevail, our fathers would've done, if only tide and wind..." Above the sailboard rental shop, grey shutters hang pocked from those same iodine winds. Beyond the adjoining beachside café, someone strapped to a launch-towed kite soars as if right out of the roof.

Nonetheless, vanilla...

This man in the creperie can't be past 35. Brown eyebrows splay his forehead. Wings again. Leitmotif of the day. *Du jour.* Peregrine wings this time maybe, or else from the spread of an old Slavic crest. The man is reading something. Sipping something too. No, yes, no, it's him, she suspects. Is his an urbane, conceptual book?

An awning's shadow angles the window, and she sidesteps out of the glare. She lifts her glasses and spies through a translucence of her haircut in a pane again, it's one of those flimsy French paperbacks he's reading. The title is...

He must sense her stare. He's smiling at her, genially enough. He returns to the book, then he must also recognize who she is, or was, maybe, because he's smiling at her again, yet this time a bit reticent. A common story. Yes. His mouth doesn't harden as many might, and also there's that blush to him. Her glasses glide back along nosebridge sweat, and the man's face turns cream-blue. Of course he's the one. Those willowy fingers. And is that not his Citröen at the curb?

But then, abruptly, she's wondering: so what? She strides across the street, past the oil stains and the stone with plaque, to the beach.

Here off the channel, tides don't fall and rise as much as they race. Every year, forewarned but heedless children five hundred meters out need rescue.

Our woman is assessing: if all this has been a set-up, some sort of willed prefix, it's been the most long-range a man could come up with, the most forbearing. Idle summer-after-summer patience. For her? His was no more than a half-minute of monologue back then. Now it's two weathered years since. So, why should he remember her with this hair? Why should she want him to?

Now a caveat.

At story's onset, three events asked to be drawn together, and having told the latest, I now begin the first:

One college summer twelve years ago, Elizabeth (I call her Elizabeth) went topless into public waters. A first for her. There'd been no men around, just three roommate friends and her. (Did her mother call her Beth? Liz? Libby?) The four young women had bared themselves at a long-ago-flooded quarry in woods north of Gloucester, Massachusetts, under the moon. Such an unquenched July moon, she recalls, and then what with the mushroom drugs they'd been minding all afternoon, their bodies lost any lesbian hunches to them, and even "bottomless" wasted into the impossible, considering that musty god of all leaves, of all eggs, of spiderwebs and satellites, of waters where granite had once rested but now shaped building-faces, in Boston probably, who could tell? These quarry waters lay just as sultry on the surface as hung the air. Tread a while and lose all notion of liquid and gas as identities more than capriced thicknesses on a continuum. But don't bother diving for any bed because no deeper than the height of a body the darkest cold waited for you, and besides, there was just no reaching.

The middle event marks a confluence of our man and our woman, oglings of France, her body and the celestial:

It was two summers ago that Elizabeth found herself at this unfamiliar Normandy beach, a house-sitter for the Language Department Chair at the Rhode Island college where she teaches. *Professeur Bookbinder,* this canvas-faced man was called. Pronounced fancophonically. The manor had been his grandparents' vacation home. *La maison aux quatre cheminées,* so locally named. Early Third Republic. Ignored over the seasons by the latest Bookbinder sons who spited our *Professeur* and still do—or so word at parties goes.

She'd just quit her third live-with mate in under six years, and here solitude's cloak pledged never to drop from her. So nicely indulgent, this. The remoteness of the expatriate-pretend. Family-styled beach as ready sanctuary. Whiffs of vanilla. (Ah, vanilla!) Of briny weeds too, and of hot-out-of-the-vat, evening lollipops. (Subsmell: Flaubert's catholic melancholies laced the winds. Did these countervail romance? Were they the stuff itself?)

Elizabeth would need no-one here, and no-one would require more of her than stylized talk, that etched politesse. She purchased wines, marketplace *chevre,* waited out a day of rain, and when it drizzled again the next, she promenaded the

99

morning seawall's length. She carried the only umbrella she'd found at the house, a cheap, clear plastic dome she had to lower over her head as if she were a wick to snuff. The first row of summer homes abutted the walk, and she strolled past their casements outswung at her ear, somber inside with low-wattaged, raw-bulbed conversations. She watched in the mist how, below the cut-stone shorescaping, a slickered girl and boy fashioned the sand around them. (One built a citadel with prosaic walls; the other carved forms thinner and less scrutable.) At town's edge stoneworks gave way to dunes, and beyond she saw the black of oyster grates, on and on and orderly in the sand like braille for fingers from the clouds. The flood tide fast erased tire-marks of tractors to and from, and our woman recalled: of course, tractors. This morning. That's what woke me up.

By noon that day, the sun claimed some sky, and restauranteurs unstacked chairs, narrowing the sidewalks she padded past. City families in thin cottons, their arms curled around baskets and towels, already dotted her path homeward to change. From past the graveyard of the Roman church, a tall father and tall teenaged son approached calmly, hand in hand.

Orange clay tiled most roofs hereabouts. In the older sections, many were slate, and a few streets back you could still find thatch, fresh weeds sprouting out of a peak. *La maison aux quatre cheminées* marked the rise of a hillock and the beginnings of bramble-fenced acres.

Elizabeth soon made again for the beach, more people nearing with her now, wending their ways through the cottaged lanes, then past fried potato and sausage redolences and the now broader crowds of the dallying continental lunch. Faces at tables gestured and spoke engagingly enough, though none drew Elizabeth's gaze. She sought only the sun with all her senses, as she bent her course toward sand and water in her new, royal blue, minimalist, lowback tank suit bought for the moment when she regained the seawall and took its stone steps down past the already drying sand shapes of those children who had left their slickers there and now splattered in nude sea.

A decade had measured past her somehow, since that last time she and the moon had floated before each other at a Massachusetts quarry. Too much scholarship, she laughed to herself as she spread her towel next to one of the jetty's rocks. How fitting, she thought. Here are quarried stones again. Water, too, of course. And what sun now! Cloud-vestiges thinned to it perceptibly above her, leaving only deference and heat.

A man and a woman in their fifties reclined in canvas chairs as if they'd been there all morning, each with a small snifter of perhaps cognac or calvados, each in briefs, the woman's breasts quite dark and broad at the aureoles, happily resting on the round of her abdomen. This was all Elizabeth needed to see, along with a nearby blonde pre-teen in bud, so that she might roll her suit down toward her hips, carefully lotion herself and lie back.

Ah, sun. Ah, skin...

Lids closed, she was wondering if such a shift of folkway from her home's side of the ocean to here meant a devaluing of breasts or a valuing of them. By what measures? Comfort? Shielding? Acknowledgement? Mystique? She considered the ancient Chinese and that clever moon-and-sun symbol of theirs. Yes, the moon's blue did shade passively, and yes, the sun's gases did exude vigour enough to reach her pores this far away—but why had those Mandarins had to fix each human gender to its one luminary, even if they did allow for those opposite-coloured, complementary spots, or eyes, or whatever those were? In time, Elizabeth found herself musing that the advantage of a family beach like this over something farther south was that people here had matured beyond body-coyness and perhaps body-rivalry too. Then she wasn't so sure. She'd never accepted people's need to pose, so she might simply have hoped it gone. And neither should her privilege here have been lost on her, childless and fit as her own body was at 28, if a bit wan.

Still, her recalling of moon and of college women friends did now leave a certain symmetry wanting. The this-for-that of matters. Might destiny somehow yield to patterns we conceive to prompt? What now then, right this day, Elizabeth glistening beneath the sun, or else above it, or else front-to-front (depending on the observer's point of view)?

Need something happen now? Why not nothing?

Silly, she thought, of me to feel I'm being watched, just because I'm not used to this.

The narrative demands more than what was at first plain. For instance, this matter of point of view:

Who was looking at Elizabeth so that she suddenly sat up? Would she have spied anyone nearby to have her doubts about had she, before she opened her eyes, been thinking of history and food? Her five most obvious senses had registered no-one. So, was it she who conceived a man to appear, in white shirt and loosened tie, seated sunlit upon a stone 40 yards away, possibly only reading the book he held open at his knees?

Or else was it my own looking at her that disturbed her? My looking, then both mine and yours. Then in due time, not my looking at all, but yours only. Altogether: your sight imagining past my eyes, mine through our man's, and his vision soon judged by what our woman supposed of him: all of us in touch with sea-air and sand, to the growing warmth of this Norman afternoon. (Elizabeth hadn't felt inclined to judge anyone, but given that she could no longer ignore this man, begrudged censure came to her as her only at-hand affection to fill the place where nothing, and no object of it, had just been.)

She hardened her face to its most challenging at the man. Even so, he didn't move; his own face remained as it was, directed into his book. Elizabeth had no proof, other than her

certainty, that he even knew she was here. The man faced his
book, yet from this distance his eyes might very well be aimed
askance toward her, and she'd be hard pressed to detect the
ploy. Yes, that's probably it, she thought, her lips tight to her
teeth. Then just as quickly as her judgment had come, she felt
silly again. Hadn't voyeurism reached from the French to the
world? What claim did she have on foreign vision anyway?
Plus maybe the man wasn't eyeing her at all—it was the sun.
Maybe she should just ease up. Tourist Elizabeth pulled her
suit slightly higher to her waist, she closed her eyes and once
more lay back.

Sand warmed her hands from underneath, sun from above,
and the thin of her lids glowed pink and white.

When she again sat up, bothered and fast glaring toward
our man, he still didn't return her look. But this time his face
was directed seaward. Oh Christ, she groaned. It's a game. It's
a goddamn game! Then, abruptly, the man did return her
look. He was raising his book and making to get back to it, but
mid-movement he must have noticed her attention because he
hesitated. He shifted to confront her, and with such a raised-
eyebrow questioning to him that Elizabeth shrank. Her head
swayed somewhat from side to side, she blew air out her
nostrils and for the third time she lay back on her towel.

But this didn't last either. Her lids' veins began to throb in
front of her: violet rivers on a pink-white map. She wouldn't
stir now though—she refused to rise unless to leave—yet the
idea did come to her: how cunning. How simple and very
cunning of the guy. One well-timed move of the head, and he
paints his high-ground with innocent stuff. Just who the hell
is this clown? Just who is he, Elizabeth both did and didn't
want to know, and she proceeded to invent him.

British. He was British, he had to be, the way he wore a tie
to the goddamn beach—so what if he had it half undone?
Either his wife was home right now doing all the work with
the kids, or else he'd never married, he lived with his mother
and he leered at women all the time. He did it so often that he

had all these eye-shift motions down pat. Sure. If it weren't for skulking to whore-town once a month, he'd still be a virgin. The whores all hated to spot him coming—he gave even them the creeps.

The light at her lids grew suddenly mauve, as if her sky had been sliced by a large bird's wings outstretched. Elizabeth heard vague, local French words into her anger and dismay. It was this man, not British at all, but directly next to her so that, up with a start, she blurted:

"Who? What?"

"*Pardonnez moi, Madame.*"

The man squatted to her height while she drew her suit toward her neck, the brown of his irises not leaving hers as he chose words in her language, apologizing, "I have inconvenienced you." Then he made a deferential, "I'm baffled myself" kind of gesture with a flutter of the head and a half upraised, loosely opened hand. He rose and made again for his rock.

A come-on? Oh, really swift, Elizabeth grimaced. But, if a come-on, then it was a rare one, she soon had to admit, because once at his rock, all he did was gather his black leather satchel by the strap, slide his book in there and leave.

But... But... Elizabeth tapped a finger into the grit, into the moist of it, the cool of it. She wanted to know what he was apologizing for, if all he'd done was heed her reproach.

Might there have been a British man on the jetty's opposite side? The wry complicator inside me wonders.

The child in me recalls a whore neighbourhood in Montréal where the faces of customers worrying from block to block breathed a fierce sadness.

By now I suspect our man's name is Edouard. He must have been born hereabouts and lives locally still. Either he sells insurance, or else he advocates cases from a one-storey office next to the village garage, across from the plain steepled church. His office's face comprises one Dutch door and one bay window only. High on the centre pane, dust and weather have eroded the blocked-ink letters of his name, yet with a squint one can still make out "Edouard." This man decides his own business hours, it seems, and summertimes he often drifts to one favourite broad and level rock among the jetty's pile where he can lean back and read and sometimes look and smell and listen and sometimes lose himself.

Was Edouard studying Elizabeth? Yes, he was. Is our man a philanderer? He lacks stark ambition, so probably not. He's been married once, loyally and amicably enough if only for a few years—trickled in time of that fast-and-ready passion his wife deemed necessary as she begged off, and he did not try to possess her.

That afternoon, Edouard could not help but notice Elizabeth, for the very reason she'd come here. This shore seldom drew her type. Women her age, yes, but more often with children, with husbands too, some pregnant and some not, though few with time to keep nubile pride before the businesses of home and blood. He'd even witnessed Elizabeth earlier that day from his office window when she strolled past the drizzled church, the way her ponytail swayed under that charmingly frugal umbrella of hers, no partner beside her. Then on his stone perch, he'd looked up from his pages to see, not 40 meters from him, this same woman as she hesitated to expose her chest (a hesitation that she had assumed lasted less than a noticeable moment). Then he saw the tender care with which she oiled her skin, and he enjoyed the smaller, classic-sculpture form of her breasts (as opposed to the shape favoured on garage calendars, which he regarded as more odd than sensual). Elizabeth's whole torso was pale, even paler than the rest of her. This paleness called out a story to him, which he mulled as he gazed, and which I've been relating to you as well as I might, allowing for imperfect translation, my own metaphors, my own confusions.

For example: was it Elizabeth who dwelled on breasts as value, or did I only imagine she did? I might've been swayed by Edouard's own contemplating at the time, of why it is that men have no equivalent to breasts: body parts evolved less for self than for others: organs that eyes might taste from, that infants' blind mouths see.

It was during such conjecture of his that our woman first sat up. Her defiant scrutiny startled Edouard. He found himself withdrawing to his book before she could isolate him, and this left him with a sense of refuge that he acknowledged with some surprise as adolescent. Ah yes, that... Adolescence... He felt as if he'd just turned a street corner and recognized an old acquaintance coming his way, someone he'd associated with but whose friendship he'd never had the desire to court. No. In fact there were two acquaintances nearing him. Edouard had known both at one time or other, but he wasn't sure if they'd shown up together back then. One was this refuge in a glance-play whose developments were perplexing him, and the other was a dimly familiar discomfort to his breathing. Might this vague pang be adolescent too? Edouard did prefer coming to terms with his impressions, and he sought a proper label.

All was fast drying around our man and our woman, puddles receding to the last of rings of algae and salt amid the jetty's stones. Breeze shifts carried in the scents of far-off, plumbless seas. Two motorboats skimmed the waves a few hundred meters out, the hums of their engines oscillating one-about-the-other so that at times a third, harmonic note droned the song of a launch that wasn't there.

Out of the vigil at his sight's edges, Edouard relaxed when he noticed our woman reclining once again. He would no longer gaze at her, yet he had to admit that now she fascinated him all the more. (Her challenge intrigued him; her form pleased him; her story kept writing itself.) In time, what Edouard did was leave the book he wasn't reading, so as to pan toward the channel and the two motorboats and the twin skiers each boat had in tow. On the way, he slowed to soak his memory's pores with as much of Elizabeth's person as he could. The skiers interwove apart then near, just as did the sounds of the boats, and Edouard watched the cat's-cradle movement of their ropes through the pale, glistening, supine image of the woman his memory held at a hover before him.

When Elizabeth rose up the second time, therefore, it wasn't our man's staring at her, but his imagining of her in front of all else, that had stirred her unrest. As he had before, Edouard noted her movement from the borders of his vision. This time he sensed her judgment even more (it had grown to disdain), and he felt that pang to his breathing again, less vaguely now.

Embarrass?
Honte?
Culpabilité?

This casino town is not large, so neither our woman nor our man should have been surprised if during the attendant week, their lives once-spliced should twine and braid. Or at least risk to... Present themselves to...

This village is small, and its market only gathers on the mornings of Wednesdays and Saturdays. Other than that hot-lollipop stand, sundowns offer one gaming-house, one cinema, one cluster of restaurants and cafés. That week the beach's radiance did invite Edouard, but he drove instead to the outlying homes of clients and of friends. He crowded his work hours. He read as he lingered over meals and drinks. Nonetheless it would happen that he'd step out of his car to buy film sometime, or he'd be walking his tattered brown accordion file to the bank, or else he'd be helping his brother unload mackerel at market and there she'd be—either in return seeing him or else not—and however much he might want something to say or do, the most he ever mustered was a nod. Each time his hands would dampen on him, and he'd remember as he regretted: *adolescence.*

That hot, sky-stirred afternoon at the jetty, somehow his fascination plus Elizabeth's shaming of him together had spurred him to a juvenile act. What tawdry deceit. The moment he'd pretended that blameless surprise, he'd felt himself diminish. Honour ebbed from him. Wisdom charged him to approach this woman so as to quickly purge his world, but he must not have defined matters enough because even as he climbed the jetty's last stone from the beach, all of life tasted rueful to him. In his Citröen that evening, he slammed a palm into his brow for it. Had his window not been rolled up at the time, he might have spat some of his abashment out. Abashment. He'd named his discomfort now, the way it could just wash back, poignant from his nostrils past his throat to his chest, the way his mother's herbal *tisanes* once had, her church-steeped mortifications too.

And as if Elizabeth's abiding before his sight all week didn't confound him enough, what should Edouard overhear one time at the papeterie but talk of the American woman who dwelled all alone in that big vined manse that hadn't sheltered human life since... When was it? Three or four summers ago, that *Professeur* had brought one of his students there. Following his groin instead of his age.

"He's done it before, you know. Do you remember the little librarian Natalie before she married Torvald Guillotte...?"

"Good day, Ladies."

"Oh, hello, Monsieur Edouard. Do you want to join our bet? How many days before the old man Bookbinder graces our streets?"

"Bookbinder?"

"Yes, you know. *La maison aux quatre cheminées.* It looks as if he's sent his new mistress ahead of him."

"Oh?" Edouard said to them.

Of course no professor would appear that week, neither here at the papeterie for pen or ink, nor anywhere else in the village. Still, once he admitted this threat to our woman's solitude, Edouard realized that as much as all else, it was this that intrigued him, that called itself to him. It was Elizabeth's solitude that kept writing itself.

How could this be? A person finds the solitude of another alluring. But to what object? How could he ever oblige the allure without forfeiting his motive to do so? Or does one wear solitude as mystique, wanted or not, our only choice whether we'll yield it, as one would clothes, to intimacy's varied lights and shades?

What was Elizabeth's solitude but a paradox?

The inside face of solitude is one thing. The mystique of a woman's public solitude, though, comprises the paradox of exposure and strength together. A man's public solitude advertises strength and ignores vulnerability.

Is this all neatly so? Will the general terrorize the particular? I see faces and faces and faces and faces. In our chronicle, Elizabeth's defiance and Edouard's public mistake reversed vulnerability and power between them.

Elizabeth did not accept Edouard's apology, and this left him frail to the judgment (he would have winters to deduce) that the churchly mortifications of his youth had moulded him to receive. For one reticent week—beneath the sun, the moon and the wafts and glides of shoreline birds—Elizabeth would not relinquish judgment. Qualms called themselves to her in time, but her purpose dissembled them.

She was no hermit. A woman's public solitude wants advantage.

The eyes in the sun and the moon stare far too meanly, from out of pupils far too small.

Every day along the coast, spent waves feed the new. Come springtides at their highest, and the jetty no longer stabs at the sea but is engulfed, whitecaps lick sky, boom at escarpment-stone, and children begin to suspect leniency in the elements.

Two years ago, what neither our man nor our woman could have known was that to Elizabeth, Edouard's sufferance of public weakness would slowly become his strength.

Forthright Edouard. Restrained Edouard. Always reading something, going somewhere, busy. An agreeably postured man, really, with graceful, long-fingered hands, our woman had once noted. With each new deference, his own mystique increased.

Such were the qualms that called themselves to Elizabeth (along with the usual dread of shallowness that earnest tourists pack), but again, because of the thick, weighty inertia of why people do what they do, she still could neither offer nor accept intimacy. Her week's stay would end, her form exit, only a story remain.

When she sighed into her taxi for the train station, it was to dawn's first umbers. The yellow of the taxi's lights now glowed the village oval, now beamed the boulangerie where she'd gone each day for loaf or tart, now the mossed stones of walls high on both sides that trenched her route up the first knoll with its lines of hedges and cultured trees. Elizabeth looked back to the village, to the unshrouding silhouettes, roof colours just starting to hint, and beyond, the darkest of ocean still. If she left her judgment behind with our story of her, she didn't notice so. Sitting back straight, she soon thought of other stories, those she was returning to, those she'd left to their own thrusts. She sensed the welling inside of a recent, yet already tired, question: What is it that I want from this earth?

That was two years ago. But now...

August sun glares overhead, and Elizabeth has inhaled once again our creperie's vanilla. She likes the sculpted weightlessness of her hair, breeze on her nape, her glasses' chromed blue. She's taken as much sun as a prudent first bright day will allow, and she's changed her mind about buying a hat tomorrow. She'll do it today. Something more nice than inexpensive, she hopes. If straw, then with a fetching kerchief for a band. Maybe... She isn't sure. She's got all afternoon. Beth the nonchalant. Eyeing shops for what's around...

This morning, at our story's start, Elizabeth spied our man at the creperie, reading a book. As she had before, she made out no title. As Edouard had before, he fluttered between reading his pages and reading Elizabeth.

New questions now arise: how necessary was this book? When first recognized, could our man have been other than reading? Is he a marionette strung to the digits of our woman's memory? Right now Elizabeth more-than-half-expects his face anywhere. Over these last seasons, her recall has collapsed the events of a week, such that if she happened upon this man six times back then, she supposes herself due for six instances today. All she's ever seen here, heard here—British radio in the grocery store, market chickens' blowtorched quills, tough-guys at the beach difficult to fear what with their Camembert and limp baguettes—all these would now echo themselves. The first day of a repeat vacation brooks few surprises.

Yet no doubt it must. Since this morning's mute, transient encounter, Edouard's face has come to light in no shop, in no café, not at the post office, not in the cinema queue for *Le Coeur Sans Griffes,* nor at the casino nor along the seawall nor anywhere near the hot candy stand. All day, though Elizabeth has been savouring the whole of our village rather than avowedly seeking anyone, Edouard's absence prods her more and more to wonder exactly why it is she has come back.

(As occurs curiously often in these matters, everyone else has posed this question already but her. Everyone in fact has answered it. Also, we might here add: given the membranes of symmetry that our story has been fashioning, is it now Elizabeth's turn to revisit adolescence?)

A television commercial stirs to mind. It's one that I watched some years ago wherein the Paris actress Catherine Deneuve handsomely and engagingly explains to us:

"I dislike very much familiarity. I think it can be a mistake. Instead, I prefer intimacy."

"Intimacy cologne," an unseen male voice adds, and though I don't

recall any words past this, I do remember pondering: what might be the difference? Is intimacy just one more cloth? The further play of scents, sounds and sights? So, what might the error in familiarity be? Some denuding of our less-than-romantic processes? The stark admissions of a future corpse?

Edouard, meantime, has been hard at work all afternoon and evening in his office's rearward rooms. He has a contract there to satisfy, labour once promised and this week come due, yet he's also secreted himself there because he wishes he might disappear awhile. This morning he recognized in Elizabeth, not her hair, nor her posture (because it too was not the same), but her pallor. He witnessed her eyes through the creperie's plate glass, then his old abashment suggested itself. This night he is shunning the abashment he has assumed up until now to be a vanished thing.

That ensuing autumn two years ago, our man indulged a tryst with one of the Lipé twins, Élodie, far too wanton for him, both understood, though he surprised her, so she told her sister, with passion overreaching his reputation in the parish. What the twins weren't privy to that we of the more compound point of view may be, is that this passion was Edouard's flushing of his soul and honour in carnality.

Magpies called their ascending whines. Clouds scudded, floated, dissipated and took new shapes. Time overlay the textures of Edouard's life with its cadences, its rote episodes. But it is all still here. Edouard in his back room feels more fatigued than he expected and hard put to concentrate. He gives up and leaves his work, late so that the moon behind that Roman steeple offers his lane its only glow. The village oval is better lit. He crosses it at an angle toward home, remnant tourists sampling the night. Our woman promenades there still. Her hat becomes her. Against the bone-colour of the pharmacy, her profile appears taller to him, either because of this up-brimmed hat, shadows' deceits, or else from the way she leans as she sways onto the pads of her careless heels. As she approaches, Edouard chooses to disregard her. Maybe he'll abstractedly reach for something into the black of his satchel's leather. But her nod to him startles him enough to also nod. They've already passed each other—yet she did utter something, did she not? He didn't quite make it out. Her French lacked music. He felt unready for this voice. (He only now determines that he never has heard her speak.) All he can be confident of is that this time she isn't judging him.

Tomorrow a migraine will enfeeble Edouard. It will consume his day, his head kept still under a bridge of pillows, one at either ear with a third across to dim his eyes and, with any hope, cool them. Tonight, though, our man dreams that Elizabeth is posing on the beach under the blackest of stars. Darkness is a liquid thing everywhere about her, but she herself glares under tripoded halogens, under a light that scribes her skin then breaks in tendrils across the sand. Except for her glasses and hat, she is naked. She shifts this way and that, pauses to advantage, shifts again. Edouard sights a camera, clickless even though he seems to regularly forward film. He pursues angulations. But he soon finds himself too close. He is so close now that the pores of her skin are warping. When he travels his lens, all he sees are a change of cells. Atoms strike his eye as the suns-with-planets he's always imagined them to be.

When people crest the arcs of their lives, they no longer sense themselves facing endless firmament. Instead what they perceive is horizon, finite and upcoming—what elders have intimated all along. People may then taste from despair, fellow-feeling, rancor, humility… They may veer toward pretence. They may not know: either what to do or that they do it.

After years of disfavouring others' urges to pose, if Elizabeth now discovers some fruition in style, she hasn't yet accosted herself in the mirror for it. She's three decades old—still shy of the age that prompts such shift—though suffering can speed tendency, and who is to say? These last seasons at home or work, something (of which our man, and we, can only guess) may have complicated her, simplified her, the two at once...

Or else maybe Elizabeth has yielded it all to vacation's allure. (Yielded, in those regions where heart meets will, where choice dances with chance.) This woman does, after all, think herself no longer a tourist here but a regular. She smiles when she wakes to seagulls' cries or to the throbs of tractors from the beach. She imagines she owns a plot here that bides, fallow for her to plant in designs she only now lays out. She's loosened the top buttons of her blouse. She awaits her crêpes in a sidewalk chair, sipping the last of a tall pastis while she peruses the village through this her second evening of blue sunglasses.

(We might here note that, symmetry or no symmetry, Elizabeth's may not be a social call from her adolescence, in that maybe she never did have much of one. From more generic youth, then, perhaps, a late burgeoning of those desires she's early on quelled to the rule of concepts. "I will not," she once wrote a lover, "appeal to anyone for less than the activity of notions that I am." But this is vacation. And academic lovers do get so calculable after a while. And desire promises like unfurling flags. It is both the flags and the wind's caprice.)

Where do the birds go in the rain? Do they yet spike the skies unseen? Even such a thin rain as drizzles Elizabeth's third day here has emptied trees, has dulled all chirrs. Our woman walks with the same umbrella in hand that she domed herself underneath before; her breath dims its meagre plastic clarity. What else does one do in falling weather but walk? She supposes she could get drunk. She could buy magazines.

A watch repairman looks up from the small of his tools to how she's slowed outside his display of the new, the pawned, the futile of payment. A mother and three children on ever-smaller bicycles pedal past Elizabeth at the curb, North

American she judges from the pastels on them, how doleful each younger repeat of the first face and how set. Elizabeth senses her limbs today, though she's also bothered by the dank thought that, yes, her week's end rises almost as close already as has ebbed its start. If she brooked no surprises her first day here, by now she worries for them. She imagines them obligated though neat.

Her second day closed to no Edouard (his skull a hot, blanched wire—what we know), and come her third morning here, Elizabeth dwells on how this man has well maintained all grace, all restraint. She relives that first sun-soaked afternoon, his confiding appeal to the largesse she wishes she'd understood to accord. She wants from his solitude. She wants from the beauty of Flaubert's melancholy that wraps him about like a dark dark scarf. On her course to market this raw-edged day, this woman's steps upon the cobblestones between the church and our village garage seem plausible enough.

A waiter at a transvestite restaurant in Vancouver had such charmed shoulders, he recognized, that he wore lowbacked clothes no matter the season. Those shoulders... How they yanked diners' eyes to them.

On the train from DC to Manhattan one day, I chanced on the rear quarter profile of a young woman's face, ahead across the aisle. I mind again the shadowed vale of her cheek, how, especially when she spoke, it dispelled all else.

Ah, there are some!

Birds, after all.

They exit and near the ancient belfry above Elizabeth. (Where to? Where from?)

They're doves, she thinks. To better behold, she has to lift her fogged cupola aside and allow wet veils onto her face. But it's worth it. Rainfall may well acquit these birds their pigeon shabbiness. Water sheens the church itself, the graveyard adjacent... Across the cobblestones, it lusters the sun-and-salt Citröen that's claiming curb by the shut Dutch-door.

So, the man's car is here. Yet his office sleeps still.

This bay window... Elizabeth has only once before looked through it. (It was dirtier then, the front room darker from dusk. She spied a large, calm desk, she recalls, the usual shelves and cabinets, and on all free walls: matted photographs.) She pauses now, she raises her umbrella again and revisits these furnishings. They're somewhat better lit, especially what's closer to the glass. One of those photographs is really a certificate. The others are all in shades of ash. That satchel was probably not on the desk last time, or...

Maybe the man lives here, Elizabeth wonders. How deep is this place? Beyond the doorway to the rear, crimson washes across a wall from the arcing out of what must be yet another door behind. An arm precedes someone. Elizabeth's man onswitches fluorescents. He's holding wet prints high on a dowel of clips. (A photographer?) He notices her before she thinks to withdraw, and she finds herself smiling at him. Edouard smiles back, bemused. She salutes in toy naval fashion to him (Where did that gesture come from?) and leaves. In her outspin, the last she heeds is this man's name on his window glass.

In a feature on Palm Beach sexuality, men were shown who, from a bluff, took telephoto shots of the skin of bathers on their towels. This promontory had its habituals, it seemed, the way a fishing wharf would, or a zoo. The bathers wore oils. The men wore as ardent a resignation as had those customers in Montréal.

Perhaps this:

Intimacy pretends to bodies which will not die, nor which were ever born. Familiarity disclaims reverence. But wherefrom this disclaiming? How to tell transcendence from depravity?

This woman—fast manifest and then just-as-fast gone—has leadened Edouard's feet where he stands. Such enzymes surge and whirl in him. Enchantment. Prurience. Worship. Dread. Atonement. Some guileless courtesy. An urge to manoeuvre too—yet how long would he remain in place if the phone didn't just now sound its protracted, European bleat? He stares toward the noise, then at his dowel of yet-damp prints, which he ends up propping flagmast-like into a file drawer he's partially pulled out. Edouard answers the phone. Discussed business draws him to a shelf, a tome of codes, a leafing through and an instant forgetting of why this page. He's already replaced the receiver. He leaves a napkin at the page for when he might remember what. He's forgotten also why he's stepped to the front. From his satchel, he lifts out a lens, a roll of film, no, not these...

This building does deceive in its depth, in that it holds a broad, many-purposed hall at its middle, then somewhere behind that a darkroom with its red-lit fixers and red-lit pans and red-lit remoteness. Most likely the taking of photographs is a sideline for Edouard, an avocation, and curiously (how Elizabeth will think), all his pictures record such scapes as the earth, the seas and heavens yield. These pictures idle with the latencies of how elements touch, they wheel with the motions of them.

Edouard pushes charged air past his lips. He presses his palms into the soft of his eyes, then pulls stretched fingers back along his temples and his skull.

Three times he's seen our woman this week, meetings prompted by her doings enough such that by now her story in him no longer tastes of judgment. Rather, all it does is invite. It calls with the enigma of her coy salute; with the way she voiced the other night that quaint, tuneless French; with the classic sculpt and the sheen of her breasts (or at least what he surmises of these from a memory seasons old). Ah... Plus her legs invite as much, the reaches of them do, hallowed at the thighs as they were just now by how her hem curtained them about on her rainwashed exit marketward.

Come noontime our man will breathe from the mystique of Elizabeth still, from the intrigue of her at a dance with wafts from his armagnac. He'll take his siesta, tend to his work, have his hair cut, and by evening rainspent clouds will wad as they recede from the grey of our sky's glad vault. They will draw all grey to themselves, an implosion of shadowplay, back from broadening veins of blue-mineral black rashed with stars, the whole sky framed for any uplooking meanderer by the brows of buildings (stone, clay and slate—their angles and reliefs); it will be Edouard this time who courses the streets, the seawall, the park with that small, carved menhir, the lane past this *maison aux quatre cheminées* with its wrought-iron gate and one upstairs dormer amber until twenty-three o'clock when it will be, like the others, dark. Tomorrow with its hot sipped espresso, broiling noontide light and resolve, Edouard will trek to the beach in his white, short-sleeved shirt and sight this woman swimming then wading obliquely back. She will sport no sunglasses. He will leave his book, his sandals and shirt and roll his pleated, taupe-coloured trousers to approach before she grants full notice to him. Her breasts will insist themselves to him, there, always hardly beneath his petition for an eye-to-eye yet with the lotioned, dripwater gleam of them just as he's imagined, even more so, her arms to the sides though slightly out as waist-deep waders will pose themselves, what with how waves can loom so slack of alarm behind.

He's been to this beach a thousand times, he's witnessed bodies here past count—and yet you don't just tread up to an altar and open doors without first uttering ovations in requisite tongue, kneeling the proper kneel... What to say? What to do? Edouard frets codes as he draws close, in awful trust to momentum, to this iodine wind of his childhood and his upbringing, to the taut down-arching of his toes as they grasp at warm sand laxities.

Yet if trust is a goblet, how often is it filled? This one won't be. And Edouard may never decipher why not.

When I first proposed to write of all this, I'd been riding old Cuban Vespas all day with my half-sister Lucia between Cienfuegos and

Sancti Spiritus. In trying to explain what I sought to compose, I mentioned to Lucia that woman on the train from Washington to New York.

I related how, from the window beyond her, sun had incandesced the down of this woman's cheek while she spoke with her mate seated next to her—the mate I'd assumed for some stops, anyway, until he got up, said to the woman, "Really nice meeting you," and left. I was musing, "...not only pretty, but congenial besides," when the woman spun in what I later gathered was a search for someone new to engage. But at the time, her move to me caught my enthrallment so nude, so vulnerable, that I fast shifted aside. The woman sat back straight, she paused, then she reached for her coat and left.

I leaned into my windowpane, tape-player in hand. I chose a cassette, and soon headphone sounds were quelling me as Wagner must once have quelled himself.

Could a village this modest (clasp-shuttered and rheumatic, no doubt, three seasons out of the year) support a photographer? One who doesn't seem to advertise, nor who retails a thing? Not likely, thought Elizabeth in her cobblestoned stride from that office and church. No. Probably not.

An artist, then. An artist sustained by profession enough to finance his own, plus, if need be, to keep any proud kin content. Talent a due surprise, really, given the story our woman wants. A surprise of the kind that thickens mystique, that splays, apt, suggesting more still. Yet artists will fashion artifacts. Elizabeth has perused the pictures on those walls, and, something, she doesn't know what it is about them cueing her: that she might discover herself there framed—or else that she wouldn't. (Crosscurrents of the private and of the vain. Our woman today senses the skin of her face less well held onto the bone.)

Rather than cede her thoughts to the marketplace, she keeps on strolling toward the casino's mouth, past it, beyond the smaller, outlying cottages on the north side of our village, an appliance store there, a trailer park... She only turns back

once among the first pastures where the roadway lies insinu-
ated with earthworms by now limpid from all this rain. She'd
have to play a troubled hop-scotch through them and loses
gait. No place, this, for the savouring of events. The quizzing
of them. Well, well, well, well...

Rainfall diminishes. Stooped peasants in galoshes and
rough wools pry snails from where garden walls rise out of the
troughs of sewers. Elizabeth returns to *la maison aux quatres
cheminées* where she sips port (too cloying, really, past the first
glass, but the only drink in the house) and she reads until all
words are a sea. She sleeps an oil-soaked sleep of little repose,
wakes early, thinks to take aspirins but minds her stomach and
chooses instead to make for the beach so as to witness dawn.
She lays out warm socks, a bikini-bottom, jeans, a short-
sleeved blouse, corduroy shirt and a navy blue sweater of our
professeur's. She'll have to wait until later to swallow anything.

Night obligingly fast dopes the jags of her head, she, star-
lit past that church once more, the high-walled graveyard,
that office, the name on it, brick sidewalks, a transformer's
buzz, motors' stains beaded with dew, sand, until she folds her
towel just-so onto the cool between seawall stones and there
sits down. "This morning, let the beach be my lover," she
whimsies, her arms wrapped tight about the lift of her knees.
First a tractor's rumble comes, its one yellow eye, then two
more pulling the dark of flatbed trailers out toward the oyster
grates, a blared yet sepulchral motion to them.

Then all is silence, it must be, except, surf reminds itself to
Elizabeth sitting still awaiting sun. Stars lingeringly concede
definitions to the mauving of her firmament; our woman sees
surf's lunar approach as a mesmerizer's fingers violet, phos-
phorescent, now as lambs capering, now as souls' silvered
cobalt throbs, until stars have dimmed hardly visible, heavens
warming, and Elizabeth expects that sun to aspire out of the
ocean's grizzle any moment now.

Yet morning has in fact bloomed far too vividly for this, and
in short time our woman can't help but notice. She reaches a

hand to the hole of her mouth. She goggles her eyes. "Ah."
Because she now recognizes how, even before any look-see over
whichever shoulder she may choose, behind her the sun
already attends.

"My, my, my," she utters to the beach's vacancy. "We'll
blame it on last night's port, yes?"

She wills shrugged laughter out. "By all means. By all
means! For my muddle alone, the planet should reverse its
spin."

*In the Overture to Wagner's Tannhauser, bass sonorities of the soul rise
up as the body's stridencies decline, in a welling cascade of the anxious
and the beautiful.*

*Hear me. I must concede this to those Palm Beach voyeurs: the bodies
on the sand before them glossed so picture-magazine stylized, with
gestures so mannered, that I suffered to conceive someone lived in them.*

It occurs to me (as it did to Elizabeth last night, sweat now
prickling her torso and feet) that Edouard is not our man's first
name at all, but rather his surname. That would be something,
Elizabeth first supposed, and this morning, to the reviewing
of this likelihood, she removes that sweater, those socks, she
unbuttons her outside shirt... The man's pane did read
EDOUARD in brown, well-blocked ink, but... Wasn't it
faded last time? Or else peeling? Dusted over? Either way, he's
had its contrasts better revealed since, and maybe it took just
such a renovation for both Elizabeth and me to realize that an
advocate or insurance man wouldn't print his first name alone
on a business sign. In our France of form, especially.

Not that it should, but this confounds much. Seasons of
pearled fancying have seeped into the understreams of a
Norman dawn, leaving hollows in Elizabeth. She's conjured
her story of our Edouard, the story I've been narrating, of our
man who is probably a lawyer or a notary, whose name it was
that much else affixed itself to, but it's likely all wrong.
Wrong enough anyway for suspicions to tunnel into those

hollows in her. (Maybe he does this with every woman. Sure. The staring game; the apology; the honourable waiting game...) We now have to call our man something else. *Monsieur* Edouard then, which (of course, of course) is what the ladies at the papeterie said, only we didn't lend enough attention at the time. How were we supposed to suspect?

What else, then, might we not know about him? It's possible that although Elizabeth never did make out the title of any of his books, what our man was reading his first time at the jetty was a French translation of the latest *Gun and Sky* western series, the fourteenth of *Le Ciel et les Revolvers*. He's read them all, and the second time when at the creperie she saw him with a book, he had in hand a tobacconist-shop novel of divorces and suicide-threats by Mineur Gantier.

Now Elizabeth draws off her jeans and lets fall her corduroy shirt. She applies sunscreen to herself, absently watching a German family approach and lay out its blanket. In time that aged couple (sister-husband-brother-wife) deliberates along the shore. A boy frustrates himself with a kite. The German mother has brought cool drinks.

Shops must be open, our woman supposes. A well-parasolled *café au lait* sounds nice, as does one of those chocolate croissants, but she still mistrusts her stomach. She would get up and stroll the oval just for that vanilla smell, yet today she worries. She worries that vanilla will yield some affection more specific than only the alcohol of it, the fermented bean. It might be... No... Yes... (Not in worded thought does Elizabeth fret; it's in how her palate thickens to all this, saline, unhappy...) Would it not have to be that heavy-sweet smell of grief?

Our woman has forgotten her sunglasses. When day gets too hot and bright, she takes off her blouse, oils the last of herself and stands so as to pad to the water, into it, shallow a long way in but soon deep enough for her to dive into the gloss of a well-bulked wave. Farther out waves don't shatter as much as bob her in her swim, Elizabeth, cadent past the jetty's tip until she tires and decides to float, on her back, hardly moving, all sounds drowned to her except for her own very loud and sloppy pulse. (Just what is it, she insists, about a person's name? I want to know. Why? Has anyone deceived anyone?) Her skin has darkened sensibly enough this week, yet she understands she should soon seek shade. Every now and then a wavelet plops at her ear or neck. Should her eyes catch salt from it, she has to right herself and tread ocean awhile. She observes the beach, how peopled it's gotten under this gull-shrieked sky, how the jetty cleaves the village from here, all so symmetrical: sand out of water on either side, escarpment walls up, housefronts like a mandible's irregular teeth gapped at town's middle where our oval opens onto stairs down one slope of the jetty and a boat-launch down the other.

It's when wading back in that Elizabeth notices our man. He's walking right toward her. (Why should this surprise? And what about surprise? Did she not woo surprise?) Shirtless his posture appeals even more—enduring, the sinewed tolerance of his stride (those quaintly typical business-pants rolled up)—and now it's our woman who pretends a gaze. Nearer in she's dropped her face toward water's distortion of the fall of feet, yet more so she's peering through air's own warps from behind the spray-laced glitter of her lashes. She realizes again the grace of our man's hands. He's got them low in front of him; they loosely touch at fingertips and thumbs.

Yet for all this dazed endearment, Elizabeth will not lift her face to our man. Her legs will veer her instead in a broad and wistful arc. (What man? There is no man. No-one hails to look behind.) Why such retreat? Something about the pose of those hands? Their aspect plies our woman with the responsibility of being hallowed, with a duty she knows not what to make of, what to do with, ill prepared, ill anointed to entertain any rites of. (She wants to reach the depths once more and swim; mineral sea will buoy her; she will swim and swim.) But what this pose of hands has afforded is only the logic to withdraw.

Because all has already proved too late for our man. All is too late for our now distant *Monsieur* Edouard. (Doesn't even his name remove?)

Water drags Elizabeth's exit out, and the thickness at her palate is a weepy clot inside. All really is all very too late, because it's our village that has died in her. It's our village, and later on, fiery-skinned and out of the water to retrieve her clothes, our woman will not return to *la maison aux quatre cheminées* by way of the oval and park, she will not dare smell, dare sample the boulangerie's tarts, purchase *Pont l'Évesque*, hear a fishseller's refrain... Rather she will follow water's rim as far as where tide engulfs the oyster grates; she will course through dunes, along pastures and apple fields, past horses and sheep and at last back to that arched, wrought-iron gate of the gardens of *la maison,* then its glassed verandah, her room... She'll have herself driven tonight to the train station. She'll ride rails to Paris and take her chances with choked-season accommodations there.

She will end up leaving this way, but right now as she forces her limbs, face-first against the surf, the salt of her and the salt of the ocean conjoin. Not yet out, Elizabeth has to let her body sag below the surface, a hand to her nose though air spattering nonetheless from her as she keeps as private as she can the violence of her lament.

When the sun and the moon navigate at right angles to our earth, neap tides hardly flow nor ebb—though our oceans are just as hard pulled.

When I mentioned to my half-sister how this woman on the train had gotten up and gone, Lucia made a wry face: "How do you know why anything? Maybe she had to leave next stop. Maybe she just went to eat with her things and there she was talking to somebody else."

Previous volumes in this series contained stories by the following writers:

Most of these books are still available. Please inquire.

Piers Plowman Studies II

THE FIGURE OF PIERS PLOWMAN

Piers Plowman Studies

I THE THEME OF GOVERNMENT IN PIERS PLOWMAN

Anna Baldwin

The Figure of Piers Plowman

The Image on the Coin

MARGARET E. GOLDSMITH

Go to the Gospel, quod she, that God seide hymselven,
Tho the poeple hym apposede with a peny in the Temple
Wheither thei sholde therwith worshipe the Kyng Cesar.
And God asked of hem, of whom spak the lettre,
And the ymage ylike that therinne stondeth?
  'Cesares,' thei seiden, 'we seen it wel echone.'
  'Reddite Cesari,' quod God, 'that Cesari bifalleth,
  Et que sunt Dei Deo, or ellis ye don ille.'

D. S. BREWER

Published by D. S. Brewer
240 Hills Road, Cambridge
an imprint of Boydell & Brewer Ltd
PO Box 9, Woodbridge, Suffolk IP12 3DF

Distributed in the U.S.A. by
Biblio Distribution Services
81 Adams Drive, Totowa, N.J. 07512

British Library Cataloguing in Publication Data
Goldsmith, Margaret E.
    The figure of Piers Plowman. — (Piers Plowman
    studies; 2)
    I. Title   II. Series
    821'.1   PR2015

ISBN 0 85991 077 6

Printed in Great Britain by
St Edmundsbury Press, Bury St Edmunds, Suffolk

CONTENTS

ACKNOWLEDGEMENTS

In learning to read *Piers Plowman* I have been sustained and carried along by a host of other readers, both living and dead. They are too numerous to name and to thank individually, and my bibliography and notes would swell out of all proportion if I were to try to mention all those who have influenced me. In practice, I have been highly selective: only those authors, scholars and critics whose thoughts I am developing, or occasionally attempting to refute, will appear by name. However, it is fitting that I should record my special debt to the late Charles Leslie Wrenn, who first introduced me to Langland and directed my early researches. In recent years I have had encouragement from my colleagues at Bristol, not least from Professor John Burrow, from whose published work and private conversation I have learnt much. He generously read and criticised the first draft of this book, to my great profit. I have had considerable practical help from my husband, and scholarly assistance from my son Michael, whose knowledge of Latin has easily outstripped my own. He has worked with me in preparing versions of the patristic material quoted in the course of the book. My manuscript has been most efficiently typed and checked by Mrs Anne Merriman. Whatever errors remain must be laid at my door. I have worked from the various printed editions of the poem, and my final thanks must go to the indefatigable editors of this difficult text, without whom *Piers Plowman* would have very few readers today.

M. E. G.

Bristol, 1980

ABBREVIATIONS

The usual abbreviations of learned periodicals are employed in the Bibliography and Notes. Books of the Bible are referred to in common abbreviations of their Latin titles. The following short forms of titles are used for reference in the Notes:

Ambr., *In Esai.*	Ambrose, *Fragmenta in Esaiam*
Ambr., *In Luc.*	Ambrose, *Expositio Euangelii secundum Lucam*
Aug., *Conf.*	Augustine, *Confessiones*
Aug., *De Trin.*	Augustine, *De Trinitate*
Aug., *En. in Ps.*	Augustine, *Enarrationes in Psalmos*
Aug., *Tract. in Ioh.*	Augustine, *Tractatus in Iohannis Euangelium*
Aug., *Tract. in 1 Jo.*	Augustine, *Tractatus X in Epistolam Joannis ad Parthos*
Greg.,*Hom. in Ezech.*	Gregory, *Homilia in Ezechielem*
Greg., *Moralia*	Gregory, *Moralia in Iob Libri I-XXII*
	Gregory, *Moralium Libri (continuatio)* (PL 76)
Jer., *In Math.*	Jerome, *Commentariorum in Matheum Libri IV*

The following initials of series are also employed:

CCSL   *Corpus Christianorum Series Latina*
CSEL   *Corpus Scriptorum Ecclesiasticorum Latinorum*
PL   *Patrologia Latina*, ed. J.-P. Migne

Anthologies of critical articles are denoted as follows:

Blanch   R. J. Blanch, ed., *Style and Symbolism in 'Piers Plowman'*
Hussey   S. S. Hussey, ed., *Piers Plowman: Critical Approaches*
Vasta   E. Vasta, ed., *Interpretations of 'Piers Plowman'*

I

PIERS AND THE MODERN READER

Piers Plowman was much read in the first century after its composition, if the numerous variant manuscript copies are anything to go by. The interested would-be reader today may choose from excellent printed editions of three decidedly different but apparently authentic versions, drearily and inescapably called the A, B, and C-texts.[1] The short title commonly used is not necessarily the one the author, William Langland, favoured himself, for none of the surviving manuscipts is contemporary with the poet, and the titles and sub-titles under which we view the poem might or might not have pleased him. Among the recent editors, Kane and Donaldson (who have the roomiest title page) have preferred the explicit *Will's Visions of Piers Plowman, Do-Well, Do-Better and Do-Best*, a title which tells the new reader something of what to expect and avoids the ambiguity of *The Vision of Piers Plowman*. Even this fuller title, however, does not indicate that Piers is an important figure in the later visions too, or that ploughing is probably the least interesting of the things he does. Piers is mysterious and enigmatic in both A and B-versions, especially in the latter. There he does two things in particular which are incomprehensible at first sight: he tears up Truth's letter pardoning him and his companions, and later he shakes and damages the tree he is ostensibly tending, instead of plucking an apple as Will has asked him to do. I imagine that the author grew tired of being asked what he meant by these surprising incidents; at any rate, he cut the pardon-tearing right out of the final version and made a more disagreeable character shake the fruit tree. So perhaps it might be argued that neither action is very important in Langland's scheme of things and it is foolish for critics to become obsessed with them. Some readers take this view. Others simply like Piers to be mysterious and his motives unfathomable. This book is not for them.

Even those who prefer the C-version — and there are certainly some good new passages in it — will probably admit that the B-text is more brilliant, lively, enigmatic and audacious.[2] The revising mind often relinquishes wit and compactness in the interests of greater clarity and a plainer moral message. If the C-version is Langland's (and this I assume without re-opening a once strongly-contested argument),[3] we may deduce that he did not wish to leave his readers mystified as to the function of Piers, but rather intended by the strangeness of his narrative to stir them into energetic rumination. He often delights in being cryptic, but it is hard to believe that he gave many years of his life to writing about the way to salvation without expecting to be understood by

1

the well-intentioned reader. I believe that his Piers is a cryptic symbol, created as such and calling for elucidation. This book tries to shed some light on him.

The appearances of Piers in Will's dreams take up comparatively little space in the narrative. The usual short title, *Piers Plowman*, rightly calls attention to the central importance of Piers in the visions, but obscures the fact that this is substantially a poem about Will and his attempts to find out the truth about the human condition, a poem in which Piers is (on the surface, at any rate) an elusive and not very approachable counsellor for most of the time. The reader accompanies Will through a long life of wandering and frustration and argument, with moments of religious fervour. We cannot help thinking as we read that there must be a lot of the author in the character of Will the Dreamer. However, we distort the poem if we therefore see Piers only through the eyes of that character, as a shadowy ideal dreamed up by Will and private to his imagination. In a recent book, Aers presents a typically modern opinion in taking as his hypothesis that Piers is something like 'the "objective correlative" of the perceiving mind'. He reasonably argues against an opposite view of Piers as 'ideal earthly perfection', but – not quite denying the possibility that Piers exists in his own right – he also says that Piers seems 'a figure with rather less independent existence' than that view assumes.[4] To my mind, the issue is plainer: either Piers is 'out there' for Langland even when Will's perception is still dull, or Piers is brought into being by Will's dreaming imagination. I would put it this way: for Langland, Will's dreams are a window on reality, a reality which exists whether perceived or not, and at best perceivable only in imperfect analogical images. The disclosures made through Will come *pari passu* with the gradual cleansing of Will's perceiving mind, and the changing guise in which he sees Piers reflects his changing comprehension. In a sense, therefore, 'Piers' is a private possession, and, for all we know, the experience of the Dreamer may reflect Langland's memory of his own growth in Christian faith and understanding. But whether Will's quest is retrospectively autobiographical or not, there can be no doubt that what 'Piers' will disclose to 'Will' is already intellectually and imaginatively present in the author's mind early in the poem, when he presents the thick-headed Dreamer in dialogue with Lady Holy Church. The comic and endearing obtuseness of Will is set against the mysterious and beautiful discourse of the Lady.[5] She speaks to him about the divine love which much later in the poem will be given expression in the actions of Piers. Will is made so lifelike that it is quite easy to forget that the author speaks through the mouth of the Lady too. She and her doctrines are obviously not private possessions of the dreaming mind, though she speaks personally to Will. Piers likewise touches Will's life and at one point in the B-text speaks directly to him,[6] but his different aspects also have public significance. The sequence of Piers's strange epiphanies has a rationale in the church doctrines which nourished Langland's imagination and out of which he created an image both traditional and unique. It is my purpose to show how this sequence stands in essential relation to the *Vitae de Dowel, Dobet and Dobest*,[7] and is predictably ordered so as to serve as a matrix against which we may judge how the easily-diverted Will is progressing towards Truth.

The key to a proper understanding of what happens between Will and Piers is the significance inherent in that initial capital letter: for Langland there is only one Truth. The fictive Will is not, in fact, learning to know the truth about himself in the way that a character in a novel might do. He is trying to find a means of reaching Truth, whose hill lies beyond the field of this world. For the medieval Christian, the way to Truth was given in the bible, and therefore Langland 'speaks bible', and Piers as guide has his credentials from the bible, and becomes more and more recognisably a biblical person.[8] While Will's adventures have some of the inconsequentiality of remembered dreams, Piers 'the ploughman' moves in great leaps towards Jerusalem. At the end he is lost to sight, because Will and his companions, whose story this is, are hindered from following him. It is open to any modern reader to think that Langland was absurdly wrong to believe in Truth on his hill, or to question his medieval way of using the bible. It is not, however, open to him to disparage the grandeur of Langland's poetic design as a consequence of blurring his vision through modern spectacles. A character in the poem is permitted to say 'Baw for books!' but it would be unthinkable for anyone to say 'Baw for Truth!' or to tell Piers that Truth's letter was a forgery. The reader must, at the least, suspend disbelief in the authority of the bible: Piers has his being from the interpreted scriptures, he is the guarantee that Truth and his shrine are 'out there', and the three *Vitae* are predicated on the strength of his credibility.

It follows that the reader of *Piers Plowman* needs some general knowledge of the medieval Christian tradition about Truth and the way in which mankind is guided towards Truth. The interpretative critic must make use of extrinsic information, and this has for some time been available in haphazard plenty.[9] As is usually the case when we study an early poem, nothing is known for certain about the books available to the poet. Possible influences are adduced and weighed and disputed. When facts about the author's life are meagre and uncertain, what criterion can we use for choosing what might be relevant to the formation of his religious views?

In considering possible influences on Langland's conception of Piers, I have taken the poet at his word in a quite unsophisticated way, with results that have increased my respect both for his learning and for his individuality. He describes, in the most transparent and (to modern sensibilities) grotesque of his allegories about Piers, how the ploughman harnesses Matthew, Mark, Luke and John as his team, and later four other stout beasts — Augustine, Ambrose, Gregory and Jerome — with whose help he ploughs and harrows and spreads his seed. Some may think that, in this rather heavy-footed and didactic piece of writing, the reference to the four great Latin Doctors of the Church is emptily orthodox. The same might be said of Scripture's earlier eulogy of Augustine and Clergy's praise of 'Gregory þe grete clerke, a good pope in his tyme'; Langland is not necessarily in agreement with Scripture and Clergy. Yet there are other occasional mentions of these authoritative teachers, as in the place where Ambrose and Augustine nourish Conscience at the dinner table, and in none of these mentions can I see reason to doubt that Langland sincerely esteemed their teaching and regarded it as supplementary to the words of the evangelists, as the 'harrowing' allegory implies.[10] Starting from this thought, I have investigated the thinking of one or more of these four interpreters of the bible in regard to themes and texts interwoven in the poem, and found in doing so that Langland's trains of thought became clearer, and in particular that the figure of the ploughman-guide and his transformations became more understandable. I soon came to believe that the

3

poet's professed veneration for Augustine as the great writer on the Trinity was sincere and based on his study of Augustine's personal search for Truth, which is bound up with his theory of love. Others have already noted that ploughing as a metaphor for preaching is elaborated by Gregory:[11] it is in Augustine too. Augustine learnt much from Ambrose, from whose interpretation of the gospels I have gained some insight into the Piers-figure who merges with Peter the Apostle. These three Doctors, I believe, gave Langland the inspiration to create the story of Will's pilgrimage and his visions of Piers. (Jerome is illuminating on some specific points in the narrative, though he does not seem to be so pervasive an influence.) How much of their works Langland had read at first-hand is a matter of surmise: flowers from their great works were of course circulated in various collections and were also frequently quoted or appropriated by later exegetes such as Bede and by many homilists.[12] Langland seems to quote from memory — even the gospels tend to become mingled in his recollection — so it is usually impossible to pinpoint exact sources. Perhaps all one can say is that he is versed in this rather ancient patristic doctrine,[13] which matters so much to him that he is heartily sick of listening to glib professional theologians in his own day using God as a talking-point and equivocating on moral issues. In the poem, Will the Dreamer gets drawn into some highly topical debates, but — with one important exception — Piers does not argue about interpretation of the scriptures. (The exception is his quarrel with the opinionated priest over the effect of Truth's pardon, and this fact in itself makes that incident important.[14]) He stands apart from other characters in the dreams in several respects, and it has seemed to me justifiable and useful to concentrate upon this one figure and the fount from which it comes. Piers does not present the opinions of Langland's contemporaries as such, and I have not tried to investigate the theological climate of Langland's time and place. What I have done is to put together what seems to me pertinent matter drawn from the interpretation of the bible by these principal authorities whom Langland venerates, disclosing (as I believe) the internal logic of Piers's multiple personality and shedding light on some little-understood passages: in particular on the episode of the Tree of Charity. The transformations of Piers are to some degree separate from the story of Will's education, which is governed by its own different strategy; moreover, Will's own words incline the reader to dwell upon the special significance of Piers in his dreams:

> Manye tyme þis metelis han mad me to stodie
> And for peris loue þe plouȝman wel pensif in herte
> [A8:13f; cp. B 7:149; C 9:229]

(The phrase 'for love of Piers the ploughman' is a little startling, and I will return to it later.) Therefore, I shall say very little about Will's incidental discussions with minor characters and practically nothing about the political import of his early dreams. My purpose is to make the direction of Will's quest clearer, and the part that Piers takes in helping Will; where Will rambles off on his own, or seemingly forgets Piers, I do not follow his adventures. One episode, the meeting of Will with Patience, comes dubiously within my purview, because it is only in the C-text that Patience is said to be

4

Ilyk Peres the ploghman, as he a palmere were

[C 15:34]

and only in the C-text does Piers himself speak in this scene [C 15:138 ff.].
I have, however, included a discussion of the episode, because the likeness of
Patience and Piers and the importance of Patience's riddle for the finding of
Piers seem to warrant it.

I have assumed that all three versions are the work of one author, and I use
all three texts as evidence of his thinking. My practice is to quote from the earliest
version, giving line-reference to the corresponding passages in the other text(s),
so that the development of the figure of Piers can be discerned. There is some
variation in line-numbering among the current editions, but it is too slight to
cause difficulty for the reader who wishes to follow up a reference.

In the presentation of illustrative material there is a substantial difficulty.
The sources are all in Latin, as are Langland's own quotations from the bible and
some of his quotations from authoritative writers. Much critical writing about
Piers Plowman assumes the reader's ability to read medieval Latin, though
Langland himself, by choosing to write in English and by explaining most of his
quotations, obviously hoped for a wider readership. The modern editors render
the Latin phrases in his macaronic text at the foot of the page or in the margin,
and several of the patristic works I want to quote are available in English
translations, so there might seem to be no great problem for the twentieth-century
student of the poem. There are, however, two considerations which need to be
honestly faced.

The first is that Langland has been taught to think in Latin about religious
matters. He is also extraordinarily conscious of word-associations, often using
what today would be dismissively called word-play to point up connections of
thought. These associations are plain in the Latin authorities, but they may
disappear altogether in translations not specifically provided to retain the
resemblance. Even Langland's own translations may obscure continuities,
simply because there are no English words precisely apt for his purposes. All his
readers know that he keeps some Latin terms, such as *Liberum Arbitrium* and
Anima, for which there are no co-extensive English equivalents; in other instances
he merely truncates Latin words to anglicise them: such are *Imaginatif*, *rect*,
infinit, *adjectif*. These are rare open instances of the Latin thinking that underlies
his treatment of philosophical or grammatical topics relevant to his religious
purpose. Generally, he finds English words to express religious and philosophical
concepts: for example, 'Kynde love' as an aspect of *caritas*. The English
equivalents fit into their immediate contexts well enough, but they tend to
disguise the lexical sets in which the Latin originals fit together: thus the over-
arching concepts of *justitia* and *caritas* which enclose the various topics of the
dreams will be much less apparent if the Latin words of quoted texts are not also
available. Modern English 'love' and 'charity' have significantly diverged in
meaning; modern English 'justice' and 'goodness' are even further divorced.
This is a consequence of changes in ethical and religious attitudes since the
fourteenth century, coupled with an essentially different understanding of the
relation between word-forms and their meanings. I take it to be the business of
historical criticism to reveal such changes as are relevant to the matter in hand,

and this cannot be done without specific attention to the words translators use in rendering the bible and the biblical commentaries into the common tongue of their readers. I have therefore found it necessary to re-translate in a literal way some biblical and other hallowed expressions which Langland either knew in a different form from the presently familiar one, or would have rendered differently, as far as I can judge.

The prime illustration of the point I am making is the complex of words expressing the concepts covered by the Latin *justitia* and the related *justus*. The modern English words 'justice' and 'just' will carry us across the leap from man's justice (and injustice) to God's absolute *justitia*, but we do not find them in the biblical translations and commentaries where Langland could read *justitia* or *justus*, simply because the English translators (rightly from their point of view) prefer words such as 'righteousness' or 'good' — words which break the semantic pattern which Langland establishes. Jesus died, Ambrose says, *ut impleret justitiam* 'to fulfil justice'.[15] This doctrine is central to Langland's understanding of the Atonement, and he shows interest in the language of the law courts and the administration of justice not as something separate from his religion, but as manifestations of a cardinal principle. To those who have studied the poem this may be obvious enough as a general characteristic of Langland's religious thought, though it may easily escape notice how often he uses quotations containing *justus* and how imaginatively he converts the idea expressed in *ut impleret justitiam* into the concrete terms of 'a justice' son' who comes into the world to 'juste', i.e. to 'joust', and to 'make just', and to 'fulfil justice'. The phrase 'a justice son' [B 16:92; C 18:126] knots together the temporal and atemporal domains. The phrase loses half its point if we do not recall that in church Latin Jesus is called *sol justitiae* 'sun of justice'.[16] The Saviour does battle to ransom the *justus*, the 'just man' of the Old Testament. Langland's strong personal sense of justice makes him peculiarly interested in the fate of the *justus* of the pre-Christian era and of infidel regions. He shows us men falling like fruit from the Tree of Charity and he quotes *Cum ceciderit justus, non collidetur* . . . [B 16:25; not in C]. His Latin quotation (itself concealing a pun on 'bruise'/'hit the ground' in *collidetur*) comes from Psalm 36:24 in the Latin Breviary; it is not in the usual Vulgate version of Jerome (where the *justus* appears earlier, in verse 21).[17] This recall of the psalm well demonstrates my difficulty: how should this verse be translated? In the English bibles we shall not find the word 'just' at all in this psalm, and in the official translations of the Vulgate we shall not find 'just' in this verse. Hence it becomes necessary to make a special translation with 'the just man' or to accept the loss of the sequence *justus* — 'justice' son' — 'juste', part of the larger semantic pattern which includes Imaginatif's quotation of Peter's words *vix salvabitur justus* [B 12:281, recalled in B 13:19; cp. C 14:203 and C 15:21 ff.] and Repentance's quotation of Christ's *non veni vocare justos* [not in A; B 5:499; C 7:139]. There is in fact no entirely suitable English word for *justus*: in the teachings of the four Doctors the word sometimes keeps its root meaning of 'one who lives according to the law' [Latin *jus*], as in the instance quoted above, *non veni vocare justos*, which Ambrose refers to those 'who are confident in the Law and do not seek for the grace of the gospel'.[18] The word 'righteous' has some of these overtones, but it will not suggest the Old Testament Law as the Latin word can do. Each biblical quotation has therefore to be considered in the poetic context: it is evident that to insert the Authorised Version in the passage about the falling fruit will make the reference considerably less apt. As given in Goodridge's translation, the sentence reads 'For it is written, "Though a good man fall, he shall not be cast away: for the Lord upholdeth him with his hand"'.[19] The change of words is slight, but the translation loses both the suggestion of the bruising apple and the reminder of Imaginatif's text 'Scarcely shall the just man be saved', quoted earlier. The consequence of using several such inappropriate translations is inevitably to dull Langland's effects, so I think we have to translate more closely, even though that means forgoing the echoes of church worship which more familiar words might carry. Similar difficulties arise when other authoritative Latin quotations are to be put into English; the available published translations, however good, may interpret rather than simply render the text, and such words as *anima*, *memoria*, *concupiscentia* present pitfalls, without a gloss. With some diffidence, therefore, I make renderings which show my own understanding of the meaning, and place the Latin texts in the notes for the convenience of those who wish to check the originals. However, since in religious matters Langland is weaving an English weft on a warp set up in Latin threads,[20] any attempt to re-state what he is saying in our single tongue inevitably makes the fabric of the composition seem looser than it is.

It even proves necessary occasionally to consider the nature of Latin grammar. Langland, as Ben Smith, Kaske, and Middleton have pointed out in various ways, at times uses the laws of language to illuminate the laws of the Christian moral and intellectual universe.[21] The laws of language for him were naturally those he had been taught in his Latin schooling, and Latin as the language of God's word was thought by medieval scholars to have a direct relationship with entities in God's universe, so that puns or analogies drawn from Latin syntax have an unassailable respectability. A simple but striking instance of this medieval dependence on the *form* of God's word is the interpretation of the plural verb *faciamus* 'let us make' in Genesis 1:26 used by a 'singuler' Person as a mark of the Triune nature of the Creator. Langland uses and develops this traditional idea: the plural verb, he says, signifies that God's Might, his Word, and his Workmanship together made man in his own image [cp. B 9:36; not in C].[22] The grammaticalness of Truth is an essential component in the riddle Patience propounds [cp. B 13:151; not in C] and the riddle cannot be explained without some attention to grammatical theory. Therefore, though it is my intention to avoid pedantry as far as I can, I find myself obliged both to employ some Latin expressions and to examine certain features of Latin phrasing on occasion.

As an essay in what has come to be known as patristic criticism, this study will not appeal to those critics who 'han pepir in the nose' when 'allegorists' or 'exegetes' are mentioned. The four Latin Doctors are all prodigious allegorists, combing the Old Testament and even the gospels for occult meanings: the effect of concentrating on those parts of *Piers Plowman* which depend on the religious tradition is to bring out the figural element in the actions of Piers and Will.[23] I can see no sign of disapproval of the Doctors' exegetical methods in Will's description of the sifting and combining of old and new texts in his last vision of Piers and his team:

7

Oon highte Austyn and Ambrose anoþer
Gregori þe grete clerk and [þe goode Ierom]
Thise foure, þe feiþ to teche, folwede Piers teme
And harewede in an handwhile al holy Scripture
Wiþ two [aiþes] þat þei hadde, an oold and a newe:
Id est vetus testamentum et novum.

[B 19:269ff.; C 21:269ff.]

These are Will the Dreamer's own words near the end of the poem; they are not undercut by suspicion of the dreamer's naivety as, say, his earlier words about Truth's Pardon might be. Nor are they put in the mouth of a possibly self-interested party such as Study or Scripture. My investigations lead me to think that the order of the names here (which is not chronological) indicates the place each Doctor holds in Langland's esteem, and his sense of their importance in promulgating 'þe feiþ'. Elsewhere, the character Scripture is made to single out Augustine above the others:

þe douȝtiest doctour or divynour of þe trinite
þat Austyn þe olde and hiȝeste of þe foure . . .

[A 11:293ff.; B 10:458f.; cp. C 11:289f.]

Thus, appropriately, Augustine is venerated chiefly for his theological insights; Gregory is an authority in a different field, and he is properly praised by Clergy for his moral rather than theological teaching:

Gregory þe grete clerk, a good pope in his tyme
Of religioun þe rewele he reherside in his morals.

[A 11:204f.; B 10:298f.; not in C]

These and other brief mentions do not of course prove that Langland had read *De Trinitate* for himself, or Gregory's *Moralia in Job*, but they do invite the serious student of the poem to consider those books as possible influences on the poet. Whether or not he had studied them, Langland is indebted to ideas promoted in these books, and also, I believe, to Augustine's *Confessiones*, and to his homilies on Christian love which go under the title *Tractatus in Epistolam Iohannis*.[24] From one of these homilies the concept of the Tree of Charity in man's heart seems to be taken.

The direct evidence for Langland's acquaintance with Augustine's *Confessiones* is questionable, but the balance of probability is that, given the poet's own interests, this book would have drawn him like a magnet. Courcelle's research has demonstrated the enormous influence that this autobiographical work had upon European literature throughout the Middle Ages. Its theme is 'a quest for truth', and Courcelle's summary of its essence might almost serve as a description of *Piers Plowman*: 'Le propre des *Confessions* est qu'Augustin y présente sa quête du vrai sous forme d'aveu des péchés'.[25] There are other points of general resemblance between the two works that I want to take up later.

The one roughly-quoted line from the *Confessiones* in Langland's work is not attributed to that book, and what it implies is a matter of argument.[26] The manner in which Scripture[27] introduces the quotation cannot give us much confidence that Langland remembered the book well:

þat [was] austyn þe olde & hiȝeste of þe foure,
Seide þis for a sarmoun, so me god helpe;
Ecce ipsi idiote rapiunt celum, ubi nos sapientes in infernum mergemur.
[A 11:302ff.; B 10:459f.; cp. C 11:290f.]

The B-version of the lines more strongly suggests that the original context of the quotation has been forgotten:

Seide þus in a sermon — I seigh it writen ones —
[B 10:460].

However, if we take the A-text 'for a sarmoun', i.e. 'as a lesson', as Langland's first thought, and the parenthetical 'so me god helpe' as Scripture's wry admission that the most learned of teachers himself knew that even scriptural learning can be a positive hindrance to faith, the A-text makes excellent sense, and for once is more pointed than B. There would be no advantage for Scripture's argument in giving the name of Augustine's book, so we cannot deduce that it was unknown to Langland.

At a later point in the narrative, the C-text has more to say about Augustine's life and writings, and a reference to his personal ecstasy, vague though it is, leads us back to the *Confessiones* and the *De Trinitate*;[28] the passage is much fuller in C than in B (cp. B 10:249ff.):

Austyn þe olde herof made bokes:
Ho was his autor and hym of god tauhte?
Patriarkes and prophetes, apostles and angelis —
And the trewe trinite to Austyn apperede
And he us saide as he sey, and so y bileve
That he seyh þe fader and þe sone and þe seynt spirit togederes
And alle thre bote o god, and herof he made bokes,
Ȝe, busiliche bokes! Ho beth his witnesses?
Ego in patre et pater in me est, et qui me vidit,
patrem meum vidit qui in celis est.
Alle þe clerkes under Crist ne couthe this assoile,
Bote thus hit bilongeth to bileve alle þat liketh to Dowel.
[C 11:149ff.]

Clergy's exclamation in the midst of this, 'Ȝe, busiliche bokes!', is rather disconcerting, but it would be absurd to suppose that Langland does not trust these 'witnesses' to 'the trewe trinite', even if he sometimes feels that 'Clergy' is over-rated. Those who do not know the treatise *De Trinitate* may be unaware that, in spite of its dogmatic title, it is actually, like the autobiographical *Confessiones*, an introspective search for *veritas* 'Truth', the image of God, through self-knowledge and true love. There is ample reason to think that Will's quest had its conceptual source in these two books.

Augustine's books include no guide such as Piers to direct the seeker after truth, and Langland finds a need to voice the question 'Who taught him?' —

Ho was his autor and hym of god tauhte?

and gives the answer:[29]

9

> Patriarkes and prophetes, apostles and angelis —
> And the trewe trinity to Austyn apperede
> And he us saide as he sey . . .

Langland's own understanding of the process of divine revelation in the saint is set out for us here: God in Trinity appeared to Augustine in one brief illumination, but he had learnt and continued to learn about God from the four named kinds of witness, whose words recorded in the bible combine into one *autor* leading him towards the truth. Have we not here a clue to the way Langland conceived the process of Will's spiritual enlightenment under the guidance and example of the gradually transformed Piers?

Many readers have concluded that in some sense or other the Piers-figure 'stands for God's ministry on earth', but there are several discordant voices when an attempt is made to describe him more precisely.[30] In adding one more voice I hope to harmonise and help to validate some of the perceptions already published, while adding my own interpretation of the first two epiphanies in particular and removing some misconceptions about the third.

My sub-title calls for some comment, though its relevance will disclose itself as the argument proceeds. Will the Dreamer hopes to find the 'tresor' described to him by Lady Holy Church; we are not told that he does find it, but his hopes rise when he comes close to Piers. In some sense, Piers is the way to Truth, and in him Will sees, however indistinctly, the image of Truth. To suggest both the treasure and God's image in man, associated with a traditional doctrine that God demands tribute in his own coin from those who aspire to Do-Best, I can find no better symbol than God's penny. To think of Piers as a dirty silver denarius is bizarre, and Langland is wise enough not to unite this image explicitly with the man who haunts Will's dreams. Nonetheless, he is sufficiently familiar with the metaphor to use it casually to contrast the false coin with the true (in the passage about 'Lussheborwes' and sterling [cp. B 15:342ff.; C 17:72ff.]).[31] Since the patristic doctrine which underlies the comparison unites the moral and theological aspects of Will's quest in some unsuspected ways, I have used this metaphor as the meeting-point of Langland's superficially various themes in the *Visio* and the *Vitae*. The coin image is a reminder of Lady Holy Church's contrast between the worldly and the seekers after Truth. The worldly pay tribute only to 'King Caesar', the prince of this world, using *his* penny. The others pay to God what he demands, namely (as the Doctors understood the text to imply), their souls — each, as it were, a coin with the divine likeness stamped upon it. Piers, the exemplary figure, is presented as a holier person each time he reappears: in the language of the metaphor, the true coin is burnished so that the King's image upon it is increasingly discernible. This being granted, it might be expected that each epiphany would hold a proper place in the process of revelation as shown in the bible, in addition to its place in the gradual enlightenment of the watcher Will. Keeping in mind, therefore, both the traditional history of mankind's salvation and Augustine's theory of love as the only restorative for the individual soul bereft of its god-likeness, I attempt to throw fresh light on Piers and his role in the structure of the poem.[32]

10

II

THE EPIPHANIES OF PIERS

I

There is unexpectedly little about agriculture as such in *Piers Plowman*. Under cover of Will's dreams, Langland sketches a lively picture of both town and country folk living their lives in the grip of self-interest and the love of money. Will's questioning of the point of it all begins with his own interest in wealth and his desire to get the best for himself. Money, wealth, treasure come frequently into the poem, sometimes in real-life incidents, sometimes in metaphor. Will wants to find Truth because Truth is treasure. Holy Church urges him to value and look for God's coin rather than coin of the realm: hence the sub-title of this book.

Will and crowds of his neighbours fully intend to find this treasure, but they have no idea of the way to it until Piers puts his head out and tells them that he knows Truth 'naturally'. By this point the seekers have realised that Truth is more like something in a shrine than a crock of gold, and they propose to hire the ploughman Piers as their guide on a mass pilgrimage. Piers rejects their money, but promises to take them when he has finished his ploughing. The pilgrimage is held up while the farm work is being done, and the start of the corporate journey is never described. The crowd disappears out of the dream-world and Will pursues his quest alone, with some help much later from an increasingly elusive and (to him) mystifying Piers. In the course of the *Vitae*, Will changes from being an amazed and curious onlooker to being a penitent and involved pilgrim, but he does not climb Truth's hill or find a resting place.

In modern times it has been a common practice to read and study Will's first two visions (to the end of Passus 8 in A, Passus 7 in B) as a poem complete in itself, a practice encouraged by some of the scribes of our extant manuscripts who put *Explicit* to signal the end of William's *Vision of Piers the Ploughman* at this juncture. Many readers may be acquainted only with the Piers who ploughs his half-acre and receives Truth's pardon: that is, the Piers of the A-text, refashioned in B. It may therefore be desirable to recall the various guises and the remarkably strange actions of Piers during the course of the three versions.

In the first vision he is introduced as an exemplary working man leading a decent Christian life. Yet even in this scene he is no ordinary ploughman. His wife and children have abstract, allegorical names.[1] Even the knight recognises his authority: he is well able to organise a proper division of labour to provide food

11

for everyone, to put down crime, to call up Hunger, and to quote scripture at the priest. His efforts fail to produce a contented community because he comes up against the shirkers and the parasites, but his political ideals are remarkably impressive. When Truth sends a pardon to him and all his people, including his posterity, it looks as if a seal of approval has been set on this reformed society, and that Langland is presenting a political solution to the world's problems. Any satisfaction that we share with Piers at this stage is utterly shaken when Piers tears the document in two and vows to cease his sowing [A 8:100ff.; B 7:119ff.; in the C-text neither the action nor the words appear]. In this moment of violent emotion, Piers's quiet self-confidence (for þauh I sigge hit myself, I serve him to paye [A 6:39; B 5:549; C 7:193]) is destroyed, and Will's confidence in him as the leader to be followed takes a knock. The A-version rounds off the scene by reminding the reader of the significance of certain dreams in the bible, so implying that Will's dream of the torn pardon has its serious import: letters of Indulgence, as he says, are no substitute for a life of good works (Dowel) on Doomsday, and we must pray for grace to live as Dowel requires. So the scene leads gracefully into the next, in which Will searches for Dowel: in the A-text there are three more passus in which Will tries to learn about Dowel from Wit and Study, among others, and is reminded that the faith of poor sinners has sometimes saved them while great scholars have gone utterly astray. In this section of the poem, Piers seems to be forgotten.[2] Thus in the A-text the consequences for Piers of his abrupt change of heart are not considered at all, and the tearing of Truth's pardon is left unexplained.

Oddly, it is in the C-version only that Piers next makes his presence known, at the dinner party in which Conscience entertains Clergy and Reason, Patience and Will and the gluttonous Friar [C 15:138ff.]. There is no hint that Piers is one of those at table, and the C-text only provides two references to him before his unexpected speech and unnoticed departure. The first describes Patience begging as if he were a palmer, 'like Piers the ploughman' [C 15:34], a phrase which would hardly suggest that Piers himself is present. The second is Clergy's deferential mention of him as *Peres þe palmare ʒent*, 'Piers the noble palmer' [C 15:131f.], whose teaching, he says, once impugned other kinds of knowledge. Immediately after Clergy has spoken, we read:

Quod Peres the ploghman: *Pacientes vincunt,*

and there follow ten lines in which Piers preaches love of God and one's enemy. He then goes quietly out, and Reason runs after him.

The gist of the same speech was put in the mouth of Patience in the earlier B-text; there, Piers is not called a palmer, and Conscience speaks of Piers's coming *in the future* to prove his words in deeds:

Thanne passe we over til Piers come and preve this in dede
[B 13:133].

The presence of Piers in the C-version of this dinner party scene thus has the marks of an afterthought, and, like several of the C-additions, it comes in awkwardly. The blunt 'Quod Peres the ploghman' is not sufficient to integrate Piers in the dramatic action. In the C-version Piers has not previously announced his intention of leading a more spiritual life, trusting in God for his sustenance

12

(as he did in B 7:118ff.), so his appearance as a palmer is very abruptly introduced. Piers the palmer is no doubt brought in to provide a second vision of Piers in the C-text, which will take the place of Piers the gardener, seen very vigorously active as guardian of the Tree in B 16:21ff., but replaced in that role in C by another character [cp. C 18:3ff.]. The two alterations in C bring the versions into line again, so that the third dream-appearance is the same in both texts.

This third appearance is so strange and awesome that Will the dreamer is not sure whether he sees Piers or not: he has to ask of Faith 'Is Piers in þis place?' [B 18:21, C 20:19], to be told in answer that it is *Jesus* wearing the surcoat of Piers, concealing his godhead in the ploughman's cloak. Again, in his next dream, Will sees the Knight, this time painted with blood and carrying a cross, and again he is unsure of his identity:

> 'Is þis Iesus þe Iustere,' quod I, þat Iewes did to deþe?
> Or is it Piers þe Plowman?
>
> [B 19:10f.; C 21:10f.]

He is answered now by Conscience: the blood-stained Knight is *Christ*, though the colours and the armour are those of Piers. Conscience further explains to him how Jesus became Christ the Conqueror through his doughty life and death on earth, and how he appeared to his followers after his resurrection. This account describes the life of Jesus in terms of Dowel, Dobet and Dobest, and with the mention of Dobest Piers the ploughman is named once more.

Conscience describes how the risen Christ came amongst Peter and his apostles, though the door of the house was barred, and how he made Thomas feel his fleshly heart:

> And whan þis dede was doon do best he [þouȝte],
> And yaf Piers [pardon, and power] he grauntede hym,
> Myght [men] to assoille of alle manere synne[s],
> To alle maner men mercy and forȝifnesse
> In covenaunt þat þei come and knewelich[e] to paie
> To Piers pardon þe Plowman *redde quod debes.*
> Thus haþ Piers power, b[e] his pardon paied,
> To bynde and unbynde boþe here and elli[s],
> And assoille men of alle synnes save of dette one.
>
> [B 19:183ff.; C 21:183ff.]

In this undisguised fashion the name *Peter* is replaced by the name *Piers* in the gospel account. The lines that immediately follow tell of Christ's ascent into heaven 'anoon after' and his promise to come again at the Last Day to judge and reward. Thus Will has been taught by Conscience to think of St Peter as Piers, and as the dream changes Will kneels before the cross and sees Piers again:

> and þanne cam, me þouȝte
> Oon Spiritus paraclitus to Piers and to hise felawes.
> In liknesse of a lightnynge he lighte on hem alle
> And made hem konne and knowe alle kynne langages.
>
> [B 19:200ff.; C 21:200ff.]

In this way the poet introduces the Piers who uses his plough in the service of

Grace. He is appointed the agent, reeve, registrar and purveyor of Grace, and his work is to till Truth [B 19:258ff.; C 21:258ff.]. Piers undergoes no further transformations: he builds a barn and works at the metaphorical ploughing, sowing and harvesting that his master requires.

II

The things that we can validly say about the figure of Piers are so multifarious that critics may conclude (and often do) that Langland was trying to express the inexpressible, or that he changed his concept of Piers during the long process of composition. Piers holds the poem together, or fails to do so, according to the reader's understanding of him.

It may be helpful at this stage to consider what kind of literary life he has. Are we to respond as to a fictional human being like the King Arthur of the romances, to a personification like Redcrosse in *The Faerie Queene*, to a supposedly historical example like Abraham in the Book of Genesis, to a parable figure like the Unjust Steward, or to a parable symbol like the Pearl of Great Price? A similar problem of mode in the dream-vision faces us when we approach the anonymous contemporary poem *Pearl*: the dreamer sees a lovely young girl who guides him to a Christian understanding of life after death. Within the poem, the girl is Pearl-like in her beauty and perfection; she seems both human and more than human. In *Piers Plowman* the dreamer sees an old ploughman, in some respects Christ-like, who guides him to a better understanding of the good life. If we were to say in the one instance, the child of the dream is the Pearl of Great Price we should be aware that the statement was figurative. When Langland says of his ploughman *Petrus, id est, Christus* [B 15:206] we are nonplussed; we do not know what kind of statement it is. Are we to think that Piers *is* Christ come again to earth in disguise? But this cannot be so, for by Passus 19 Piers *is* quite unmistakably St Peter founding the church. We might fall back upon the idea that there is some Piers-quality which the English ploughman shares with Christ and Peter: is it simply humanity? Is Piers representative of mankind? Up to a point this interpretation satisfies. We can see the early Piers as the typical son of Adam, in the sweat of his face winning bread from the earth [cp. *Gen.* 3:19], appearing in the later visions as Christ the second Adam, and as St Peter the provider of spiritual food. But there are some objections to this view: it does not account for the authority of the Piers who organises the would-be pilgrims in the *Visio*, and it does not explain the strange allegorical names of his wife and children. Nor does it explain why Will expresses deep love for him even before he has seen him in his Christ-like guise. What does Will love in the plough-man of his vision? He admires him, we may say, because he is honest and fair and compassionate in his dealings with his fellow-men, but what cause has he to *love* him?

This question may help us to approach the fundamental question of the mode of Piers's literary being by another route, avoiding the impasse which faces us at *id est*. In the *De Trinitate*, Augustine desires his reader to love Truth, as Langland does in his poem. But he is well aware that to 'love' what we can neither see nor even imagine in any ordinary way is to love in no familiar sense of that verb. He therefore prefaces his main enquiry with a more general consideration of what it can mean to love someone we only know from written records. He believes that he loves the apostle Paul, and he analyses how this can be so:

> Come back with me then, and let us consider why we love the apostle. Assuredly not because of that human form which we know well and attribute to him because we believe him to have been a man? Not so: else what we love no longer exists, since that man is now no more; for his soul is parted from his body. But we believe that what we love in him still lives on; for we love the righteous soul. But this implies that we can move from the general to the specific — that we know what 'a soul' is, and what 'righteous' is.[3]

He then argues that we all know what a soul is, because we have one. His word for 'righteous' is *justus*: somehow we *know* what *justus* means, before we are 'righteous' ourselves. This kind of knowledge comes, he thinks, from an 'inward truth'. The only way in which a soul can become righteous [*justus*] is by holding to the pattern [*forma*] of righteousness [*justitia*] which it can contemplate within itself: 'Thus love for the man who is believed righteous is based upon that pattern and truth which he who loves perceives and understands in himself'.[4] Augustine's way of explaining how we can love the soul of a holy man whom we cannot meet in the flesh may help us to clarify that 'Piers-quality' shared by the ploughman, Christ, and St Peter which from the first generates love in Will, and causes him to engage in dialogue with his own soul [*Anima*] in his search for 'that inward pattern and truth' which will tell him how to Do-Well and to reach Truth itself.

As Augustine develops his argument, he insists that the searching soul must first learn 'the nature of true love — or rather the nature of love, for only the love which is true deserves the name. All other is cupidity . . . For this is true love, that we *live justly* [*juste vivamus*] clinging to truth, and on that account we put no value on any mortal things compared with the love of men through which we desire them to live justly'.[5] Following a similar path, Will the dreamer, learning to love, has first to recognise cupidity for what it is (pondering the power of Lady Meed) before he can discover for himself the validity of Piers's (and Augustine's) teaching that God is not to be found in travelling the earth but rather in his own heart:

> Thow shalt see in thiselve Truthe sitte in thyn herte
> In a cheyne of charite, as thow a child were
> To suffre him and segge noght ayein thi sires wille.
> $$\text{[B 5:607ff.; cp. C 7:255ff.]}$$

Augustine expresses his belief that we shall find this inward truth and love if we love our brother man. If we desire the welfare of our neighbour we exercise the true love which is an inward part of our being. He amplifies this thought:

15

Lo, *God is* Love. Why should we go rushing to the height of the heavens or the depths of the earth looking for him who is in us if we are willing to be in him? Let no one say, 'I do not know what I am to love'. Let him love his brother and he will love that same Love; for he knows the Love through which he loves better than the brother whom he loves. God can be more clearly known because more present; more known because more inward; more known because more sure.[6]

Thus, in *De Trinitate*, Augustine joins together the love of God and neighbour, and arrives in exaltation at his proof-text: *Quoniam deus caritas est, et qui manet in caritate in deo manet* [1 *Ioh.* 4:8].[7] A similar belief infused *Piers Plowman*, uniting the search for Dowel and its mainly social concerns with the pilgrimage to St Truth: they are discovered to be one and the same progress towards the restoration of man to his true self. Langland's Wit puts the belief plainly, using the same text as testimony:

> And alle that lyven good lif are lik to God almyghty:
> *Qui manet in caritate, in Deo manet, etc.*
>
> [B 9:64f.][8]

Any man who follows Piers's road will become more and more Christ-like; that is, more God-like (according to the evangelists). If we examine Augustine's argument further, we observe that he describes the sin of pride as a cancer, destroying the health of the inner man so that he can no longer discern God naturally by reason of his inborn likeness to his Maker. The conclusion reached in this chapter is that the soul must be cleansed of pride and cupidity before it can begin to recover its natural understanding of Truth, an understanding which has degenerated but is never entirely lost. By willing the welfare of his brother man, the questing soul recovers the capacity to *love*, i.e. to know God and to be in the presence of God. Only when it is filled with love will the soul really know what goodness is and what is meant by living well [*juste*]. The reader of *Piers Plowman* will find this doctrine quite familiar. Langland plots Will's progress from his confessed lack of 'kynde knowing' of Truth [cp. A 1:127; B 1:138; C 1:136], through an intellectual search for Dowel hampered by pride (note Anima's rebuke to his ambitious wish to know 'kyndely' all the knowledge in the world as being like Lucifer's lust [B 15:49ff.; C 16:210ff.]) to a 'lovedreem'[9] which begins his spiritual movement towards Calvary and his vision of Christ. Nevertheless, though he grows in understanding of Truth, Will remains entangled in the love of the world: we do not see him climb Truth's holy hill. The part played by Piers is very different. He from the first claims to know Truth 'kyndely', and in his various guises he acts as an example and pattern of righteousness which draws Will to him even while the dreamer only obscurely knows what he is looking for. Will, taught by Holy Church, is looking for nothing less than the very pattern of love and goodness, that which *is* love and goodness. Augustine, in the chapter from which I have been quoting, insists on the supreme reality of the pattern itself, and he sees in the life of the apostles and other holy men something that kindles *caritas* in other people:

So the love we bear for that pattern [*forma*] which we believe they followed in their lives leads us to love those lives themselves, and their life, when we believe it, excites in us a more ardent charity towards that same pattern; so that the more ardently we love God, the more surely and more clearly we see him; because in God we perceive the unchanging pattern of righteousness [*forma justitiae*], in accord with which we judge that a man ought to live.[10]

Piers, the just man of Langland's poem, embodies, I would suggest, that 'pattern of righteousness' which has the power to stir Will to 'a more ardent charity'. This view of Piers, which would make him neither a single soul nor mankind as a whole, still less a literary personification as such, will need some refining, but from this standpoint we can begin to see more clearly how Will and Piers interact within the scheme of the poem.

> But here let us pause in our exertions: not supposing that we have found what we are looking for, but rather, as happens, that we have found the the place in which to look. The thing is not found yet, but where it can be looked for has been discovered. What has been said is enough: we shall be able to weave the rest from a new starting-point.[11]

So Augustine ends the first part of his investigation in *De Trinitate*, and in the same spirit I now want to approach the transformations of Piers from another point of view.

III

Before the *Vita de Dowel* begins, Piers the faithful ploughman undergoes a painful spiritual awakening. When the import of Truth's 'pardon' comes home to him, he is both angry and sorrowful, and he vows to change his way of life [A 8:100ff.; B 7:119ff.; not in C]. The significance of the pardon and his violent reaction will require special consideration below, but the fact of his sudden conversion to a life of prayers and penance calls for explanation, if, as I have argued, he presents a pattern of goodness for Will to follow. It is evident that he cannot be a pattern of *perfection*,[12] since he himself sees his need for penance. He speaks as if his values had been wrong all his life, in spite of his loyal service to Truth, and this moment of shock has proved a source of confusion to interpreters of the poem. Again, Augustine's personal search for Truth can help us. In his autobiographical *Confessiones*, he describes how, while reading the bible, he suddenly found that the words held a new and potent meaning which caused him to cry out in an intensity of feeling. Importantly, as we shall see, for our understanding of the themes of 'letter and spirit', Old Law and New Law, as they bear on the change in Piers, Augustine's sudden spiritual illumination brought the words of the psalms he was reading to new life. The passage is worth recalling:

> And I cried out, as I read this outside me and felt its meaning within me.
> I did not wish to be 'increased' in worldly goods, wasting time and wasted

17

by time, since I should have in eternal simplicity other 'corn and wine and oil'.[13]

(The second sentence echoes Psalm 4, which he was reading when the illumination came.) The phrase here rendered 'felt its meaning within me' [*agnoscens intus*] has a peculiar ambiguity. Pusey's translation brings out the sense explicitly: 'as I read this outwardly, finding it inwardly'. The earliest English translator of the *Confessiones*, Tobie Matthew (1620), expands what the phrase implies: 'reading these things in the letter and finding them to be verified in the spirit'.[14] Augustine is saying that the man he *was* before this moment could see the literal meaning of the psalm, but the man he now *becomes* can *feel* its meaning for his own life. In the language of St Paul, he has been transformed from 'carnal' or 'animal' man into 'spiritual' man.

This is the transformation which Dunning recognised in Piers, in his important article published in 1956, though he did not speculate on the source of Langland's inspiration.[15] Piers, it will be remembered, quotes verses from the Psalms as he vows to be less busy about his 'bely ioye' in the future.[16] His first text is *Si ambulavero in medio umbre mortis Non timebo mala, etc.* [B 7:120, not in C]. The significance of this psalm-verse and the following verse 'Thy rod and thy staff, they comfort me' is very clear in Augustine's later gloss on the verses:

Even if I walk in the midst of this life, which is the shadow of death . . .
Thy discipline, like a stick to a flock of sheep and like a rod to sons who are growing and rising from the animal life to the spiritual, do not afflict me, they are more of a comfort, because thou art mindful of me.[17]

What I deduce from a comparison of this incident in Augustine's life with the changes in Piers in the poem is that the 'pattern' which is to kindle *caritas* in Will (and in the reader) first 'grows and rises from the animal life to the spiritual' and then becomes more and more illuminating in the way that the people of the bible may become greater witnesses of divine love when their words and deeds are felt 'in the spirit' by the receptive soul. Augustine's description of the new meaning for himself of the old words of the psalmist is purely autobiographical, but it is also testimony of the prophetic power of David's inspired language. For Augustine, beginning to do well, as Langland too recognises, involves reading the bible with the heart, finding new meaning in the old texts. The infusion of new meaning into the old scriptures was traditionally supposed to be figured in the gospel by the changing into wine of the jars of water at the marriage in Cana, the first public miracle performed by Jesus; it is later recalled by Langland in these words:

In his Iuventee þis Iesus at Iewene feeste
Water into wyn turnede, as holy writ telleþ.
And þere bigan god of his grace to do wel:
For wyn is likned to lawe and lif holynesse,
And lawe lakkede þo for men lovede noȝt hir enemys
And crist counseileþ þus and comaundeþ boþe,
[Boþe] to lered and to lewede, to lovyen oure enemys.
[B 19:108ff.; C 21:110]

The implication of this passage is that the *Vita de Dowel* will be accompanied by a new understanding of the meaning of the scriptures. The old ploughman, Piers, quits Will's *Visio* after such a moment of revelation as Augustine describes, and until this happens the *Vita de Dowel* does not begin. The exemplary man whom Will has been admiring has to be seen with other eyes before he can lead the folk on their pilgrimage, and when he appears again in Will's dreams he hardly seems to be the same person.

The spiritual reawakening of Piers may thus be regarded as an essential feature of the journey towards Truth, and it is bound up with the difference between Old Testament and New Testament revelations of God. The gradual disclosure of the Christ-likeness of Piers has some affinity with the revelatory process shown forth in the bible itself, in which various prophets, and especially the psalmist, are understood in later years to be foretelling the Incarnation of God and his descent into hell to free mankind.

III

IMAGES AND TRANSFORMATIONS

If I am moving in the right direction by finding in Piers the Christian's pattern, the *forma justitiae*, which is nothing less than man bearing the Image of God, dimmed since the Fall but recoverable in the new life of Grace, the patristic symbol of the coin with its scarcely-decipherable head of the King would manifestly provide an analogical metaphor for the poet. Equally manifestly, it is not a metaphor which permits extension in dramatic form, and therefore the poet must look elsewhere for images which can be activated in his plot. Where could he turn for an acceptable image other than to Jesus, whom the bible calls 'the image of his glory'?[1] In some fashion he must confess that the pattern is Christ (*Petrus, id est Christus*), albeit disguised, as he is in the Messianic prophecies and (as was thought) in some of the parables and miraculous events of the gospels.

Am I in danger of losing sight of the undisguised realities of the poem? It has certain practical aims; it urges moral, social and political reforms; it satirises hypocrites, and hints that a ploughman might be a better example to follow than a cardinal. If the main practical purpose were to present Christ in a humble working man (a tacit — or more or less tacit — derogation of the princes of the church), why not Piers the Carpenter as the hero? Or if to present Christianity in the simplicity of the first apostolic mission, why not Piers the Fisherman? Why Piers the ploughman, Piers the gardener, Piers the knight who lends his 'cote armure' and his plate-armour to the jouster,[2] and Piers the harvester? When I ask the questions like this, I see my way to an answer. Jesus in the carpenter's shop and Peter in his fishing-boat belong to 'the real world': metaphors can of course be derived from their activities, as when Peter is called 'a fisher of men'.[3] But the activities of ploughing, gardening, jousting, reaping are not labours that Jesus and his disciples actually engaged in: these unhistoric actions *force* a symbolic reading not bounded by time. They release their meaning only as we ponder what ploughing, gardening and jousting are *for*, and so they work upon us like the cryptic sayings of the bible, revealing Truth *per speculum et in aenigmate*.[4]

The parables of the New Testament and some of the more obscure sayings of the prophets were normally read as allegory in the Middle Ages, as any dip into the regular commentaries will show. The derived secondary senses tend to become permanently attached to the texts and then they do not have to be made explicit in use. In the tradition of the commentaries, the penny promised to the vineyard labourers as their wages signifies (even to Jerome, a comparatively restrained allegorist) the familiar coin 'which bears the image of the king', implying that the reward God offers to his faithful servants is 'his own image and similitude'.[5] So the work of priests as God's labourers brings naturally to Langland's mind both 'Go into my vineyard' and 'cristes tresor' [cp. B 10:480ff.], the salvation of souls. For him, Holy Church is speaking quite plainly when she tells Will the dreamer that the man who lives in truth and charity 'is a god be þe gospel on grounde and on lofte' [cp. A 1:86ff., B 1:88ff.; C 1:86ff., interpreting *Luc.* 8:21, and perhaps *Luc.* 6:35 and *Jo.* 10:34]. The Lost Coin of the parable in *Luc.* 15:8ff. invites further extension of the allegory and enriches the concept of 'cristes tresor'. Ambrose interprets the lost coin with a pun on *census* and *pretium* which interlocks the separate doctrines: that each soul has a value (*pretium*), the sum of souls making up the wealth (*census*) of the Church; and that the king's image on the coin (*imago regis*) is the mark of its value, its enfranchising possession (*census*) which gives it the right to be included in the treasury.[6] Langland, as mentioned before, does not expressly identify the exemplary Piers with the coin that will be included in God's treasure; instead he warns the hypocritical priests who contrast with Piers that they are like bad pennies, apparently bearing the king's mark, but inwardly adulterated and destined to be rejected when God weighs them at the judgement [cp. B 15:349ff. and C 17:72ff.], so making a variation of Ambrose's idea that the image on the coin will make it acceptable to God. Though I quote the idea from Ambrose, such allegorical symbols became common property, as Raw has noted,[7] and we have no means of tracing the transmission of the symbol to Langland. (This point applies to all the parable symbols I am discussing.)

The two parables of the Sower (cp. *Matt.* 13:3ff., *Luc.* 8:5, *Marc.* 4:3ff.) likewise pass into the tradition with orthodox extensions of their original significance, and Langland's ploughman-harvester obviously has a model here. The derived doctrine of the three different yields of 'fruit' produced from the Sower's tillage creates the idea that there are *three stages* of spiritual growth (suggesting the three *Vitae*) and also the idea that there are three classes of good souls, the wedded, the widowed or continent, and the virgin, ranged in order of their dedication to eternal Love.[8] These ideas are completely absorbed by Langland and imaged afresh in Piers's fruit.

Meanings traditionally attached to the parable of the Samaritan similarly become part of the poet's material.[9] The distinction between the *parable* and *allegorical* significances is very clear to see in this instance. As a parable, the story answered the question 'Who is my neighbour?' by showing a foreigner taking care of a wounded Jew after his own priests had ignored his plight. As an allegory (as the four Doctors read it) the wounded man is Adam, mankind set upon by the Devil: the Jewish priests do not help him, but Christ, in the guise of the Samaritan, lifts him up and heals his wounds. The derived, allegorical meaning became so much a part of the faith that it needed no explanation. There is a very good illustration of its living significance for Augustine near the end of *De Trinitate*, when he addresses his own soul:

And you, my soul, where do you feel that you are? Where do you lie, where do you stand, until he who has shown mercy upon all your sins shall heal all your sicknesses? Doubtless, you find yourself in that inn to which the Samaritan brought the man who was found half dead from the many wounds laid on him by the robbers.[10]

In a different context, the same writer would find the main purport of the story to be helplessness of the patriarchs and prophets to bring about the recovery of fallen man, or, in other words, the inefficacy of the Old Law to bring men to salvation.[11]

The allegorised parables can be seen to offer scriptural models of a semi-dramatic kind uniquely apt for presenting 'in an enigma' a revelation of God working in and through mankind. What is more, the common store of derived meanings could provide the poet with links of allusion to join one narrative episode with another. Thus the ripening ears of corn produced by the Sower merge with the ripening fruit on the Tree, and the fallen and bruised fruit of the Tree with the bruised and prostrate traveller.[12] These links of habitual association have been to a large extent broken in recent times, and one of the effects of this has been to fragment some of our early religious poetry. The critic is forced to attempt a reconstruction (though to spell out the point of an allusion is inevitably to dissipate whatever natural appeal there was in its allusiveness, and to accentuate what might be called cleverness in the composition).

There can be no gainsaying that Langland exploits the derived meanings of the Sower and the Samaritan parables. He also incorporates the derived Christian meanings of such Jewish events as the breaking of the tablets of stone on Sinai, and the meaning of such dark sayings as Isaiah's 'Why are your garments red . . .?' [cp. *Isa.* 63:2].[13] These supposed prophecies are brought vividly to life, not as matters of past history, but as part of the revelation present in Will's mind. I do not think we disparage Langland by acknowledging that he was sustained in his re-creation of the history of salvation by a host of other artists in stone, stained glass, and dramatic presentation — and of course by the preachers with their own verbal art. All these had brought the major prophecies, signs, and parables into everyone's consciousness, literate and illiterate alike.

In order to derive Christian truths from the cryptic sayings and pregnant events of the Old Testament it was the practice from the time of the apostles to combine and harmonise selected texts. (This is one of the methods by which the four Doctors 'harrow' after Piers's seed has been planted.) A medieval poet thus inherited a number of thematic schemes created from these interdependent texts: some he would know from the church services, some from homilies and biblical commentaries. Drawing on them, he could evoke a dense cluster of doctrines in comparatively few words, as is the case with Langland's Tree of Charity. A given text may occur in several schemes and it is quite possible for the modern explicator to bark up the wrong tree. My experience has been that certain associations of texts favoured by Augustine have suggested submerged trains of thought beneath the surface of *Piers Plowman*. As a pertinent illustration of this kind of textual linking, I return now to the associations of Psalm 4 as they appeared to Augustine in his moment of enlightenment at Cassiciacum. The passage illustrates the secondary meanings which the psalm then came to hold for him, several of which bear on the theme of a quest for the true good.

What is described by him is a new life inwardly entered upon. He uses here some of the language of Paul, who taught his disciples each to cast off his old self — the 'old man' — and to 'put on' the new self which could grow in likeness to God. The two kinds of life are treated in three of Paul's epistles: in the Epistle to the Galatians he characterises them in a metaphor of 'sowing' and 'reaping' first 'in the flesh' and then 'in the spirit' [cp. *Gal.* 6:7ff.]. There he includes the phrase *dum tempus habemus* [v.1. *est*] *operemur bonum* 'while we have [*or* there is] time, let us do good'.[14] Langland's adoption of the first part of this phrase as the name of Piers's wife in the *Visio* suggests that he planned to bring out this Pauline contrast between carnal and spiritual sowing through the figure of Piers and his work on the half-acre. What he required was a means of presenting this vital conversion, since the parable figures I have been discussing do not undergo a personal change. Augustine's meditations on Psalm 4 as he described his own conversion would give him a model. A cluster of scriptural doctrines is attached to the question 'Who can show us any good?' The psalmist's question [cp. *Ps.* 4:7] is essentially that which the pilgrims of the *Visio* are asking when Piers comes on the scene. Augustine's 'inward' reading of an answer in the next sentence of the psalm itself: *Signatum est super nos lumen vultus tui, Domine*, 'stamped upon us is the light of thy countenance, O Lord',[15] rather surprisingly involves the whole doctrine we have seen accruing to the coin-image, assuring Augustine that true goodness is discoverable within oneself when the dimming effect of sin is penitentially removed. This belief leads him to a personal interpretation of the preceding psalm-verses: the obscure words 'Sacrifice the sacrifice of justice and hope in the Lord' [*Ps.* 4:5] [16] imply for him that he must slay his former sinful self — 'the old man' in Paul's terms — which must be 'sacrificed' in an act of penance, so that a new life of spiritual joy can ensue. Out of his contrition and grief comes a hope which he desires to share with the other hungry souls who are starving in spite of an abundance of corn and wine and oil. There is a striking similarity here to the events at the end of the *Visio*, when the old man, Piers, vows to give up his sowing and concern for 'bely joye' and instead to take a plough of prayers and penance [B 7:115ff.; cp. A 8:102ff.; not in C]. So apt is this sequence to explain Piers's conversion to a new life that I have used Augustine's account of this experience more fully later in the book in discussing Piers's 'tene' and the tearing of the Pardon. The central text from Psalm 4, the *lumen vultus Domini* verse, has been seen by others to be illuminating for *Piers Plowman*, and its association with the coin-image remarked: Smith notably used it in his attempt to solve Patience's riddle, quoting Augustine's *Enarrationes in Psalmos* as witness that this verse 'was conventionally connected with the denarius mentioned in *Matt.* xxii, 17-21'.[17] But I do not recall that any interpreter of the poem has observed the *context* of the *lumen vultus Domini* verse, or the train of thought it initiates in the *Confessiones*, significant as these are as parallels to the movement in Langland's poem from the general labouring of the folk to satisfy Hunger to the personal introspective pilgrimage which brings hope and spiritual joy to Will.[18]

The connections and reinterpretations of texts sketched above bring into being a doctrine of spiritual growth which involves penitence and a re-dedication of life. These are associated with the death of the 'old man', and an inner quest for the *imago dei*. This quest, as I have summarised it from Augustine's account of his own experience, is an active progress in learning to love God in oneself and in others; as the soul progresses in love, the light of God's countenance becomes

23

visible, the man grows in likeness to his Maker; the coin is brightened, the royal stamp is clear upon it. Then the burnished coin can be rendered to God and accepted into his treasury. In this metaphorical language the doctrine is intellectually comprehensible but (as with all such analogies) translation into fictional activity, the external manifestation of the soul's progress, proves impossible.[19] The gradual restoration of the *imago dei* in man defeats the resources of fictional allegory. Piers, as the pattern who is to reveal the nature of *justitia* and *caritas*, must impress the reader as more and more god-like as he draws the errant Will after him towards Truth. This cannot be done by direct means: if it is achievable at all, it can only be done by recall of the biblical revelation of God. It is noteworthy that the final epiphany of Piers is as the Apostle Peter filled with the Holy Spirit; the parable figures are for the time being set aside, and the vision of Pentecost comes straight from the New Testament account.[20] Only the bible itself, as traditionally interpreted, could reveal the Christian message of the reconciliation of God's justice with his love. Only if Langland can succeed in giving poetic form to the changing concept of godliness communicated through the bible — through the righteousness of the patriarchs and the penitential hope of the prophets to the Christian charity of the apostles — can he provide a pattern for Will to emulate at each stage of his own progression from well-meaning worldly life to a state of inward grace. Given the Pauline and Augustinian doctrines of holy living, it is clear that Will's example and guide must change and be transformed in Will's eyes as the seeker's spiritual education proceeds. In subsequent chapters I shall examine each of these transformations: but first the troublesome question of the time-scheme of Langland's narrative must be faced.

In a sense, everything happens in the fourteenth century, during the life-time of Will. In his dreams Will may find himself a witness of Christ's entry into Jerusalem, and Abraham and Moses may tread the same earth. There is no difficulty here. The problem is centred in the *Visio*, in which Piers is undoubtedly a fourteenth-century Christian ploughman, and yet, as has often been observed, he takes the role of a patriarch leading the people out of the wilderness.[21] In this matter too, Augustine's thinking can help us. Piers and his companions, genuinely seeking 'the good', are still spending their days 'increasing earthly goods, wasting time and wasted by time';[22] until Piers tears the pardon they seem to be doing well enough, but theirs is the condition of the 'old man'. Their state is that described by Augustine in another discourse: they are 'living under Adam' though physically alive in the Christian era and ostensibly living a 'Christian' life. Augustine sees this as a hopeful condition from which people may progress to a state of grace; he tells such men that they must 'for the time being look for even temporal goods from none but the one God, thus serving him according to the Old Testament, so that they may attain to the New'.[23] This way of thinking about the spiritual life of individuals and societies allows the religious poet to postulate for any soul in any period of the Christian era a time of living 'under the Law' before the moment of dedication which Augustine associated with 'the sacrifice of justice' begins the process of restoration.

The double time-scale of the Ages of Man and the aging of Will as an individual man was familiar enough to Langland's first readers.[24] The compression of centuries of history into a life-time, and of a life-time into the seasons of a single year, is a feat which the traditional church services had made unremarkable. The liturgy with its seasons of Lent, Easter and Pentecost is explicitly used by Langland to mark Will's progress, and the bible readings included in the liturgy associate the providential events of mankind's history as recorded in the scriptures with the gradual revelation of Truth. Piers, as guide to revealed Truth, can be placed in any one of these time-schemes, or, since time dissolves in dreams, in more than one of these time-schemes even in a single vision.

I think it is evident that Raw speaks truly, though it is only a partial truth, when she says: 'The restoration of the divine image in history and in the individual soul is the unifying theme of *Piers Plowman*'. Her own documentation can be amply supplemented and the metaphors traced back to Jerome and Ambrose as well as Augustine. Her article does not point out that the idea of paying in his own coin what is owed to God (his tribute money) also goes back to Augustine, though she quotes a pertinent and explicit passage from Bede which neatly draws the doctrines into one statement about salvation and judgement:

> Just as Caesar demands from us the imprint of his image, so God must receive back the soul adorned and sealed with the light of his countenance.[25]

There is one more strand in the associations of the coin: the strange story of the silver coin miraculously provided for Peter to pay the Temple tax gave Ambrose an opportunity to speak of *Christ* as the coin which pays the price of our redemption.[26] I mention this because it fills in another part of Langland's belief about salvation: that the wretch who has nothing to offer of his own may yet find that by confessing Christ he has miraculously been given the means to pay what he owes to God [cp. A 5:242f.; B 5:461f.; C 6:316f.]. The passage quoted earlier about the base-metal coins being offered to God shows Langland harping on the need to pay God honestly: this is another aspect of the theme of *justitia*.

Though the speeches of Holy Church to Will when he first questions her have been given a good deal of critical attention, the full significance of her quotation of the *Reddite Cesari* passage from the gospel seems not to have been noticed. As the first words from Jesus quoted in the poem, this sentence must carry great weight. Langland has introduced them solemnly:

> Go to þe gospel, quaþ heo, þat god seiþ him seluen.
>> [A 1:44; B 1:46; cp. C 1:44]

Holy Church does not directly answer Will's naive question 'Who does all the treasure in the world belong to?' Instead she recalls the words of Jesus:

> *Reddite cesari*, quaþ god, þat *cesari* bifall[iþ]
> *Et que sunt dei deo* oþer ellis ye don ille.[27]

Five passus follow in which Will is allowed to brood on the first half of this text, watching Meed and False subverting justice and the wasters cheating their fellow-workers; in contrast with these, Piers, law-abiding and fairminded, is, one would say, doing well, paying due deference to God's commandments. But Langland is keeping back the full force of the second half of the text, which tacitly constrasts God's coin with Caesar's penny. As I have indicated, anyone who had read

25

Augustine on Psalm 4, or heard the Psalm glossed in this way, would be able to understand why Piers found the stark judgement of the 'pardon' so shattering to his peace of mind:

> In two lynes it lay & nouȝt lettre more,
> And was writen riȝt þus in witnesse of treuthe:
> *Et qui bona egerunt, ibunt in vitam eternam;*
> *Qui vero mala, in ignem eternum.*
>
> [A 8:94ff.; B 7:111ff.; C 9:286ff.]

I think we have to take Holy Church's words about treasure and Caesar's penny as pregnant with foreboding for those 'living under Adam'. Like her other teaching to ingenuous Will, her famous description of love [A 1:83ff.; B 1:85ff.; C 1:81ff.], the words she speaks carry import which some readers will grasp at once, though the fulfilment or explication of them may come much later in the poem.[28] Before Piers comes on the scene at all, a general contrast is drawn between those who receive their reward in this world and those who serve Truth and hope for his treasure.

It is against this background that we must interpret his work for the folk in the *Visio*. The hints are there from the first that this ploughman is no ordinary person, though it is not until his second epiphany that the reader can be certain that Piers is specially endowed with authority in spiritual matters. In the next C-text appearance he is a preacher to whom Clergy himself must defer; in the second B-text appearance he guards the tree which grows in man's heart and teaches Will about man's need for salvation. Even before he becomes indistinguishable from the *deus-homo*[29] in Jerusalem, it has become evident that his life in the poem is not bounded by the span of one mortal life.

To sum up: Piers, I have argued, gives imagined life to a traditional Christian concept of exemplary human nature transformed over the centuries of sacred history. He presents, more and more openly, the *imago dei*, the 'true nature' of human beings, as it is thought to be manifested in certain chosen messengers of God, the 'apostles' who offer a *forma justitiae* for their fellow-men. This theory requires that in him 'the light of God's countenance', the *lumen vultus Domini*, is more strongly recognisable than in most men, and this holiness becomes clearer to see as the perception of the watcher pierces the fog of error, passing through the stages of revelation which match the eras of salvation history. In action, his primary role is that of the Sower, since the mission of the messengers is to prepare the hearts of men for the seed of the Word. To define the literary status of Piers is peculiarly difficult, because he is neither a single character nor, strictly speaking, a personification. However, the dream-vision genre uniquely permits that he may appear and disappear and change in outward characteristics without straining probability. Such things happen in dreams. He can appear as a tiller of the earth, as a preacher or a priest; he can reflect the personality of Moses or Peter or Jesus himself, but the action in which he is involved can only reflect 'in a dark allegory' the essence of the doctrine. The symbol of the King's denarius, rather than any single individual or rank or calling, epitomises what the ploughman, gardener, knight stands for in the poem, because the coin represents the true treasure, the salvation Will hopes for: the discovery of Truth within the soul.

IV

PIERS, PETER AND THE LAW

The contrast between Meed's followers and those who try to live by moral law is explained, suitably enough, by Conscience — but Conscience in the *Visio* appears to have received his idea of God's rewards and punishments primarily from the Old Testament. He looks back to David as an authority, and when he does quote Jesus his quotation is the grim

> *Amen, Amen, receperunt mercedem suam.*
> [A 3:233; B 3:252; C 3:310; cp. *Matt.* 6.2]¹

His account of God's 'meed' contrasts Saul and David; the doctrine is taken from the psalms, and particularly from Psalm 14 *Domine, quis habitabit?* 'Lord who shall stay in thy tabernacle; who shall dwell on thy holy hill?' In the A-text, one line only is quoted from this psalm, but in B several lines paraphrase this question and the psalmist's answer:

> Lorde, who shal wonye in þi wones and with þyne holy seintes,
> Or resten in þyne holy hilles? þis askeþ David.
> And David assoileþ it hymself as þe Sauter telleth,
> *Qui ingreditur sine macula & operatur Iusticiam.*
> Tho þat entren of o colour and of one wille
> And han wrouȝte werkis with riȝte and with reson, etc.
> [B 3:235ff.; cp. A 3:221; C 2:38]

Neither David, nor Conscience as he quotes David, expresses doubt that any man could walk 'immaculate' (*sine macula*) or be able to 'do what is right' (*operatur justitiam*). To question man's capacity to live without sinning would not suit Conscience in his argument before the king, which is to the effect that God rewards justly those who live justly. At this stage, Conscience reveals no anxiety about what 'doing well' might involve:

> þere arn to maner of medis, my lord, be ȝour leve.
> þat on, God of his grace gyueþ in his blisse
> To hem þat werchen wel whiles þei ben here.
> [A 3:218ff.; B 3:231ff.; not in C]

It will be recalled that Psalm 14 was invoked by Lady Holy Church herself as she censured Meed:

27

How construeþ David þe kyng of men þat [cacceþ] Mede,
And men of þis moolde þat mayntaneþ truþe,
And how ye shul saue yourself? þe Sauter bereþ witnesse:
Domine quis habitabit in tabernaculo tuo, etc.

[not in A; B 2:36ff.; cp. C 2:39]

This psalm is first presented, by Holy Church, as David's answer to the
question Will has asked her, 'How may I save my soul?' It lists the moral virtues
required of a just man living under the Law, and it has to do with clean, kind and
honest living. However, it is not the answer that Jesus gives to fundamentally the
same question. The response of Jesus to the man who asked 'Good Master, what
must I do to obtain eternal life?' was 'Why do you call me good? No one is good,
save God alone. You know the commandments . . .'.[2] Langland is very much
aware of the difference between David's prescription for doing well and the
boundless demands made by Jesus. He returns to *Domine, quis habitabit* as one
of only two proof-texts cited by Clergy as the teaching of Piers, but in the
latter citation he significantly adds the doctrine that Dowel and Dobet are
'infinites', and in the C-version bluntly says that Piers also teaches that everything
on earth is imperfect:

> And preueth by puyre skile inparfit alle thynges,
> *Nemo bonus,*[3]
> Bote lele loue and treuthe, that loth is to be founde.

[C 15:136ff.; cp. B 13:126ff.]

Thus, the psalm which Conscience brings to mind seemingly describes a moral
path to God's holy hill, but in the teaching of Piers in the *Vitae* (as also in the
writings of Ambrose and Augustine) its meaning is less clear-cut and confident.
The Doctors respond to the psalm with a sense of their own unworthiness.
Ambrose, for example, uses some of the words of the psalm in writing on John
the Baptist's call to repentance.[4] Langland shows us Will's subconscious mind
responding similarly, for the dream of good government ruled by Conscience is
closely followed by another dream in which Conscience's big public sermon,
exhorting the crowd to seek St Truth, brings *Repentance* on the scene. (In the
B-version it is Reason who preaches the sermon, but with the same effect.) All the
folk are then moved to confess their sins. However, we must note that this move
towards repentance by Conscience (as by Reason in B) is *not* caused by a sense
of his own unworthiness to dwell with God, but instead by a fear of God's wrath,
brought on by experience of storms and pestilence. And, when preaching, though
he carries a Christian's cross, he proclaims the punishment sent by the Lord like
some Old Testament prophet (see, for example, *Isa.* 24:1-13; in C, Isaiah is
actually quoted).[5]

Holy Church has set Will upon his search for Truth, but he does not immediately
find his way out of 'the maze'. The world, governed by Meed's followers, moved
by competing interests and compulsions, is full of people scurrying this way and
that, and Lady Holy Church's first words to Will bring in the (Augustinian)
metaphor of the winding ways of error:

> Sixt þou þis peple
> Al hou bisy þei ben Aboute þe Mase?

[A 1:5f.; B 1:5f.; C 1:5f.]

The phrase 'the maze of error' (*circuitus erroris*) appears in Augustine's *Confessiones* to describe the aimless movement of the soul directed away from God.[6] A great conversion of the folk must occur before they dedicate themselves to the pilgrimage to the hill of Truth, and they will need a call like the Baptist's before they decide to forsake Lady Meed. Though Conscience predicts that one day Reason will reign, Meed be put down, and trespassers against truth be dealt with by Justice according to the law,[7] no such reign of peace and love ensues in Will's dreams. On the contrary, with the best advisers in the world, the king still cannot dominate Meed. Reason then speaks out strongly for due rewards, heavier punishments, and no leniency in return for gifts:

> For *nullum malum* [þ]e ma[n] met[t]e with *Inpunitum*
> And bad *Nullum* [*bonum* be] *irremuneratum*.
> > [A 4:126f.; B 4:143f.; C 4:140f.]

The party of law-and-order thus gains the upper hand, and Meed is disgraced, but the poet makes us very uneasy about the naked justice being advocated by Reason and the harsh attitude taken by Conscience. The tale that Conscience offers as a warning to the king, concerning the punishment of King Saul for listening to Meed rather than to God's command given through the prophet Samuel, is quite horrifyingly related. Samuel's words to Saul as paraphrased by Conscience have no vestige of compassion in them:

> Wende þidir with þin ost wommen to kille;
> Children & Cherlis choppe hem to deþe.
> Loke þou kille þe king; coueite nouȝt hise godes;
> For any mylionis of mone murdre hem ichone;
> Barnes and bestis brenne hem to deþe.
> > [A 3:252ff.; B 3:259ff.; C 3:407ff.]

This tale vividly presents Old Testament justice at its most appalling. The king's advisers in Will's dream also express themselves with a most disagreeable callousness:

> 'Be hym þat [rauȝte] on þe rode,' quaþ Resoun to þe king
> But I reule þus þi reaum, rend out my ribbes . . .
> > [A 4:148f.]

However, the next dream does not advocate, as this one does, that wrongdoers should get their just deserts, so we should be chary of concluding that Conscience and Reason here speak for Langland.

The repentance of all the people is presented through the confessions of the Seven Deadly Sins. (We recall Courcelle's epitome of Augustine's spiritual journey, 'Le propre des *Confessions* est qu'Augustin y présente sa quête du vrai sous forme d'aveu des péchés').[8] A full study of Langland's unusual portrayal of the sins is not germane to my theme, but it may be noted that there is much emphasis on false speaking, cheating and ill-will, together with self-indulgence. Some of the faults may seem mere peccadillos, but they all work against the two commandments 'on which hang all the Law and the Prophets', and they negate the simple moral code expressed in David's psalm *Domine, quis habitabit*. One striking addition to the queue of penitents is Robert the Robber, one of those wretches whose need of Christ as the coin of his redemption I have already mentioned:[9]

> Robert the Robbour on *Reddite* he lokede
> And for þer nas not wher-with he wepte ful sore.
> [A 5:242f.; B 5:469f.]

Robert has no hope of ever earning enough to pay what he owes, but when he remembers the thief whom Christ pardoned on Calvary he too can pray for mercy. In the C-revision, Robert is moved from his place with Sloth and put less conspicuously and more conventionally with Coveytise [C 6:316ff.], in the company of a Welshman Ʒeuan-ʒelde-aʒeyn. Through these characters, the doctrine of restitution (also derived from Augustine)[10] is brought in to reinforce the theme of Justice, at the same point in the poem as the unbounded mercy of God is illustrated.

Langland's insistence that everyone must be given what is rightfully his matches Augustine's thinking in his discussion of the meaning of *justus* and *justitia*, which I quoted earlier. Augustine makes use of Cicero's definition of *justitia*, quoting 'That soul is righteous (*justus est animus*) which *apportions to each his own*'.[11] Langland's robber and cheat have flouted justice by taking what was not their own. Ʒeuan promises contritely to pay back everyone he has cheated: he will not allow it to happen

> That eche man ne shal haue his ar y hennes wende
>
> [C 6:313]

Thus, in the dream of general forgiveness, Langland never loses sight of the principles of natural law and justice. At this stage of the poem, Truth and Justice are shown to be aspects of God which must condemn the sinners in the maze.

In the B-text, Repentance offers a long prayer to the Saviour for them all, before the pilgrims move off. In that prayer, he quotes both the text that reminds men that they were made in God's image [*Gen.* 1:26] and the New Testament text that offers hope of the renewal of the image through love [1 *Jo.* 4:16]:

> *Et alibi, Qui manet in caritate in deo manet et deus in eo*
> [B 5:486][12]

Holy Church's earlier appeal to the text *Deus caritas*, and her promise that man can become 'god . . . ylik to oure lord', spoken when she set Will on his pilgrim way, are brought back to mind as the general pilgrimage begins. One final telling point in this preliminary exploration of what it means to be 'just' is the quotation from the lips of Jesus himself [*Matt.* 9:13; *Luc.* 5:32]:

> *Non veni vocare iustos set peccatores ad penitenciam*
> [Not in A; B 5:498; C 7:139]

These words, full of hope for the penitents, simultaneously rebuke the self-righteousness of those who carefully observe the Law. (Ambrose's comment about those 'who are confident in the Law', quoted earlier, makes a gloss to be borne in mind as the *Visio* proceeds.)

With Repentance's evocation of the text *Non veni vocare justos*, this extended prelude to the appearance of Piers the ploughman comes to an end. In it, Langland has set about shaking some ordinary preconceptions about justice and mercy. For the most part, it seems that he favours beating villains and chaining them up; his Reason is ruthless:

> And ȝit (quod Reson) bi þe Roode I shal no reuþe have
> While Meede haþ eny Maystrie to Mooten in þis halle.
>   [A 4:117f.; B 4:134f.; C 4:131f.]

And yet – 'by the Rood' to have no pity? This is one of many instances in which Langland uses an expletive as a kind of comment on the speaker who uses it.[13] Reason or the Rood, punishment or pardon, justice or mercy: these are the matters which the poem must somehow resolve, and the punishment of Meed's henchmen is only part of the answer, as the hope of Robert the Robber reminds us. There is no reasonable doubt that he should be condemned and yet, 'by the Rood' on Calvary, Christ pardoned that other robber, Dismas. This must upset those who trust the dictates of Reason.

At this juncture, the crowd of would-be pilgrims sets off with no clear idea of direction. For a long while they are wandering like blundering beasts. They question the much-travelled Palmer, and, when he says that he has never heard of anyone seeking St Truth before, a ploughman explodes with the oath 'Peter!' It turns out that he is swearing by his name-saint; the pilgrims address him by the English form of that name, Piers. Later, when the people are afraid to go off without a guide, Piers swears again 'bi peter þe Apostel' [cp. A 7:3; B 6:3]. Since in his final epiphany Piers is shown receiving the Pentecostal Holy Spirit and taking on himself the mission of the Apostle Peter, this first utterance of his cannot be dismissed as a mere exclamation.[14]

There are several indications that Piers and Peter have more than a name in common even at this stage. In the first place, there is Piers's claim to know Truth 'kyndely': Peter, it will be recalled, was the one disciple who, from untutored inner conviction, acknowledged Jesus as the Son of God (cp. *Matt.* 16:16). The name Peter which Jesus gave him was supposed by some medieval scholars to mean 'knowing' (*agnoscens*). This interpretation of *Petrus* was repeated even by those who were also aware of Christ's equation of *Petrus* with *petra* 'rock'.[15] Piers claims the natural knowledge of God which was a distinguishing mark of his namesake. Then, the pilgrims' first thought is to offer him money for his services, and we recall that Peter rebuffed those who tried to buy the spiritual services of the apostles (cp. *Act.* 8:18ff.). Piers speaks to the pilgrims with authority and with simple confidence in himself and his master. He manifests the same strong certainty in his faith as Peter showed. In his first appearance, however, he is like the spiritually unillumined Peter, obedient to the Jewish Law, religious but limited in his understanding of Christ's message.[16] We observe that the prescription he offers for reaching Truth is naive in form and founded on the elementary principles of being obedient and speaking the truth. The highway that he describes is formed on the words of the Law rather than on specifically Christian teaching. For example, he speaks of not harming one's neighbour, rather than of loving one's neighbour [cp. A 6:54f.; B 5:573f.; C 8:211f.], a precept closer to Psalm 14:3 than to the New Testament formulation of the

31

commandment, which leads into the parable of the Samaritan [cp. *Luc.* 10:27ff.]. Indeed, the spirit of Piers's advice throughout is similar to that of Psalm 14, which is apt enough in a just man's account of how he hopes to reach Truth's hill, for, as Conscience has reminded everyone, the man 'who does what is right' and 'speaks the truth in his heart' . . . 'and does no wrong to his neighbour' shall dwell on the Lord's holy hill [*Ps.* 14:1-3].[17]

When Piers speaks of the truth in his heart in terms of a person sitting there [A 6:93f.], the figure is one of a lord enthroned; in the B-text amplification, the image is of a child and a stern father. These images are not, of course, incompatible with Christian belief, but they emphasise 'the fear of the Lord'. So does the latter part of Piers's description of the route to Truth's castle: he is conscious that it is very hard to enter, that one may be locked out; there is a dread of punishment. It might be argued that Piers is talking to the crowd in language suited to their understanding, but his own simple expressions of obedient loyalty are not essentially different. His attitude may recall Paul's way of referring to his own spiritual immaturity, when he 'spake as a child' and 'understood as a child': these words precede the famous image of man's imperfect vision, *Videmus nunc per speculum (et) in aenigmate*, from which the Doctors took support for the doctrine of the dimmed *imago dei* [cp. 1 *Cor.* 13:1f.]. Though Piers is here like Peter in his intuitive recognition of Truth, he is not at this stage like the apostle filled with the Holy Spirit (as he is later), but more like the Peter whose earth-bound worship of Jesus was rebuked in the episode of the Transfiguration. The significance educed by the Doctors from Peter's ascent of the mountain, with his vision of Moses, Elias (Elijah) and the glorified Christ, is, I believe, pertinent to our understanding of what is involved in following Piers-Peter up the hill to Truth. According to the gospel account, Peter at first proposed to build three tabernacles there for the three prophets, 'not knowing what he said' (cp. *Luc.* 9:33). Living as he then was 'under the Law', he responded to his vision as any devout Jew might have done, not knowing (as Ambrose puts it in his explanation of the event) 'that a human being in this corruptible body is not capable of making a tabernacle for God'.[18] Ambrose relates Peter's experience to the Christian's experience of 'seeing the Law in the Gospel', and 'seeing Elias with the Word of God'.[19] What he is saying is that the Christian who follows Peter in his ascent of the holy hill will discover that the language of the Old Testament takes on that enlightening inner meaning which we have already seen to be part of Augustine's sense of spiritual renewal. This is a matter pertinent, I think, to Piers's own renewal of life at the end of the *Visio*, and I will pursue it later. Here I want simply to suggest a comparison between Peter and the first Piers in respect of their down-to-earth faith and worship. Piers, like Peter, will later transcend this simple observance of moral law and religious precept, but in this first scene, as he preaches the commandments and does what he can to put down wrong and promote brotherly love, he seems to be in like case with the honest disciple in the early days of his commitment to Jesus. The ploughman is god-fearing and righteous, but not a truly spiritual leader.

For Ambrose, as for Augustine (whose teachings, it should be remembered, are the food of Langland's Conscience at the comic but serious dinner-party), the understanding of the bible, the word of Truth, expands and develops with the change in themselves as they feel that they are making spiritual progress, i.e. moving towards Truth. The event of the Transfiguration provides an image apt for combining the ideas of ascent in virtue and greater clarity of vision. Ambrose urges each of us, his readers, to 'be Peter' — *Esto ergo et tu Petrus* — to be the disciple climbing the hill to see the face of God and the glorified, once veiled, face of Moses.[20] He conceives that Jesus chose Peter, James and John to climb the hill with him as representatives of mankind. For him, the special vision granted to Peter indicates to later Christians that they will discover the full message of the prophets only by following the way of Jesus.[21] Unenlightened people are in the case of the Jews who could not bear to look on the glorified face of Moses after he had spoken with God on Sinai; the prophet had to cover his face with a veil [cp. *Exod.* 34:29ff.]. It is the belief of both Ambrose and Augustine that in 'unveiling' the words of prophecy they are coming closer to Christ; the revelation of God is not merely something to be learnt about, but something to take into oneself, so that to reveal the Truth in Moses is at the same time to reveal the god-likeness in oneself. Ambrose puts it like this, expatiating on the meaning of Peter's vision:

And today Moses teaches and today Elias speaks, and today we can see Moses in greater glory. For who cannot, when even the Jewish people could see him, indeed did see him? For they saw the glorified face of Moses, but they looked on the veil, they did not ascend the mountain, and therefore they went astray. Those who saw Moses alone could not at the same time see the Word of God. Let us reveal our face, therefore, 'that we all, with face revealed, beholding as in a looking-glass the glory of the Lord may be changed into the same image'.[22]

In this last quoted sentence Ambrose is remembering Paul's teaching on the letter and the spirit, the tablets of stone and the tablets of the heart, in the passage which ends with Paul's hope that all men may be transformed into the image of God [cp. 2 *Cor.* 3:18]. We note that the ascent of the mountain is another way of speaking about the growth of spirituality in the Christian soul: we are urged to make the climb, following Peter, in order to see our true selves as in a mirror. Ambrose believes that on the mountain-top we all become one body in Christ.

This doctrine, I think, can also illuminate some of the mystifying words of Anima to Will in the Dowel section of *Piers Plowman*. When Will communes with his own soul — beginning to 'know himself', when he begins to 'reveal his true face' as if looking in a mirror — as he searches for Piers, he becomes capable of glimpsing Charity in person. Piers himself, by becoming like Christ, can lead Will to be 'transformed into that same image': *Petrus, id est, Christus.*[23] Paul's metaphor of the 'face revealed' looking into the mirror has the same essential meaning as the metaphor of the restored image on the King's penny.[24] The veiled face, the dimmed likeness, belong to the man who lives 'under Adam', just and law-abiding though he may be. This traditional way of regarding the Christian life makes explicable Langland's need to start a new quest for Dowel just when the penitent folk seem to have found a satisfactory way of living together for their common good. It explains why Piers is not delighted when he understands the import of Truth's letter to him, and accounts for his immediate resolve to change his way of life.

The Piers of the *Visio* has put off the pilgrimage to Truth's tower on the hill: he flatly insists that it must wait while he farms his field. Though he is confident that he knows what Truth requires of his servants, he does not, in the event, make good his offer to lead the pilgrimage. At this important stage in the narrative, his decision to put the farm work first obviously calls for explanation. Some critics suppose that Langland has chosen to indicate through Piers's action that he distrusts pilgrimages as worthwhile Christian enterprises. It might even be argued that the replacement of the pilgrimage by useful work for the good of all indicates that Langland is dubious about the value of ascetic Christianity as preached by the Doctors. However, such argument will not explain why Piers later thinks he must give more time to prayers and penance, nor why Langland involves him in the *Vitae* of Dowel, Dobet and Dobest, which certainly indicate improvement of life and a lack of concern for ordinary practical bread-winning. As will be evident from what I have said so far, the structure of the poem accords best with a figural reading of the *Visio*. That is to say, the ploughing and harvesting can be read literally as mundane and proper social activity, good and profitable in itself, but at the same time it can be interpreted as a figure for human life 'under Adam', which can be morally good and yet unsatisfying to the soul.

Will's dream concerning the half-acre, as I understand it, explores the possibility that Truth will be found in honest labour, just as his earlier dream explored the possibility that a fairer system of reward and punishment would create a world of peace and concord. Langland did not rest his hope there: much improvement in the way people treated each other was effected by those other reforms, as here in the agricultural scene, but only by taking cruel measures against the disrupters — and even then with only temporary success. Repentance and the Confessions of the Sins then showed Langland's belief that lasting reform can be assured in one way only: men must recover the true purpose of their earthly lives. Only if general *good-will* drives out ill-will can any enduring betterment ensue for all the folk of the field. The folk at first willingly accepted Piers's advice and authority, but even with the threat of starvation facing them some proved unneighbourly and practically unlovable, and even Piers was not able to offer a social panacea. In the *Visio*, the culmination of Piers's stewardship over the field is the alarming wrangle over Truth's Pardon. The whole controversy turns on the validity of the Church's claim to issue 'pardons' with power derived from Peter [cp. *Matt.* 16:19], a power associated with the giving of the name *Petrus*. The Pardon granted to Piers invites comparison with 'the power of the keys' given to Peter. So, from first to last, the Piers of the *Visio* sporadically makes us think also of Peter, but not so as to suggest an identity of the two.

Piers shares certain qualities with Peter, as is proper in a Christian *forma justitiae*, but it will, I hope, be clear from my earlier discussion of Augustine's theory of goodness that I do not imply that Piers is simply Peter in a contemporary guise. Peter's progress in spiritual understanding and faith is more fully chronicled in the gospels than that of any other apostle, and it is therefore natural that the Doctors should regard his life as a model or pattern for later Christians. Gregory, for example, notes how he grows in virtue, first like a blade of corn, next forming the ear, and, finally, the full grain in the ear: three stages of goodness remarked in different episodes from the gospels.[25] Langland would not lack for a model in creating a guide for Christian folk in their ascent of

Truth's hill. If we think of the first Piers as similar to the loyal but unillumined Peter, who initially failed to understand that he would be given a New Law superseding the Law of his fathers, we can explain both the rather Judaic tone of his instruction to the folk and his failure to appreciate the need for the pilgrimage. This Piers of the *Visio* must be 'transformed into that same image' in the manner that Ambrose describes, before he can lead Will to Truth, and his ploughing must be of another kind.

Readers of Langland criticism will be aware of Gregory's use of the metaphor of ploughing to describe the work of Christian preachers. Some of the pertinent quotations from the *Moralia* have been published by Barney (1973) in support of his thesis that 'Piers's agnomen "the Plowman" is an outgrowth of the symbol of the plowman as preacher'.[26] He suggests that Piers stands for something like — if we had the word — 'priesthoodness'. His wish for an abstract noun more abstract than 'priesthood' shows that he is aware of Piers as a *pattern* rather than an individual, but his theory suppresses unduly the Piers who inhabits the world of the palmer, the cutpurse, and the patronising priest. Most critics of the poem would prefer to think of Piers as, in some sense, a real ploughman. A figural interpretation allows that he has a role as a real ploughman, but one whose actions and words carry figurative meaning of which he and his companions are not aware, or only partially aware. When we cast about for an abstract noun to denote his figural significance, we might make do with 'apostolate'.

Though in recent English usage the word 'apostle' has a rather specific application to certain followers of Jesus, the Middle English *apostel* carried the wider sense of the original Greek *apostolos* 'one who is sent', i.e. a messenger (of God). In the Latin bible, Jesus himself is called *apostol* [cp. *Hebr.* 3:1]: the Messenger is also the message, the Word. An apostle's life and teaching make one testimony; he may come from any walk of life, but his vocation is to give the word of God to others. The fisherman-apostles were called to be 'fishers of men'; the ploughman-apostle of Langland's vision is charged to bring his harvest to God's barn. However, it will not do to think of Piers simply as a latter-day apostle called from his farm as Peter was called from his boat, because the Piers of Will's dreams has his being in biblical times and places as well as in Langland's English countryside. In a dream, time is dissolved and the people we think we see may merge or vanish disconcertingly. By giving Piers the insubstantial life of a figure in a dream, Langland is able to merge him with Moses or Jesus or Peter so as to suggest the historical continuity of the divine revelation. The poet even speaks as if the later Piers were God himself:

> 'Clerkes haue no knowyng,' quod he, 'but by werkes and wordes.
> Ac Piers þe Plowman parceyveþ moore depper
> What is þe wille and wherfore þat many wight suffreþ:
> *Et vidit deus cogitaciones eorum.*'
> [B 15:198; cp. C 16:337f.; and *Luc.* 11:17, *Matt.* 9:4, where *Jesus* is the
> subject of *vidit*].

This altered quotation from the gospel shows plainly that, for Langland, Jesus, the God-man, was able to see and judge men's motives in a way not open to ordinary human minds. However, this extraordinary discernment also characterises Peter in his dealings with the liar Ananias [cp. *Act.* 5:3], from which it may be inferred that an apostle is not simply a mouthpiece for the proclamation of God's message: the Word is an indwelling presence which sanctifies his judgements. So Langland claims no more for Piers than might be expected of a figure representing the apostolate.

The corollary of such belief is that Peter's power to pardon or not to pardon is rightly given only to those priests in whom Truth is a living presence, those who are brothers in Christ in more than name. Langland's Piers constantly shames those contemporary priests who claimed Peter's authority but who could never have seen the face of Charity in the mirror. Langland frequently addresses himself specifically to them, and much of the poem applies to men in holy orders rather than to laymen. Nevertheless, Christ's injunction to his disciples to 'be perfect' makes no distinction of persons or status, and Langland sets no barriers before anyone who may be inspired to emulate Piers.

Sharing Will's visions of Piers, the reader is invited with him to climb the mountain as Peter did. There he may reach some understanding, partial as it must be in mortal life, of the nature of Truth. The Piers of the early vision reminds us in indirect ways that even the man who headed the followers of Jesus served at first with an uncomprehending devotion. The Piers of the last vision is quite obviously modelled on a Peter guided and transformed by the Holy Spirit. Peter, though himself no paragon in the gospels, is eminently, for Christian writers, a paradigm of man's restoration. To become a veritable paragon in the eyes of the Doctors, he must enter unity with Christ. Langland's Piers, because he is a figure in a dream, is able to portray Peter quintessentially and also to hint his apotheosis. Will's lifelong quest is a struggle to 'be Peter' in the sense that Ambrose's exhortation requires, but *amor mundi* often conflicts with the love he comes to feel for Piers, and this keeps them apart. Will becomes an old man in the course of the narrative, and physical cares still surround and grieve him. He presents for us the many who have looked for a true purpose in life and have had some indistinct perception of the divine. He concurrently stands as representative of the human will throughout salvation-history, and therefore the Piers that he sees moves in spirit through the eras of the Law and the Prophets and the ministry of Christ. For Piers, as for Will, what emerges is man's need for pardon, and the mystery of Truth's Pardon and what it means to Piers deserves our special consideration.

V

PIERS AND THE PARDON

I

Truth's letter of pardon to Piers is one of the great stumbling-blocks to modern readers of the poem. In order to appraise its significance, it is necessary to consider what leads up to it. For the whole of the previous passus Piers has been in charge, not of the proposed corporate pilgrimage, but of the farm work on the half-acre. Piers, though he has volunteered to lead the folk to Truth's castle, is not ready to start. In the event, they have all delayed until harvest time comes round. Is this delay blameworthy, or simply common sense?

On this debatable question, I want to make three points about Piers's decision and what follows:

> Quaþ perkyn the plouȝmon, 'be peter þe apostel,
> I haue an half akir to er[e]n be þe heiȝe weiȝe'.
> > [A 7:3f.; B 6:3f.; C 9:1f.]

First to be noted is the oath, reminding the reader even more forcefully than his exclamation 'Peter!' when he came on the scene, that the designated leader of Christ's errant flock, charged by Jesus to feed them, was St Peter [cp. *Jo.* 21:15ff.]. Peter was evidently commanded to give spiritual food to the people under his care; Piers, on the other hand, shows himself primarily concerned with physical provision for them. The second point is this: the half-acre is said to be 'beside the highway', and the phrase itself implies that he is stepping aside from the road, the pilgrim way. (Two of the C-MSS have scribal headings introducing Piers's description of the way to Truth's castle which make the significance of the highway more explicit: *alta via ad fidelitatem est obseruatio .X. preceptorum, ut dicit Petrus Plouhman.*) It may be relevant to note also that this phrase 'beside the (high)way' (*secus viam*) occurs in *Matt.* 21:18 in the description of the barren fig-tree, and that Jerome, the least extravagant of the four Doctors, assumes that the phrase has covert significance. It intimates, he thinks, that the Jews (symbolised by the tree) remained at the side of the road instead of following Jesus: 'For they kept to the Law, and [the Synagogue] was *beside the highway* because they did not believe in the Way'.[1] My third point is a larger one: if Piers's work on the half-acre is what Truth requires, why, we must ask, does the *Vita de Dowel* not begin here instead of later on, after the pardon-tearing?

Facing these questions, we observe that Piers (like many of his modern

37

admirers) believes that he is serving Truth to the best of his ability.[2] We can have no doubt that he is honestly rendering unto Caesar the things that are Caesar's, and he is obviously paying some dues to God. Are they enough? If (as many readers think) the toiling in the field is a metaphor for fallen Adam's legacy of toilsome life,[3] can we not legitimately infer that Piers, the faithful servant of Truth, is, like Adam, spiritually *semivivus*:[4] in the same case as the wounded traveller in the parable who could not move from the side of the road without help from the Samaritan? Piers does not seem to Will or the reader to be in this desperate situation, and yet his own recognition at the end of the *Visio* that his salvation is not ensured by the Pardon, and his resolve to start a new and different life, do accord with such an interpretation.

There is some direct evidence, too, that his delay in order to do the ploughing is reprehensible. As often, the C-text reveals more of what Langland was thinking than the earlier versions: at the point where he described the crowd getting ready for the pilgrimage, he was thinking of Christ's uncompromising parable about the men who made excuses for not coming at God's call.[5] In the C-version of this episode, there is one man who insists that he must plough with his five yoke of oxen instead of going on pilgrimage. It is hard to see why Piers's reason for postponing the start should be regarded differently. The parable of the procrastinators, as elaborated by Ambrose, symbolises God's call to come to his Kingdom, where 'we shall be like him' [cp. 1 *Jo.* 3:2], that is, where we shall be restored to the image of God. For good measure, Ambrose contrasts the man who chose to put the ploughing first with Eliseus [Elisha], who was called from his ploughing by the prophet Elias [Elijah]. Eliseus killed his team and burnt their yokes when he was called by God:[6] the meaning that Ambrose derives from this embellishment of the parable is that 'the yoke of the Law' (consisting of the Ten Commandments or the Five Books of the Old Law) must be cast aside when the new life is begun at God's call.[7] In the parable, the man with the oxen is one of several representative people who are thinking of the things of the world, not the things of God; what they are doing is in no way reprehensible in itself — it only becomes so if they regard it as more important than God's work. So, Ambrose concludes, those people who put other things first when Christ calls them are shut out of the Kingdom: and amongst these, according to his reasoning, is the man who chooses the yoke of the Law rather than the obligations of Grace.[8]

That Langland conceives the work of Piers on the half-acre to be no equivalent for the Christian's journey to Truth is also indicated in other indirect ways. Piers at this stage judges more like Moses than a Christian: he utterly condemns the vagabond and the prostitute, quoting *Deleantur de libro ... et cum Justis non Scribantur* 'Let them be blotted out of the book [of the living] and not be written with the just' [*Ps.* 47:29, *Vulg.*]. Though he adds a pious hope that they will amend, there is no forgiveness in him; he does not mention Mary Magdalene or the penitent thief. His language is that of record-keeping and proscription.

Facing the thought of the pilgrimage still to come, and feeling the weight of his years, Piers decides to write his testament, arranging for the legal disposition of all that he owns. In the A-text the combination of the 'old man' and the phrase 'I wole ... write my Testament' looks like a reminder of Moses, the supposed author of the Pentateuch and mankind's inheritance described therein.

However, we obviously would not say that Piers at this stage *is* Moses,[9] any more than we could say that he *is* Peter. His more abstract genesis is evident when we consider his family. The wife and children to whom he bequeathes his honest gains are not individuals, but moral qualities which law-abiding people share. The allegory appears at first sight to be quite unsubtle, of the same naive kind as Piers's first directions to the pilgrims. The surface meaning sorts well with Piers's hard line towards shirkers, his apportioning of tasks among the folk, and his readiness to use Hunger to bring down the murmurers and wastrels. In itself, this part of the poem can be taken as a plea for fair dealings towards honest labourers and as a clear warning to labourers themselves to accept authority and to have no sympathy with rebellion. Yet nothing in Will's early dreams is necessarily to be taken at face value, and the scene must be read in its place in the strategy of *Visio* and *Vitae*, not primarily as a political tract.

The names of the wife, son and daughter invite closer consideration. As I have already indicated, the good Dame bears a phrasal name with religious overtones: 'Werche-whanne-tyme-is' is fairly certainly an adaptation of half a text from *Gal*. 6:10.[10] It would be entirely in Langland's manner to signal with half a text that half a truth was being ignored.[11] A reader who recognises the Pauline echo will be aware that the verse sums up a passage about 'doing well' [cp. *Gal*. 6:9] expressed in the metaphor of sowing and reaping. Since Paul is there contrasting 'sowing in the flesh' and 'sowing in the spirit', there is a covert reminder to clerical readers (and those who remembered their sermons) of the vital difference between carnal and spiritual work. With this good wife Piers begets offspring who are allegorically named so as to signify good works done in obedience and fear. Neither the wife nor the children have any mention in the other epiphanies of Piers; they belong only to this phase of his service to God.

The matters I have been discussing suggest at least two concurrent meanings for the ploughing scene. Langland uses the scene in its secular aspect to commend disciplined work and to berate spongers and law-breakers, and at the same time his biblical echoes give a different aspect to the attitudes and judgements of Piers himself. Piers shows himself to be an efficient reeve; his authoritative measures work rather well; we incline to forget that he had offered to lead the pilgrimage and has not done so. He gives the wasters what they deserve, but here as in the court scenes naked justice is unpleasant to contemplate. Hunger is his dubious adviser in making the lazy farm-workers do their share of the farm tasks. Unexpectedly, Hunger tells Piers himself that he eats too much, and Piers accepts the 'lesson': later he accuses himself of being too busy about his bodily sustenance.[12] Clearly, this Piers of the *Visio* is not very Christ-like. In a limited way he serves as a moral example to the rest; as *forma justitiae* in this phase of the narrative his affinities are with Moses, the lawgiver, and with Peter as he was before the Passion, dedicated but weak in the flesh[13] and unable to comprehend that the Kingdom is not of this world.

Both Moses and Peter were practical men called on to give judgement on others, and on occasion they found food for the hungry, but it is not for this that they were venerated. Each was marked by his special vision of the light of God's countenance; the *lumen vultus Domini* stamped on mankind was revealed through them to future generations. Each was given a prophetic hope, though for Moses it was a hope unfulfilled before his death. Piers in the *Visio* is an old man, facing death with equanimity until the moment of shock when the words of Truth's Pardon are read out to him. After the *Visio* his age is not alluded to, and he does not grow decrepit with the years as sad Will does. It may therefore be assumed that his condition as an old man when he comes on the scene has more than mundane significance. Both Moses and Peter, the two traditional leaders of the pilgrimage of man into the Kingdom, are usually represented in art as old men, and Moses, it will be remembered, died before the people crossed into the Promised Land. Peter, as we have seen, underwent a kind of renewal of life. Augustine, influenced by Paul, experienced something which seemed to him like the death of his old self. These eminent examples would go to confirm the doctrine of Paul concerning carnal and spiritual sowing and reaping, the 'old man' and the 'new man', in Langland's mind. His old Piers as leader of the folk ought typically either to die like Moses, having travelled as far as he could, or else to take a new road, like Peter and Paul and many of their saintly successors. As leader in the *Visio*, Piers does a great deal of good; he helps his fellow-men to become more just and more concerned for each other's welfare. Yet it is also to be confessed that he has given only verbal directions to Truth's hill, and none of the pilgrims has come within sight of Truth himself. Truth seems quite far off; he 'herde telle' what Piers was doing, and sent him a message inscribed in a document.

It seems to me evident that those critics who have associated this Piers with *homo carnalis* are substantially right. If Piers at this stage in the poem had the kind of insight that characterises the Piers of the last epiphany, he would be urging his folk to 'sow in the spirit' if they desired to come near to Truth. Ambrose expresses this view of the Christian life very plainly in the metaphors of Paul when he comments on the man 'out in the field' and the women 'grinding corn' in Luke's account of the way the Kingdom of God will come [cp. *Luc.* 17:31 ff.]. He takes the opportunity to exhort his readers to work on their own field: he wants them to smell of the field as Jacob did — but the seed to be sown is the word of God, and the cultivation, within the soul:

> Till your field, then, if you want to be guided to the Kingdom of God.
> Make a fruitful crop of good merits flower abundantly for you.[14]

In the same passage from Luke, the man who is forbidden to go back even to put on a tunic brings to Ambrose's mind Paul's image of 'putting on the new man' [cp. *Col.* 3:9f.] [15] and the two women 'grinding at the mill' suggest to him the unacceptable wheat of the Synagogue on the one hand and the harvest of the Church, prophesied for those 'who sow in tears' [cp. *Ps.* 125:6] on the other.[16] The complex of scriptural verses assembled shows how completely Ambrose was imbued with belief in the changed meaning of Scripture and the changed requirements of a virtuous life involved in 'putting off the old man'. Langland, presumably taught to read the gospel with a gloss like this, would have authoritative precedent for transforming his exemplary figure, so as to make him 'sow in tears' [cp. A 8:106 ff.; B 7:124 ff.; not in C] and eventually prepare a harvest for God's Kingdom.

The momentous event that marks this change in Piers is his sudden comprehension of what Truth's Pardon must mean, both for himself and those who have decided to follow him. He has assumed a responsibility for all the would-be pilgrims, and the Pardon when it comes is puzzlingly said to cover him and them *and their posterity*. As we have remarked above, Piers's posterity is abstract, not flesh and blood. Perhaps we can learn something more on this matter from the strange name of his son, given in the previous passus:

> His sone hattiþ suffre þi souereynes to hauen here wille
> And deme hem nouȝt for ȝif þou dost þou shalt it dere abiggen,
> Let god worþe wiþal for so his woord techiþ.
>
> [A 7:72ff.; B 6:82ff.; C 8:82ff.]

The last part of this unconscionably long name brings the reader's mind once more back to Moses: 'Let god worþe wiþal'. The C-text expands the 'name' further and makes the reminder of Moses more explicit by adding

Super cathedram Moysi sedent, et cetera,

a quotation from *Matt.* 23:2 '[The scribes and the pharisees] sit in the seat of Moses'. The phrase 'Let me alone' is said by God in wrath to Moses [*Exod.* 32:10] when the people of Israel had 'turned aside out of the way' and worshipped the golden calf. Through the name of Piers's son, Langland gives a warning to everyone not to usurp God's place as judge, and covertly, to those who can place the allusion to God and Moses, he says two other things. Juxtaposed with his text *Super cathedram Moysi*, the phrase 'Let god worþe' expresses confidence in the scriptural message, however unworthy the person who preaches it; put back in its historical context, the same phrase offers a hope that the expected divine retribution is not inexorable. Hearing 'Let me alone' from the Lord, Moses in fact prayed that his people might be spared, and in answer to his prayer God pardoned them.

The 'pardon' which Moses received for those who had been worshipping the golden calf consisted in the restoration of their inheritance as sons of Abraham: the possession of the Kingdom. In Christian teaching, this inheritance passes to the Church through Peter and the other apostles. The word 'testament', as I have already remarked, can imply the disposal of property after death, and this indeed is the meaning attached to the 'New Testament' in the Epistle to the Hebrews [cp. *Heb.* 9:15f.]. This instrument is thought to grant the Hebraic Promised Land, figuratively understood to be the Kingdom of Heaven, as a legacy to Christian people.

Augustine picks up this idea from the Epistles and impresses on his readers that 'our Father's testament' [*testamentum patris nostri*] is no ordinary will that may be contested; he contrasts it with 'any worthless document made by some man or other'.[17] It is therefore to be reverently guarded. This contrast is made in the context of Psalm 36, which says a great deal about the inheritance of the land: in his discourse, Augustine reproaches those sinners who 'take his testament in their mouth' without profit to themselves, expatiating on the unmatchable importance of the sacred text.[18] As we shall see, many things in this discourse pertain to the thought of *Piers Plowman*, and I would make a guess that Langland's idea of contrasting Truth's document with 'any worthless document made by some man or other' under the name of a pardon germinated while he was studying the inward meaning of this psalm under the tutelage of the Doctors. All my argument so far leads to the conclusion that Truth's letter to Piers is to be identified with 'our Father's testament' which becomes valid 'on the death of the testator' [cp. *Heb.* 9:16]. (The reason for its being divided in two will emerge later.)

Psalm 36 is an antidote, Augustine thinks, for the soul-sickness which afflicts those who question God's justice because they see corrupt men prospering in this world. There are promises in the psalm for those who 'dwell in the land' and blessings on David's seed. To make a specifically Christian interpretation, such promises had to be read prophetically and allegorically. The extension of *spiritual* benefit to a man's heirs (which the prophetic reading requires) raises a difficulty: the same difficulty as critics have found with the provision of Piers's Pardon which releases him and his heirs from the guilt of sin for ever:

> And purchasede him a pardoun *A pena et a culpa*
> For him, and for his heires ever more aftur.
>
> [A 8:3f.; B 7:3f.; C 9:3f.] [19]

As Bennett puts it: 'No papal pardon presumed to extend its benefits to a man's children'.[20] Similarly, Augustine, faced with the psalmist's 'his seed shall be blessed' [*Ps.* 36:26], assumes that 'his seed' does not mean 'offspring' here, but, rather, the good works that he sows; in explaining the verse, he draws on the verses from Paul which we have seen to lie behind the name of Piers's wife:

> *His seed* is what he leaves behind, that from which he sows here and will reap hereafter. And so the Apostle says: *And in doing good, let us not fail. For in due time, we shall reap, not failing. Therefore, while we have time,* he says, *let us work good to all men.*[21]

Psalm 36, as interpreted, thus joins *spiritual sowing and reaping within the land* with God's promise that the *justi* will inherit the Kingdom. If we use this teaching to interpret Truth's Pardon to Piers, it will be seen that the outward, expressed meaning of Truth's words promising possession of the Kingdom to the folk entails their being 'just' under the Law, whereas the 'inward', derived meaning requires that they sow and reap 'in the spirit' in order to claim their inheritance under the Testament. Piers's wife's name points to this inward meaning. Psalm 36 also states that the Lord will uphold the just man and provide his bread (in verses which Langland appropriates, the one in the clauses of the Pardon and the other later on in the description of the Tree of Charity). As for the wickedly prosperous, the psalmist dooms them, and Augustine advocates leaving them to God's retribution. (We recall the name of Piers's son.) In speaking of this coming retribution, Augustine quotes Christ's prophecy of Doomsday [*Matt.* 25:46]; this includes the words Langland uses (in a slightly varied form) for the 'two lines' of the Pardon, as read by Will and the priest:

> In two lynes it lay & nouȝt o lettre more,
> And was writen riȝt þus in witnesse of treuþe:
> *Et qui bona egerunt ibunt in vitam eternam;*
> *Qui vero mala in ignem eternum.*
>
> [A 8:93ff.; B 7:110ff.; C 10:286ff.]

In Augustine's discourse, this Doomsday prophecy is coupled with the prophecy which ends the parable of the Sower and the Weeds [cp. *Matt*. 13:36ff.], so bringing the metaphors of sowing and reaping to their ultimate conclusion: the harvest at the end of the world.

The arrogant priest who reads out the two lines of Latin from the Pardon is quite evidently one of those who are described in Augustine's words as 'taking his testament in their mouth' unprofitably.[22] Like a pharisee, he reads only the letter of God's testament. Langland has set before him this solemn text as it appears in a creed, a variant of the gospel words of Jesus.[23] He speaks his empty creed to his own condemnation (while recalling to us, by his oath, Peter's power to pardon, passed down to such as he is): 'Peter! ... I con no pardoun fynde' ... [A 8:96; B 7:115; C 9:290]. Will the Dreamer, looking over his shoulder, also sees only the words that the priest reads out. Piers himself has no ready contradiction of the priest's words. Instead, with an upsurge of 'pure tene', he tears the document:

> And Pers for puire teone polled hit a-sonder.
> [A 8:100; B 7:116; not in C]

Whatever the meaning of the 'tene' and the gesture, the words he then utters are of walking through the valley of the shadow of death; no more, he says, will he be so busy about food for his body: he will trust in God and spend his days in penance and weeping; his tears will be his bread. In this moment of realisation, his former way of life suddenly seems misdirected, his confidence that he has been giving Truth satisfactory service is broken. The shock of this revaluation vibrates through Will to the reader. On our understanding of this climactic moment of the *Visio* our interpretation of the whole of *Piers Plowman* will depend.

Piers's 'tene' and his ambivalent gesture have generated a critical literature of their own, and there is no consensus of opinion.[24] The phrase 'pure tene' has no simple equivalent in modern English. 'Pure' may mean unmixed, or unsullied, 'tene' anger or grief, or sorrow tinged with anger.[25] Piers might be irritated with the priest who is showing him up as an ignoramus. He might be vexed with himself for not having understood the truth before. He might be angry that 'pardons' are sent to deceive the people. He might be grieved that all his hopes for himself and his followers are dashed. He might be sorrowful that he has proved an inadequate guide to the others, or contrite because he has paid too little heed to the gospel. In Piers as a *person* any or all of these feelings might be his immediate response to the shock of the priest's words. As a man rocked on his heels by unwelcome self-knowledge, he might tear up the incriminating document in a rage, irrationally, as if to nullify it and all it implies. The gesture is psychologically *right* — and yet it achieves nothing. Truth is unmoved. The quest is still to be fulfilled, and the words of Truth cannot be destroyed. Will the Dreamer seems to have come to an impasse. His ploughman-guide is at odds with the priest; Truth promises Paradise to those who deserve it; but the priest's reading cannot be gainsaid, and who can be sure of his own deserts?

Some critics think that Will the poet has reached his own impasse here.[26] But even in the A-text the impugning of the Pardon is not the end of the poem and the Life of Dowel is begun in the next Passus. Will the Dreamer's spoken conclusion as he meditates on the matter is that it must be unsafe for the sinner who breaks the Ten Commandments to rely on buying his way into heaven; his final prayer is for mercy and grace to do well. This rounding-off of the *Visio* is an important indication that Will has learnt 'to know the false'. But this is only the negative side of his religious formation; he has as yet no inner understanding of goodness and forgiveness. He has observed what the world reflects: bewilderment and injustice, abortive good intentions, scorn and distress. He has learnt to love Piers, the just man, and at the end of his vision he has seen him broken in spirit. Without full awareness, he has been drawn towards righteousness [*justitia*] and has seen the human face of righteousness humble and sorrowful before the demands of Truth's Law. To learn more, he must follow Piers in a different domain.

Langland ends his first version of Will's dreams with a quotation from Augustine's *Confessiones*.[27] I have already suggested that in describing Piers's conversion he was recalling Augustine's personal experience, and I want now to focus upon a singular feature of that experience. Augustine's illumination, it will be remembered, came through the words of Psalm 4. Surprisingly, he writes of his *anger* as the inward meaning of the psalm struck him. He read the words 'Be angry and sin not' [*Ps.* 4:4],[28] and he describes his response to them in this way:

> I read, 'be angry and sin not', and how deeply I was moved, O my God, for now I had learned to be angry with myself for things past, so that I might not sin in the future . . . Nor were my 'good things' now outside me, nor were they to be sought with bodily eyes under this sun.[29]

Augustine had earlier felt great anger against those who seemed to him to be opposing the truth, but in this moment he feels only grief for them and turns his anger upon himself. He takes to himself the words of the Psalmist, as I have described in Chapter 2. His account interweaves the phrases of the psalm with his own words:

> But there, where I was angry with myself in my chamber, where I felt the stings [of contrition], where I had offered my sacrifice, slaying 'the old man' and beginning the resolve of my new life, putting my hope in thee – there, thou didst begin to grow sweet to me and to fill my heart with gladness.[30]

There follow the sentences I have already discussed:

> And I cried out, as I read all this outside me and felt its meaning within me, etc.[31]

I referred above to the meaning Augustine attaches to the obscure *Sacrificate sacrificium iustitiae*; his understanding of it is further elucidated in his discourse on Psalm 4 in the *Enarrationes in Psalmos*. No doubt thinking of Paul's quotation of the verse 'Be angry and sin not' in the context of 'putting on the new man' [cp. *Eph.* 4:23ff.], Augustine takes the 'sacrifice' to be an act of penance at the start of a new spiritual life.[32]

There is thus apostolic and patristic precedent for an accompaniment of anger with the sorrow and hope which a man might feel as he dedicates himself to a more spiritual way of life, and Augustine is pursuing the implication of Paul's words when he finds this experience to be also a dying to the life 'under Adam' and a rejection of the 'letter', the surface meaning of the Scriptures, in favour of an inward understanding. All these feelings and discoveries seem to be appropriate to Piers at the end of the *Visio*. Langland's phrase 'pure tene', implying anger which is not sinful, would very aptly denote anger such as Augustine describes, directed at his own shortcomings, its destructive force turned upon the old, rather complacent, servant of Truth who has relied on obedience to the Law. Both the gesture of tearing the sacred document — the 'letter' itself — and the sorrowing resolve to lead a new kind of life appropriately mark the change of the pious ploughman-preacher into a humbler, yet paradoxically a more awesome, leader of the Christian folk. The outward gesture manifests (as several critics have suggested) that Piers is freeing himself from the letter of the Law which, in Langland's view, still trammels many of his pharisaical contemporaries. The inward change is both a sacrifice and a renewal: he feels that the light of God's countenance is stamped upon him. That Psalm 4 meant something like this to Langland as well as to Augustine is further indicated by the later passage in which Peace quotes from this psalm, at the moment when Righteousness is reconciled with Peace and Mercy with Truth [cp. B 18:185; C 20:191]. Peace offers the quotation as part of an 'open letter' — 'Loo, here þe patente!' — confirming that, as the C-text explains,

> '. . . Crist hath conuerted the kynde of rihtwisnesse
> Into pees and pyte, of his puyr grace.'

That is, the very nature of righteousness has been converted in the Atonement. Piers in responding to the inner meaning of Truth's letter at the end of the *Visio* signals a change in his nature as *forma justitiae*: he is thenceforth ready to render God's coin back to God by progressing in Christ-likeness.

Several other meanings have been proposed for the gesture of tearing the Pardon: the tearing-up of a sentence of death, the wiping-out of the record of man's sins, the breaking of the tablets of the Law, the rending of the veil of the Temple, even the killing of Christ on the Cross. All of these present different ways of describing the conversion of Piers in his figural aspect. The personal change in him which is like Augustine's own illumination represents the historical change in human nature which is the essence of traditional Christian teaching. We should not interpret the giving or the tearing of the Pardon as the re-enactment of one single biblical event in the earthly life of Moses, Christ, or Peter: it can signify several moments of prophetic revelation because essentially it signals the sealing of the New Covenant which destroys the 'letter' of the Old Covenant and at the same time makes the 'testament' effectual. It betokens the self-sacrifice of Justice which Piers, now understanding 'inwardly', takes into his own religious life in a new way.

The words of the Pardon hold the promise of salvation, but, like the Old Testament texts it uses, its meaning is ambiguous and opaque to the secular mind.

Truth apparently commands Piers to till the land, yet Piers resolves to cease his sowing; there are provisions which apparently promise Paradise among the patriarchs, yet when the document is unfolded before the priest and Will they can see only two lines of letters. Unless the poet wished to undermine belief in the truth of Truth, which would effectively destroy the foundations of his narrative, these surface inconsistencies must be explicable. They seem to me to be so only if we apply the doctrine of inward and outward meaning.

The provisions of the Pardon are the great hope of just men in their several walks of life. Their confidence can rest on Psalm 14, *Domine quis habitabit* [cp. A 8:47 and 55; B 7:49f.]; all are offered the same pardon as Piers if they live in love and in law. It follows that, when the Pardon is revealed as a decree of just reward and retribution, their hope must falter. The scriptural texts on which they have relied come from 'þe sauter and sapience boþe' [cp. A 8:47 and B 7:41ff.]. Truth is said to have sent a letter 'under his secre seal' [cp. A 8:25; B 7:23; C 9:27] implying, I suppose, that what Truth says is not open to all eyes. It is a striking fact that the A-text Pardon contains no New Testament texts, and in the B-text a solitary quotation from Matthew [7:12] turns out to be the rule of life summed up in the words 'For this is the Law and the Prophets'. The one other reference to the gospels is to Luke's parable of the Talents, in which Truth shows himself to be a hard master [cp. *Luc.* 19:23, quoted in B 7:83]. On the surface, the 'talents' are material possessions to be increased by proper use, but this is a parable which demands a non-literal reading. In Gregory's *Moralia* the money entrusted to the Lord's servants is construed as the due of preaching which a pastor owes; this is part of his discourse on 'the ploughshare of the tongue'.[33] For Augustine, as for Gregory, the parable teaches that those who are given the word of God must put it to good use for the benefit of others, remembering the condemnation of the servant who buried the talent entrusted to him.[34]

It appears therefore that the texts which Langland uses as the guarantees of the Pardon will have special meaning for priests and preachers (who can read 'under the secret seal'). The promises given under the Law and in the words of the Prophets hold good for all who do well to the best of their ability, once they are redeemed by Christ. The various provisions of the Pardon respecting people in different callings ask no more than honest and righteous dealing with others, and in this they match the moral teachings in the Psalms and some of the other Judaic scriptures. But Langland is very much aware that Jesus asked more than this of his disciples, and the parable of the Talents, which he quotes, has disquieting undertones, especially for those who are following Piers in the vocation of preaching, and for all who ponder on the significance of the buried talent.

The characteristic differences of the three versions of *Piers Plowman* are quite evident in the three accounts of the contents of the Pardon. Each of them makes the fundamental point I have been considering: that the fair-sounding Old Testament promises are bound up with the stark justice of Old Testament Law. The A-text does not elaborate the point. The B-text introduces cryptic texts which have barbed significance for neglectful priests and complacent Christians generally. The covert significance of these puts the informed reader in the right frame of mind to understand both why the mocking priest impugns the Pardon and why Piers must tear up the 'letter' of the Old Law in beginning his new life. However, the enigmas of the B-text have often baffled willing readers and it is not hard to suppose that the plainer and more explicit C-text was written because the B-version had frequently been misconstrued.

The C-text Pardon elaborates two matters implicit in B: the rights and wrongs of almsgiving to the deserving and the undeserving poor, and the wickedness of uncaring pastors. The two cryptic texts I have quoted from B have no place in this differently directed argument, so the underlying theme of the transformation of Piers 'under the Law' to Piers looking for Grace (with its metaphorical relation to the coin which alone will pay man's debt to God) is buried in C under a heap of castigations. The new material also includes more quotation from the gospels, as if the immediate moral lessons of C had to take precedence over the former logic of the poem's structure, but, even so, the texts used do not mingle the provisions of the Pardon with the New Life. There are two sorts of quotation, each reminding the reader of the disciples of Jesus. The first group [cp. C 9:118ff.] recalls that the disciples were sent out *selverles, in a somer garment*, and that they wandered the streets reverencing no man, like the *lunatik lollers* the poet is commending to his readers' care. The second group of texts [cp. C 9:255ff.] admonishes slack bishops and priests by reminding them that Peter's charge has fallen upon them, and by linking them with Simon Peter in his fleshly weakness at Gethsemane. Christ's charge to Peter to feed his sheep and his reference to hireling shepherds lie behind a vigorous attack on bishops who neglect their flock. The C-text Pardon thus comes back to the theme of rendering one's account, of having a debt to pay. The false shepherds who have lived by simony, with 'have þis for þat' [C 10:277] have placed themselves under the Law, and they will be judged, as they have judged others, by that Mosaic principle. It is clear from this passage that the poet has not lost sight of the relation of Truth's Pardon and the Old Law, but in this last version he wants to speak out more plainly about the worldliness and sloth of the contemporary successors of Peter. He does away with the grand symbolic gesture of the tearing of the Pardon, presumably because it had failed to make its point. He reverts therefore to a more commonplace attack on the hireling shepherds and to his earlier themes of meed and mercy. This drives home the doctrine 'with what measure you mete' which runs through the whole *Visio*, and brings the reader to the same conclusion as in the previous version: that the Law condemns. But C has clearly lost not only the dramatic incident of the B-text, but with it the sense of an all-encompassing providential movement towards man's salvation. The great poetic vision is occluded and a good sermon preached instead. The poet's anger finds vigorous expression, but the C-text simply tells us what we are to feel: in the B-text the splendid anger of Piers shows us a moment of terrible and irreversible commitment.

The illumined Piers understands a different meaning in Truth's command to him to take his team and till the earth. Suddenly, he acknowledges that he must *live* the words he has known so long: that he must seek the Kingdom of Truth inwardly, in a spirit of penitence, that his leadership of the others will in future be a spiritual leadership − a ploughing with the tongue. Like the prophets of former times he must draw the people back to God. When Will meets him again, it will be in the role of prophet, revealing God in mysterious signs, *in aenigmate*.

VI

PATIENCE AND PIERS THE PALMER

I

Will the Dreamer goes his own way for a long time without seeing Piers again. This part of the poem allegorises a period of study and introspection in which he tries to find answers to his questions about the life that will lead to salvation. In this respect he resembles the Augustine of the *Confessiones*, who turns from his ordinary work to a scrutiny of his inner self, discovering through wider self-knowledge what it means to be a man made in the image of God. In this process, Augustine becomes more than ever conscious of conflicting desires within himself: his understanding of sin deepens with his spiritual growth. Will similarly discovers more about sin than about charity as he questions himself. Before he can open himself to the love of God, he has to reach a state of receptive patience which is foreign to his ungoverned temperament. Even when (as the allegory presents it) he becomes the companion of Patience, his strong curiosity and impulsive anger burst out. His struggle to be humble and charitable is comically dramatised in the scene at the dinner table [B Passus 13; C Passus 15] where, from his lower place beside Patience, he watches the fat Doctor of Divinity savouring the rich meal and hears him pontificating on the subject of good works. He succeeds in swallowing his vexation, since he goes on his journey by the side of Patience, and so he reaches a state in which his heart and soul can come close to Piers and learn more of divine love.

In the bible, patience is an important virtue, often linked with hope and especially with the hope of the prophets awaiting the Messiah. In Paul, the life of the individual soul seeking to do well essentially involves patience:

> To those who after patience [*secundum patientiam*] in doing well [*boni operis*] seek honour, glory and immortality, he will give eternal life [*Rom.* 2:7].[1]

The 'ploughman' to whom even Clergy defers in the dinner-party scene speaks the doctrine of Paul [cp. 1 *Cor.* 13:1f. and *Rom.* 1:22]. However, Clergy does not quote Paul's words. He claims that Piers's teaching depends on two texts only: these texts are in fact the basis of the Old Law. The special interest of these two texts is that they demonstrate the continuity of God's Law: 'love God and your neighbour' is the message of *Deut.* 6:5 and *Levit.* 19:18, endorsed by Jesus in *Marc.* 12:33ff.[2] (Gregory, discussing these two precepts of charity in the *Moralia*, reminds his readers that Jesus is quoting the Law when he gives these injunctions.[3]) The second fundamental text ascribed by Clergy to Piers is the familiar Psalm 14, which sets out the virtues of the just man. Clergy thus stresses that Piers has always preached love of God and care for one's neighbour. The same emphasis is to be found in the speech of Patience, which follows, for he amplifies the words *dilige inimicos* 'love your enemies' not with the words of Jesus but with reference to the 'coals of fire' of *Proverb*. 25:22. In the C-text only, the 'coals of fire' passage is put in the mouth of Piers himself (though his presence has not been hinted as the guests assemble). When he has uttered this one speech, he slips unnoticed from the room and Reason follows him.

Much praise has been given to this scene for its psychological realism and humour, but its place in the progress of Will's quest has not been so well understood. It is plain enough that the Doctor does not live up to his own very limited idea of what loving his neighbour involves, and also that Will is reproved for being impatient with him. However, it is less clear what the text *patientes vincunt* has to do with Will's search for Truth. It proves again to be an Augustinian association of ideas, to be found quite fully expressed in *De vera religione*. This is a tract in which Augustine argues that reasoning can help us to discover Truth, though Truth is not *reached* by reasoning, but by a disposition of mind. He reasons that man has a disposition to rule, which may lead him to pride and ambition to subdue others, or more happily to subjugation of his unruly desires and control over his own life. The victory, which only the patient know, will come when *cupiditas* (imagined as a woman) is subdued, and other vices brought under control:

> He who has conquered his vices cannot be conquered by man. For he is not conquered unless what he loves is taken away from him by the adversary. Therefore, he who loves only what cannot be taken away from the lover, is indubitably unconquered, and is tormented by no envy . . . For he loves God with all his heart and with all his soul and with all his mind, and his neighbour as himself . . .

> Then, as the commandment requires, let us love even our enemies, if we wish to be truly unconquered. For no man is unconquered in himself, save by the unalterable law under which only those who serve are free. For thus what they love cannot be taken from them, and this fact alone makes them unconquered and perfect men.[4]

Augustine's argument in this treatise depends on the central tenet of his religious faith that man's purpose on earth is to reach towards God by loving: first by loving the true self, the soul, and then by embracing with the same love the true selves of all other men:

> Whoever loves another as himself ought to love that in him which is his true self. Assuredly, bodies are not what we truly are. So what we are to covet or desire in a man is not the body. In this, too, the commandment is valid: *You shall not covet anything belonging to your neighbour*. Because of this, anyone who loves anything in his neighbour other than what is truly himself does not love him as himself.

Why, therefore, should he not be unconquered who in loving a man loves nothing in him beyond what is truly man, that is, the creature of God made in his image, and can he find wanting the perfect nature that he loves, since God himself is perfect?[5]

The passages I have quoted seem to me to shed light on Langland's conception of Patience and the teaching he offers, more particularly on the difficult lines which lead into the riddle. Patience quotes his old 'lemman' Love, on loving one's own soul and others as oneself (thus repeating Augustine's theory that we know Love before we love another being) and then adds:

> For he þat loueþ þee leelly litel of þyne coueiteþ.
> Kynde loue coueiteþ noȝt no catel but speche.

> [B 13:149 f.]

Even an enemy must be loved as oneself: so 'casting coals of fire' upon his head, we must try to win him over. Even an enemy may thus come to 'love lelly', coveting no bodily property in the other, desiring from him nothing but communion in speech. The ambiguity of the word *kynde* makes for uncertainty here, but, if we follow Augustine's theory, we shall take this 'kynde love' to be that which belongs to man's essential nature (that which he shares with Kynde, the Creator), and therefore to be completely different from 'natural love' based on physical ties.

At the centre of the passage concerning 'kynde love' we come upon the celebrated riddle of Patience. It is a riddle of power: Patience can confer mastery 'þoruȝ miȝt of þis redeles' [B 13:167]. Though it does not directly impinge upon Piers, it prepares Will and the reader for the grand enigma of Passus B16 and so comes within the scope of my study.

> Wiþ half a laumpe lyne in latyn, *Ex vi transicionis*,
> I bere þer [in a bouste], faste ybounde, dowel,
> In a signe of þe Saterday þat sette first the kalender,
> And al þe wit of þe wodnesday of þe nexte wike after;
> The myddel of þe Moone [i]s þe [m]yght of boþe.
> And herwith am I welcome þer I haue it wiþ me.

In these words, Patience describes the mysterious box which will arm the bearer against all tribulations, quoting as testimony *Caritas nichil timet* and *Pacientes vincunt* [B 13:151 ff.].[6] The argument from *De vera religione* quoted above, if brought to bear here, will lead us to expect that Patience's box contains some symbol of 'true love'.

The researches of several critics, including notably Kaske and Smith, have prepared the ground for interpretation of these cryptic lines.[7] All would now agree, I imagine, that the mention of day, week and month refers to Easter, and that the strange Latin *Ex vi transitionis* puns upon 'the power of transitivity' and 'the power of the Passover'. Smith has offered us one 'lamp-line', Kaske another. Kaske favours a metaphorical *bouste*, Goodridge an actual box carrying a wax Agnus Dei. Their respective elucidations, especially of the grammatical term, are subtle and very elaborate. Langland can be playful and profoundly serious at one and the same time, as the whole scene demonstrates, and it is likely that he is provokingly obscure in *Ex vi transitionis* in order to underline the point that, before God became incarnate, the prophets spoke of him *in aenigmate*.[8] Will is passing from the Old Law period to the New; the New Testament will be sealed at the first Eastertide, and Will must travel patiently towards the revelation that Easter will bring to him. Some obscurity in the words of his guide is therefore apt. Nevertheless, to be obscure is one thing, to be incomprehensible quite another, and I can hardly believe that Langland meant to be incomprehensible to all but grammarians. The published hypotheses about the meaning of Patience's riddle seem to require the reader to be well-briefed in grammatical theory of a rather technical sort. The solution I am going to propose involves grammar in a much more rudimentary way, and it is based on Augustine's own use of grammar in his exposition of the nature of love. If we continue to follow Augustine's path to Truth, we also come across a 'lamp-line' which seems peculiarly apt for Patience to hold in mind.

I have already had occasion to quote several passages from Augustine's disquisition on love in *De Trinitate*; it is again central to my interpretation here. It will be recalled that Augustine's personal search for Truth begins with belief that we love what is good, and with some analysis of what it means to say 'we love':

> For this is true love, that we *live justly*, clinging to truth: and on that account we put no value on any mortal things compared with the love of men, through which we desire them to *live justly* . . . Since there are two commandments *on which hang all the Law and the Prophets: love of God* and *love of neighbour*, it is not improper that Scripture often puts one of them for both . . . We find many other places in Holy Writ in which only love of our neighbour seems to be taught as a requisite for perfection, and nothing is said about the love of God, though the Law and the Prophets hang upon both commandments. But this is because he who loves his neighbour must necessarily first love Love itself. *God is love, and whoever abides in love abides in God*. It follows, therefore, that he must first love God.[9]

(This insistence that the love of Love precedes the love of others explains, as I have indicated, why Langland's Patience has Love as his 'lemman'.)

Significantly for our enquiry into Patience's mysterious 'power of transitivity', Augustine next considers the grammar of the verb 'to love'. His reasoning turns on the fact that the verb requires an object: we cannot conceive of loving without loving someone or something. Augustine does not expressly use the terms 'transitive' or 'transitivity' in this argument, but he clearly uses *verbum* in the sense 'transitive verb', for without the grammatical concept his reasoning would make no sense. It is my supposition that Langland, adopting the reasoning, has made the grammatical point explicit by using a technical term of the schools, having also in mind the pun he can make with that term. The phrase *Ex vi transitionis* can both encapsulate the Augustinian doctrine of love's need for an object and punningly suggest a 'crossing-over' which invokes the traditional significance of the Jewish Passover. This is the relevant part of the argument:

For when we love Charity [*caritas*], we love something that loves; we love it *because* it loves something. What, then, does Charity love which makes Charity itself loved? For it is not Charity if it loves nothing. But if it loves itself, it must have some object in order to love itself *as charity*. Just as a (transitive) word implies an object — it denotes itself but does not denote itself *as a transitive word* unless it indicates that it implies an object — so similarly Charity indeed loves itself, but unless it loves itself loving some object it does not love itself *as charity*. What therefore does Charity love unless it is what we love through charity? And that, as we advance from what is nearest [*or*, if we start from our neighbour] is a brother.[10]

Augustine's purpose in this part of *De Trinitate* is to show that God, who is *caritas*, has three aspects, as lover, love and beloved, and that the human spirit 'walks in an image' of God. To grow in love is to move towards the perfecting of that inward image, and its perfecting is the meaning to be understood in the text: 'we shall be like him, for we shall see him as he is'.[11] Langland's view of 'charite' and his concept of the three *Vitae* owe much to the doctrine developed in *De Trinitate*, as I have tried to show, and it is my belief that the passage I have quoted about the verb 'to love' put in his mind the association of verbal transitivity and the contents of Patience's box. Augustine's argument proceeds to the proposition that 'man has no means of loving God, unless it comes of God'; in my view this corollary to his teaching about charity explains why Patience needs 'half a lamp-line' as well as the 'box'. The 'lamp-line' must be one which gives Patience hope of the enabling power which Augustine describes in this same passage:

God the Holy Spirit who proceeds from God, when he is given to man sets him alight with the love of God and of neighbour, and is himself Love. Man has no means of loving God unless it comes of God.[12]

Whichever scriptural 'lamp-line' we adduce in solving Patience's riddle, there is to my mind no doubt that it refers to the flame of love kindled by God in man's soul.

At first sight, Smith's identification of the lamp-line with the *lumen vultus Domini* text from Psalm 4 is very attractive.[13] We have already seen that this text is important for the underlying thought of *Piers Plowman*. There is, however, a difficulty which Smith's exposition glosses over: namely, that *lumen* in the psalm does not refer to the light of a *lamp*, but to the brightness of the divine image impressed upon the human soul. It would obviously be preferable to adduce a text which refers directly to a lamp (remembering also that Langland earlier used the metaphor of a lighted lamp for the soul aflame with charity).[14] The context requires an allusion to the lamp of a patient soul who loves God; such a text occurs in Psalm 17 *Diligam te, Domine*, a psalm which promises, to the man who has kept the ways of the Lord, his mercy and the strength to make his way perfect. The first *half* of the verse in question reads:

Quoniam tu illuminas [v.1. *illuminabis*] *lucernam meam, Domine.*
'For thou dost [or wilt] light my lamp, O Lord.' [*Ps.* 17:29][15]

The aptness of this text becomes apparent when we note its interpretation by

Augustine, who likes to quote it, especially with the *illuminabis* which implies hope for the future. In the *Confessiones* he uses it about his own search for the light of Truth:

Thus it was then with me, since I did not know that my soul had to be illumined by another light, so that, not being in its own nature of the Truth, it might become partaker of Truth. 'For thou wilt light my lamp; the Lord my God will lighten my darkness.'[16]

What this enlightenment meant to Augustine is apparent in *Enarrationes in Psalmos*: in one discourse he imagines this 'lamp' showing pilgrims the way back to God; writing on *Ps*. 52:3f. he quotes the half-verse from *Ps*. 17:29 as the words of a man *who knows who he is* because God's light is in him.[17] Evidently this is the lamp which Will's Patience must carry. Will must keep the commandments and 'possess his soul in patience' [cp. *Luc*. 21:19] until he receives the light by which he can truly know and love his own soul: and when he communes with *Anima* he will be led to a vision of *charite*. First, he must part company with the worldly-wise like Friar Jordan, whose hearts are dark.[18] Patience's riddle means nothing to Jordan, though he is confident that he knows what Dowel is.

It seems probable that Langland's inspiration for the contrast between the self-indulgent worldly diner and mortified Will with his pilgrim companion Patience was the Epistle of James. We find there an attack on those who 'respect persons' and care nothing for the poor, and also advice to the brethren to follow the 'royal law' of love of one's neighbour in order to *do well* [cp. *Jac*. 2:8]. Moreover, this epistle also urges the brethren to 'be patient' like a farmer waiting for the fruit of the earth, and to take example by *the patience of the prophets* [cp. *Jac*. 5:7 and 5:10].[19] Patience in *Piers Plowman* carries Dowel in his box and waits for the light which will disclose the deep meaning of his riddle.

The fact that Patience carries Dowel (rather than the higher virtues)[20] consorts with his intermediate placing as a pilgrim between the beginning of Will's journey and the vision of the Tree of Charity. He carries with him the doctrine of love which safeguarded the godly men of the Old Testament, and waits in hope like the prophets. If my interpretation is valid so far, there remains only the matter of the 'box' which he carries with him. It can hardly be mere coincidence that the Israelites were enjoined always to keep with them and to 'bind for a sign' upon their hands and upon their foreheads certain texts which bid them hear God's word and teach it to their children, and to love God [cp. *Deut*. 6:8]. These commandments could be summed up in the words *disce, doce, dilige*, which Patience repeats [cp. B 13:137f.]. A godly man living under the Old Law always carried with him *a box* containing these texts together with the verses from *Exodus* 13:1-10 which command a yearly memorial of the Passover. This box, the phylactery or 'safeguard' which the Old Testament requires the people of Moses to carry, is a uniquely fitting sign to prefigure the fulfilment of the Law at Easter, when the Jewish Passover is given a new meaning as prophecy of the sacrifice of the *Agnus Dei*.[21] Friar Jordan, like the scornful priest of the pardon scene, does not perceive the 'inward' meaning of the old scripture; his attitude is very worldly. But Patience eats the 'sour loaf' of the Passover meal and preaches 'Kynde love', which is his protection on his pilgrimage.

Thus, Langland has used the character of Patience to bring out the continuity of the Old Law and the New Law of love. Ingeniously, by using the 'coals of fire' text, he has shown that the Old Testament even taught love of one's enemy. If we take this scene, like that of the Pardon, to have both personal and historical significations, the cryptic *ex vi transitionis* and the ambiguous 'Kynde love coveiteþ noȝt no catel but speche' will now disclose satisfactory meanings on each plane. This latter sentence will yield fuller meaning yet.

On the personal and atemporal level, Augustine's theory of love accounts for the 'kynde love' which desires only communion in speech. In *De Trinitate* he makes an analogy between the desire of a loving friend to put his feeling into words and the expression of God's love through the incarnation of his Word.[22] Such a train of thought would fit well into Patience's education of Will. It would also suggest how the phrase 'no catel but speche' can bear an additional significance in the history of God's relations with mankind. Before the incarnation of the Word, man's worship was expressed in terms of cattle offered in sacrifice. During the ministry of Jesus, a more spiritual understanding of worship was spread among the Jews,[23] as is shown in the passage from Mark which I cited at the beginning of this chapter. Patience, a character still living under the Law, seems to me to fill the shoes of the scribe in this dialogue:

> And the scribe said to him, 'Well, Master, you have spoken truly: for there is one God, and there is no other but he.
>
> And to love him with all the heart, and with all the understanding, and with all the soul, and with all the strength, and to love one's neighbour as oneself, is more than all burnt offerings and sacrifices.'
>
> And Jesus, seeing that he answered wisely, said to him, 'You are not far from the Kingdom of God.'
>
> [*Marc.* 12:32ff.]

This scribe understood what 'kynde love' required of him, and he knew that no 'catel' could serve as substitute offerings. His journey to the Kingdom was almost over.

II

I turn now to the rather different C-text version of the scene. Early on, Patience is said to be:

> Ilyk Peres the ploghman, as he a palmere were
>
> [C 15:33f.]

This is the first hint given to the reader of this version that Piers may now be travelling as a pilgrim. The Dreamer has not seen him since his quarrel with the priest over the meaning of the Pardon, and he does not, in fact, see him come in at any point in this dream, though he hears him speak. As I have already indicated, in the C-text Piers takes over the speech of Patience which leads into the riddle, and the riddle itself is deleted. The speech itself is simplified and shortened so as to remove the (Augustinian) mention of loving Love and one's soul: the effect is to leave the dogma of the Old Law, *disce, doce, dilige deum*, the 'coals of fire' injunction, and the aphorism *Patientes vincunt*. The only new element here is that Piers promises

> Byfore perpetuel pees y shal preue þat y saide
> And avowe byfore god, and forsaken hit neuere . . .
>
> [C 15:139f.]

The phrase 'before perpetual peace' is susceptible of various interpretations; I do not find the phrase as such in the biblical glosses, though the Kingdom of God in *Isa.* 26:3f. [*Vulg.*] is a hoped-for place of peace *in perpetuum*. If 'perpetual peace' can be regarded as equivalent to 'perfect peace' we might gloss the phrase with the help of Gregory's thoughts on *Job.* 5:24, among which appears 'For our peace begins in longing for the Creator, but is perfected by a clear vision'.[24] The sentence I have quoted occurs in a passage about learning how to love one's fellow men. Piers's role is ill-defined at this point in C, but he appears to be prophesying that Christ, as man, will prove his love for mankind, even for his enemies, in laying down his life: this act of supreme love must precede the perfecting of the vision of God. His words encourage Conscience to go with Patience 'parfitnesse to fynde' [cp. C 15:184].

Before we leave the C-additions in this scene, there is another alteration to observe. Clergy, speaking just before Piers, excuses himself here rather differently from answering the question 'What is Dowel?' He will debate such matters, he says, only in school, 'for Peres love þe palmare ʒent'. Leaving out at this point the evocative but difficult teaching ascribed to Piers in B,

> And seith that Dowel and Dobet arn two infinites
> Whiche infinites with a feith fynden out Dobest
>
> [B 13:127f.]

he adds in the later version a new proof-text, quoting *Marc.* 10:18:

> And preueth by puyre skile inparfyt alle thynges,
> *Nemo bonus*,
> Bote leel love and treuthe þat loth is to be founde.
>
> [C 16:136f.]

The simple effect of this addition is to reinforce the doctrine that every man needs grace, but it comes in abruptly and lacks a clear transition from Clergy's speech to Piers's first words '*Pacientes vincunt*'. The new text *Nemo bonus* is excerpted from the answer Jesus gave to the question 'Good master, what shall I do to inherit eternal life?' [cp. *Luc.* 18:18f.], so it brings the reader's mind sharply back to Will's questions to Holy Church and the purpose of his quest.[25] Clergy's reference to 'pure skill' makes it evident that he, as a debater, admires the cleverness of the answer Jesus gave on that occasion. (Ambrose, commenting on the text, makes a similar point — *versuta interrogatio et ideo arguta responsio* 'the question was crafty and the answer correspondingly clever'.[26]) However, it would be wrong to infer that Clergy simply identifies Piers the Palmer with Jesus,

55

for the other proof-texts are from the Old Testament, and indeed *nemo bonus* repeats the thought of Psalm 13:3, 'there is none that does good, not even one'.[27] For Ambrose, the *nemo bonus* text cryptically distinguishes Christ, the divine Wisdom, from all other men, and he goes on to quote from the Book of Wisdom:

> For he is the brightness of everlasting light
> And the immaculate mirror of the majesty of God,
> And the image of his goodness.
>
> *[Sap.* 7:26][28]

Thus, in the C-version, Clergy's newly-added scriptural text is charged with meanings for Will in his search for goodness: fundamentally, it implies that no human teacher can lead a man to Truth, and that goodness cannot be achieved without the action of divine love. The connotations of this new text must dash Will's hopes of obtaining straight answers from the professional theologians to his questions about salvation but they also mysteriously point the way to the *deus-homo* of C Passus 20, love's proof in deed.

The important place assigned to Patience in a man's progress towards salvation is traditional. Gregory, like Langland's Conscience, recognises patience as leading to perfection of virtue.[29] The biblical authority for this is *Matt.* 10:22, but it may also be relevant to note that the bible gives the promise of a crown to the man who 'keeps the word of patience' [cp. *Apoc.* 3:10ff.].[30]

To conclude, the dinner-party scene in both versions I believe to be a bitterly comic parody of the Jewish Passover meal. The suggestion made by Goodridge that Langland's word *transitio* is a mistake for *transitus* 'passing over' cannot stand, in view of the excellent sense made by reading the phrase as a grammarian's expression, but his insight is not therefore valueless.[31] Will the Dreamer's choice of Patience as a companion leads him to the realisation to which Piers came much earlier: that one should not be too careful for the needs of the body [cp. B 14:33], and that the 'sour loof' of penance is princely food [cp. B 13: 52ff.]. So Will slowly prepares to cross into a life of grace. Patience, according to my reading, is waiting for the coming of the Light, as were the Old Testament prophets, and, like them, he keeps the Passover, the first of the three pilgrim-feasts of the Old Law [cp. *Deut.* 16:3]. As Goodridge points out, the March moon 'set the calendar' first for the Jewish Passover, and later for the Christian Easter.[32] The transformation of this feast is an important part of the fulfilling of the Law by Jesus. The beginning of the Passover ritual as laid down by Moses was the slaughter of a sheep or calf in the place of worship and the ceremonial eating of this beast [cp. *Deut.* 16:2]. For the seven days after, the ritual meals contained no meat, but only 'the bread of affliction' and bitter herbs which commemorated the flight from bondage in Egypt. If Langland has the Passover in mind, it will be evident that the line

> Kynde love coveiteþ noȝt no catel but speche
>
> [B 13:150]

has particular point when referred, not merely to a general change in worship, but to the Christian replacement of this ritual sacrifice by the services of Holy Week and Easter. The Passover ritual is laid down in a long speech by Moses which also gave God's commandments and initiated the custom of carrying the phylactery. The speech includes a teaching which Jesus himself repeated: '. . . *quod non in solo pane vivat homo, sed in omni verbo quod egreditur de ore Dei* [*Deut.* 8:3; cp. *Matt.* 4:4, which Langland quotes when Patience brings victuals out of his bag for Haukyn at B 14:47; C 15:245].

Finally, we must note that this speech by Moses was made on the day that the Israelites were to cross Jordan into the Promised Land: *Audi, Israel: tu transgredieris hodie Jordanem* . . . [cp. *Deut.* 9:1]. The verb *transgredior* also has the sense 'surpass': I cannot believe that Langland's quick ear for a pun missed that one when he made Friar Jordan the target of Will's justified resentment and the only notable member of the company to be left behind when the pilgrims went on their way.

Piers has no essential part to play at this stage of Will's journey. Clergy and Patience can speak for him, since the Law and the Prophets have joined in one message and one expectation of the Messiah's coming. In the C-version he makes a token appearance, to remind the reader that Patience takes his strength from the support of Piers, though Piers himself is out of sight, and to give his own promise that he will appear in the fullness of time to give living proof of his doctrine of love. In the B-version that doctrine is presented to Will in the lively symbolism of the fruit-tree of Will's next vision, a tree cultivated and protected by Piers in person.

VII

PIERS AND THE TREE

I

The enigma presented by Piers when Will encounters him for the second time (in the B-text) has at its centre the strange fruit tree which is said by Anima to be 'charite'. The Tree should, therefore, symbolise that 'Kynde Love' which, as we have seen, was thought to unite the Creator with his creatures and each man with his neighbour — if each man could but live according to his true nature. What inhibits the operation of this Kynde Love is sin, which separates man from God and sets him against his fellow-men. The tree symbol, presenting 'charite' in the world, inevitably shows love and sin in conflict, and, because Will is in process of learning to 'know himself' and has been urged 'to examine the nature of sins rather than the nature of things' [cp. B 11:228f.), we find that this vision has more to reveal about the effects of sin than about the operations of love.

Throughout the previous passus, Will has been listening to Anima, and it is Anima who directs him back to Piers. In introducing Anima, Langland found it necessary to list the different faculties of the soul, paraphrasing Isidore of Seville on the subject. This part of the poem is not to modern taste (in spite of a little joke about bishops) and somewhat confusing, because the faculties of the soul listed here do not include *Liberum Arbitrium* 'Free Will', who turns out to be (in Anima's next bit of teaching) the important faculty whose business is to cleanse the heart — clearing it of 'weeds' — under the guidance of Piers.[1] The poet himself was apparently dissatisfied with this dry exposition; in the C-revision *Anima* is not personified and *Liberum Arbitrium* becomes Will's adviser and his guide to the country of *Cor-hominis* where the Tree grows. It should not go unnoticed that in analysing the functions of the soul Langland names Augustine alongside Isidore as an authority [cp. B 15:37; C 16:198]; in fact, he seems to be drawing much more on *De Trinitate* than on Isidore, in spite of the initial quotation. One telling point will illustrate this. Isidore's account says, ordinarily enough, '*dum recolit, memoria est*', 'when it recollects, it is [called] Memory'. Langland's Anima, however, does not stop there, but unexpectedly relates *memoria* with the soul's turning to God, as in *De Trinitate*, where Augustine's theory is that the mind has the innate power to *remember* and love its Maker, and therefore in 'knowing itself' comes to know God.[2] Further, Augustine believes that the mind must reflect upon itself: 'fixing upon itself the direction of the will which was wont to stray elsewhere'. He describes how the mind

58

occupying itself with 'restless pleasures' and 'bent on the acquisition of knowledge from external things' becomes disfigured by its love of corporeal things, images of which adhere to it, from which it must be separated before it can know its true nature.[3] Will the Dreamer's spiritual education is evidently proceeding along the lines Augustine has laid down, and he will now come to the knowledge of love in his own heart, in his inner vision of *Cor-hominis*.

It remains to be asked why Anima was replaced in the final revision by *Liberum Arbitrium* [cp. C 16:89]. The effect of the change is to make plainer that Will's progress towards Truth must be directed by a faculty which is 'Cristes creature' [cp. 16:166], namely, a special power of the *redeemed* soul which enables it to know and love the good.

> But by the law is the knowledge of sin; by faith is the obtaining of grace against sin; by grace is the healing of the soul from the harmful effect of sin; by the healing of the soul is freedom of the will (*liberum arbitrium*); by freedom of the will is the love of righteousness (*justitia*); by the love of righteousness is the operation of the law.[4]

In these words, from *De spiritu et littera*, we have Augustine's view of the function of *liberum arbitrium*, the freed and healed will. In the poem, Will the Dreamer has already learnt something from Patience about the harm done by sin, and its remedy in the sacrament of penance [cp. B 14:96] dispensed by the successors of Peter,

> For sith he hath the power that Peter hadde, he hath the pot with the salve
> [B 13:254; C 15:225]

Patience invites people to partake of *Fiat voluntas tua* [cp. B 14:48f.; not in C], so enabling the will to conform itself to the will of God, to root out sins and to progress towards righteousness. The C-text rearrangement of the roles in this important scene emphasises that it is the healed spirit that can see God — though only in the *mirror* of its burnished self and in an *enigma* [cp. C 16:293ff.].[5]

The Augustinian road to Truth through introspection brings the Dreamer to the enigma of the Tree in its personal and atemporal aspect. In *Cor-hominis* he can see *Liberum Arbitrium* rooting up the weeds which represent the corporeal loves which compete with *caritas*. What is Piers doing here? He is 'the apostolic farmer' who helps the soul in its work of cleansing the heart, and by his words plants and nurtures charity:

> He sees men's hearts as a field: but in what condition does he find them?
> He finds weeds; he roots them out. If he finds clean land, he plants.
> He wants to plant there *the tree charity*. And what weeds does he want to root out? Love of the world. Listen to him who roots out weeds.[6]

Through this image, Augustine urges his hearers to listen to John the Apostle, discoursing on Christian love. He develops his metaphor of the *verba extirpantia* and the *exstirpator*, the 'words that root out' and the 'rooter-up' of these wild growths that prevent charity from flourishing.[7] (For John, the competing growths are the three false loves, *concupiscentia carnis*, *concupiscentia oculorum* and *superbia vitae* [cp. *1 Jo*. 2:16], figures the reader of Langland will recognise: Will met them earlier as clinging damsels rather than as choking weeds [cp. B 11:

13ff.; C 11:175ff.]. This passage, from Augustine's homily on John's First Epistle, the only specific reference to *the tree charity* that I know of, appears in a context so appropriate to Langland's thought in this passus that I myself have no doubt that this is one conceptual source of the apostolic gardener and his tree in *Piers Plowman*.

Piers the gardener, if derived from this source, would seem to be a New Testament character, but he proves to be another transitional figure. Though the Augustinian weeding metaphor is indisputably connected with the Apostle John, the planting of charity in the breast of man is an image used by Gregory in the passage on love of God and neighbour which I have already quoted above: that in which he says that Jesus speaks 'through [the words of] the Law'.[8] The Lord, as he puts it, 'first fixes the root of his love in the soil of our breast, so that afterwards in the branches the love of our brethren may shoot forth'. Langland's elaboration of the image with the winds of temptation probably owes something to Gregory; the moral teachings about patience, simplicity of heart, the results of brawling and trying to do mischief against one's neighbours are to be found scattered in the *Moralia*. One passage in particular, which uses the metaphor of the 'blossom' falling so that the 'fruit' does not form (when good intentions are overcome by earthly desires or strife with others), is especially close to Langland's moral Tree image: Gregory sadly concludes that 'such things often happen to those who do not follow God with a pure and single aim'.[9] For both Gregory and Langland, single-minded perseverance in 'the rule of perfection' is necessary for the maturing of charity: it is in this sense that 'Pacience hatte the pure tree, and pure symple of herte' [B 16:8].[10]

There is absolutely no reason (and here I agree with Aers against Smith and others[11]) to look for covert allegorical meaning in Anima's description of the Tree. Anima speaks in a general sense about the virtues; it is left for Piers to speak more ecclesiastically on these matters. Before we pass on from the *Moralia* to other traditional church teaching which helps us to elucidate what happens when Will questions Piers, it is to be noted that Gregory's usual practice in explicating a biblical text is to treat it twice over, first 'morally', then 'allegorically'. He is not, of course, the only exegete to expound the Old Testament in this way, but we need look no further than the *Moralia* for instances of the kind of double perspective on a single object that has made Langland's elaboration of the Tree image incomprehensible to so many modern readers.

I think Langland's first readers must have been used to this double perspective. Without it, we cannot make complete sense of the Pardon or of Patience's box, or, I would say, of the Tree. Each symbol has both an atemporal significance which can fit into the 'now' of Will's dream and a time-related significance which gives it a place in the historical process of salvation. Putting it another way, each says something about both the progress of the individual soul towards Truth and the progress of the Church towards Truth. These are not separate stories in the mind of the poet because they are both educed from the same scriptural texts, and the progress of the individual cannot be divorced from the growth of the Body of which he is part. It is the doctrine of the unity of *caritas* which makes Will's progress every man's progress; and quarrelling, backbiting, heresy are all offences against *caritas*.

This love is altogether of one piece, and as it is itself compacted into a unity, so it makes into one all that are dependent upon it, like a flame fusing them together.[12]

In these words, Augustine sums up the teaching of John in the homilies from which I have quoted. Like Langland, Augustine was writing in a time when the unity of the Church was endangered by heresy and schism. Paul had met the same danger of the fragmenting of the new Church when he learnt that different communities were making personality-cults of the apostolic preachers who were their various founders — and the image he found to quash this sectarianism was that of the planter and the gardener who look after the growth of a tree [cp. *1 Cor.* cc. 1-3 *passim*, and especially *1 Cor.* 3:6-9]. Whether Paul or Apollos or Cephas (Peter) is the teacher, Paul says, the voice is the Spirit of God; all the apostolic labourers 'have the mind of Christ' [*1 Cor.* 2:16]. So Augustine, grieved by the quarrelling voices of different teachers in his own day, naturally found Paul's words apt for his own homilies. He not only amplifies the metaphor of the farmer tending the tree; he also reiterates that his own teaching is like the work of the man who plants and waters; he cannot form the fruit himself:

> The sound of our words strikes upon ears, but the Teacher is within. Do not think that anyone learns anything from a man. We can give reminders with the sound of our voice, but if he who teaches is not within that noise of ours becomes useless . . . Outward teachings are helps and reminders of a sort. He who teaches hearts has his chair in heaven.[13]

It is central to Langland's whole purpose in writing *Piers Plowman* that Piers should give such helps and reminders, and his role as gardener caring for the Tree is peculiarly appropriate to remind the reader that Peter, Paul, John, the inspired prophets of the pre-Christian era, and the inspired Fathers of the Church, all give one testimony to the meaning of Kynde Love. The poet has to show that the Church grows on the stock of the Synagogue, that God's love was in man from the beginning, though the fruit of that love was meagre, abortive and bruised. His Tree in its historical aspect requires a source in the Old Testament which can in some pertinent sense foreshadow the redeeming love of the New Law.

This 'allegorical' aspect of the Tree has proved an insoluble enigma for modern critics, as Aers shows in his ruthless scrutiny of the various untenable theories.[14] The general opinion has been that Langland had in mind a Jesse tree such as is commonly found in ecclesiastical art. However, though the pictorial shape of such a genealogical diagram may have inspired his imagination to some extent, it is quite clear that his tree description is different in detail and effect. As Aers trenchantly observes, 'a Jesse tree without the Virgin Mary and without Jesse and without Christ is not a Jesse tree'.[15] I believe, for reasons given below, that Langland's concept comes from an utterly different biblical source.

The Jews were required by the Law to keep an annual festival to celebrate the in-gathering of the fruits. It was (and still is) marked by an unusual ritual of prayers and meals held in special booths constructed out of leafy branches and decorated with fruit, in which the families sat. It was also marked by a complete reading of the Mosaic Law. It might seem fanciful to suppose that Langland's people among the tree-branches have anything to do with this ritual, were it not that this festival was instituted when the Temple was rebuilt at Jerusalem, thus combining a thanksgiving for God's care for his people's welfare in the annual harvest of fruit with the re-founding, as it were, of the Synagogue, and the re-affirmation of the Law. The festival is called, from the booths, The Feast of Tabernacles. Now, Jesus was celebrating the Feast of Tabernacles when the Pharisees accused him of breaking the Mosaic law by healing on the Sabbath [cp.*Jo.* 7:24], and it was at the end of that Feast that he refused to countenance the legal stoning of the woman taken in adultery. It may therefore be said that Jesus used this Feast which affirms the Law as the occasion to transcend the letter of the Law in acts of love.

If this allusion holds, a very satisfactory pattern of incidents marking the Christian transformation of the Old Law is discernible in the structure of *Piers Plowman*. The first Piers reminds us of Moses on Sinai and the pardon he obtained for the idolatrous people; Patience (Piers's double) reminds us of the binding of the Law on the Israelites and the institution of the Passover Feast as they prepared to cross Jordan; the Piers of the Tree scene reminds us of the re-affirmation of the Law when Nehemiah (*Neemia*) instituted the Feast of Tabernacles. All these prophetic incidents have their Christian counterparts, the 'inward meaning' given them by Jesus, and Piers on each occasion intimates that the prophecy will be fulfilled.

Nehemiah is not much read today, though some readers will recall that T. S. Eliot used him as a character in his first religious play, *The Rock* (a pageant structured on lines not unlike those which govern the epiphanies of Piers). As the re-builder of the Temple, this prophet has had a special place in sacred history, and Bede thought highly enough of him to write a book, *In Ezram et Neemiam*, explaining the Christian significance of the Temple and the Feast of Tabernacles and various signs given by the prophet. It is of particular interest that one of these signs is the shaking out of the prophet's garment to show the people that anyone who mistreats the poor should be 'shaken out' (*sic excutiat*) of God's house: Bede takes up the point and tells us that anyone who shows no mercy to the poor will be 'shaken out' of the Church and will get no 'fruit' from his labour of good works.[16] Piers, we remember, both stones and shakes the Tree from which the people — its fruit — fall down.

II

We are now, I think, in a position to understand how Langland's mind is working when he creates the Tree scene. Other traditional doctrines are drawn in from several biblical references to trees. The bible many times uses fruit trees — the olive, the fig, the grape-vine — as symbols of mankind. The prophet Isaiah symbolised the people of Jacob suffering God's wrath by an olive-tree with almost all its fruit shaken off [cp. *Isa.* 17:6]; Jesus, it has been thought, used the fig-tree as a symbol of man barren of good works. The barren fig-tree story may lend something to Langland's picture: the land around the fig-tree needs to be dug and manured to give it a last chance of fruiting, and Ambrose fills out the metaphor with 'apostolic mattocks' working the hard soil of Jewish hearts.[17] The one extra year's grace given to the unproductive tree is associated in *De Trinitate* with the Last Age of the world in which the Son of God will come 'to reform us in the image of God'.[18] Preachers naturally used as metaphors the kinds of tree their audiences were used to seeing every day, and the exegetes extracting the 'kernel' of truth from such passages pay scant attention to the species of fruit in the story. Ambrose, reading John the Baptist's words about the axe laid to the root of the trees [cp. *Luc.* 3:9], at once thinks of the barren fig-tree, and prays that the *bonus cultor agri* will have patience with us in our unfruitfulness.[19] When he reads how Zacchaeus climbed into a sycomore-fig tree so that he might see Jesus pass, Ambrose's fancy sees him as the fruit of a New Age, in which with Christ's coming the Tree will bring forth not fruit, but men: for him Zacchaeus is a type of mankind rising above the Law to be reborn as a Christian.[20] It would seem, then, that Langland is by no means uniquely fanciful in portraying men both as producers of fruit and as themselves fruit of a tree that spans the ages.

Piers's tree, however, is not a Palestinian tree, but, surprisingly enough, an Anglo-French apple-tree which produces both apples and hybrid Cailloux pears ['Kalewey bastard', B 16:69]. Even to the non-gardener, this must indicate that there has been a grafting on the old stock, and this Pauline metaphor for the growth of the Church out of the Synagogue is adapted so as to make the apples of the old stock suggest those 'living under Adam' and the pear-fruit near the crown of the Tree those who have given up earthly loves to become 'angels' peers' [cp. B 16:67ff.]. If we compare Ambrose's exposition of the fig-tree incident again, we find that he talks about 'two fruitings' on some trees, so accounting for the fall of the 'fruit' produced by the patriarchs to make way for the riper fruit of the new era.[21] Langland seems to have refined on this so as to bring in all the connotations of Adam's apple and the pun on the sweeter pears. In his eclectic picture, God's people are shown to be part of a living organism of mixed stock, upheld and protected by divine love, the organism itself maturing in love, yet not wholly sheltered from the agents of corruption which can destroy the fruit piecemeal. Piers the apostolic gardener tries to prevent the Tree from being damaged: he advises and works with the restored human will, *Liberum Arbitrium*.

We may now look afresh at what happens between Will and Piers in this scene. The first thing that Will notices is that the Tree is shored up: it would be blown down by the winds if it were not supported by three matching wooden stakes. As we have already noted, the imagery of temptation used here has a Gregorian ring. In several places Gregory speaks of 'the wind of temptation', as, for example, in his comment on 'And behold there came a strong wind from the desert' [*Job* 1:19]:

The 'desert region' is the heart of unbelievers, which, when the Creator has abandoned it, has no inhabitant to care for it. And what other than strong temptation is the 'strong wind'?[22]

He also combines this image with that of a man blown down like a leaf from a tree. On *Job* 13:25, he writes:

> For what is man but a leaf, who fell in Paradise from the tree? What but a leaf is he who is caught by the wind of temptation and lifted up by the gusts of his passions? For the human mind is shaken by as many gusts as it suffers temptations.[23]

Thus Langland has a precedent for filling the garden of *Cor-hominis* with strong winds, though Gregory does not use the tree image in precisely the same way as he does.

Piers's answer to Will's question about the stakes under the tree shows doctrine dominating the development of the image. There are three component metaphors overlapping here: the endangered tree menaced by the gales, the fruit-blossom which the cold wind may destroy, and the worm which eats away the blossom and spoils the fruit. These literary vehicles present aspects of man's growth in *caritas*, a growth which may be stunted or aborted by the external forces of the Devil and all his works. The gardener's aids against these forces present aspects of God's power and support. When Will last saw Piers he heard him quote the psalm,

> For though I walk in the midst of the shadow of death,
> I will fear no evils, for thou art with me.

[*Ps.* 22:4]

Now that he meets him again, he sees the metaphors in the remainder of that verse turned into solid objects:

> Thy rod and thy staff, they comfort me.

Both Psalm 22 and Psalm 36 [cp. B 16:26] portray God's help as a support to a stumbling and fearful walker: apt metaphor for the pilgrim, but not easy to transpose into gardening terms. Langland's solution is to make the rod and the staff into props for the Tree, and to add a third staff corresponding to the Holy Spirit, the Comforter. God's supporting love for man is thus symbolised in trinity. However, the poet also wishes to show his gardeners themselves constantly active in controlling the pests and counteracting the blighting effects of the winds. Since their efforts will not avail without the help of God, by the logic of the doctrine their weapons against the pests must be those same staves which are there to prevent the Tree from falling. If the gardening image, the vehicle, were dominant, Piers might lay hands on other sticks with which to crush the pests, and leave the stakes in place, but, as it is, his tending of the Tree is governed by the theological and moral points. This part of the teaching is given to us in Piers's own graphic description of his work.

The connection between the Tree that Piers describes and the Tree introduced earlier by Anima has been the subject of much critical discussion. The 'leaves' and 'blossoms' of the two descriptions have seemed to some to be inconsistent in a rather absurd way. Aers has made an uncharacteristic move towards patristic exegesis to point out that 'the bare leaves' which are all that the 'worms of sin' leave behind when they have destroyed the fruit-blossom may indeed be, as in Anima's description, 'Lele-Wordes the lawe of Holy Cherche' [B 16:6]. He says,

Now the effects of the wind of Carnality include not only the destruction of all possibility of fruition, but also the reduction of the plant 'to the bare leaves', which, as Professor Salter says, would suggest to Anima's reader, 'the bare text of God's scripture'. But in the new context this gloss has striking ramifications. For Carnality, in medieval thought, causes 'the death of the soul'; and one of its manifestations is when the text of God's Scripture is reduced to a barely literal understanding.[24]

This interpretation fits well with Langland's general attitude towards 'living under Adam' and it could be further strengthened by reference to commentary on the leaves of the barren fig-tree.

After describing the Tree, Piers gives Will a sort of pastoral sermon, in which he lists the various classes of sinners whom he helps. The first set of people he talks about are those that 'willen truthe' [cp. B 16:27] but who lose sight of the Creator in worldliness: the Serpent in the Tree is always promising them earthly satisfactions and they are the prey of concupiscence. (We remember the followers of Lady Meed.) Piers helps them with reminders of the wrath of God, raising his staff to call down destruction on the wicked, and so instils holy fear. These sinners are like the man of the Sower parable who 'became unfruitful' because of the cares of the world [cp. *Matt.* 13:22]. (The 'yield' from the various kinds of person in the parable is woven into the later part of Piers's account.) The second set of people are those who are plagued like Paul with 'the law in their members'. They are constantly being drawn back into carnal life. To help them, their pastor Piers lays hold of Wisdom like a staff to drive out the harmful carnal thoughts. The 'secounde pil' which he uses is here called *Sapientia Dei Patris* [B 16:36], an idea perhaps suggested to Langland by Gregory's sentence on *Sapientia Dei*:

Again, by a 'tree' the incarnate Wisdom of God is figured, as it is written of her: 'She is a tree of life to those who lay hold of her'.[25]

[*Prov.* 3:18]

The fruit on this middle part of the Tree are the converts, those who have given up the ordinary life of the flesh to live the life of the spirit: such as were Peter, Paul and Augustine. As the former group of rather worldly people can be called *Matrimoyne*, because they are still married to earthly loves, this second group can be called *Continence* or *Widwehode* because they have given up earthly loves. These are less holy than the virgins, and, in Langland's gardening terms, they are the hybrid pears [cp. B 16:69].

The word *peeris* offers Langland the chance of another pun. The third group of people Piers watches over are those who have dedicated their lives wholly to the love of God in perpetual virginity, those who will be near to God in the Kingdom of Heaven, taking the place of the fallen Angels. They are therefore rightfully called 'aungeles peeris' [B 16:71], and they are the special object of the Devil's envy for this reason. They are to be found at the crown of Piers's tree, and it is at this 'crop' that the fiend throws his missiles. He tries to reach them through unkind neighbours, backbiters, quarrellers, brawlers — all those 'children of the Devil' who hate their brother-men [cp. *1 Jo.* 3:10] — in hope of provoking them to give up their 'buxom speche and benigne lokynge' in rebellious and irate retaliation. He also tries to reach them by means of lies, since he is 'the father of lies'. (We remember Wrath at work in the convent garden [cp. B 5: 137 ff.].)

When these holy souls are under attack, there is no need of lawgiver or prophet and Piers has no part in this contest. By a subtle use of the phrase 'manacen bihynde me' [B 16:49], Langland recalls that Christ rejected the final temptation of the Devil with his 'Get behind me, Satan'.[26] As prophesied in Peter's vision, the Law and the Prophets have merged into Christ, and the human faculty which chooses between good and evil, *Liberum Arbitrium*, has been freed. It is therefore *Liberum Arbitrium* who carries on the battle with the Devil. The holy soul is filled with the Holy Ghost, and *Liberum Arbitrium* guards the heart with the power of that Spirit, having in himself the God-given strength to quell the forces of evil. (Because free-will under grace has this power, it sins like Lucifer himself if it chooses evil, and like Lucifer is utterly condemned [cp. B 16:48a].)

Piers's sermon thus gives to the enquiring Will a metaphor of the good life that he is searching for, with its hazards and hindrances and need for perseverance. Above all, he himself illustrates the lovingkindness of God towards his people and the means of grace open to all who seek it.

But Will the Dreamer prefers to come to forbidden knowledge by Adam's route. He wants to talk theology. His first question was about 'thise piles' [B 16:24], and when Piers triumphantly rounds off his pastoral sermon Will thanks him for his interesting account of 'the power of thise postes' and immediately reveals that what he has been thinking about is where these staves come from — i.e. what is the origin and nature of the Trinity. Piers gives him a short answer and a sharp look, and so brings him quickly back to consideration of the three kinds of fruit on the Tree.

Speculation about the legends which might underlie the imaging of God's supporting hand as three pieces of wood has been plentiful and not, to my mind, very profitable. Langland refuses to pursue the matter, and he does not take up this image again when he offers various analogies to the Trinity later in the poem. For the purpose of showing the operation of Father, Son and Holy Ghost aiding mankind against the Devil, he needed to describe three supports, three instruments of power. Beyond this, it was important to emphasise that there were not three separate sources of power; hence these pieces of wood all grow on one root.[27] The only other quality of God which is pertinent to Piers's exposition is that he is the source of all goodness; so Piers's staves grow in the ground called Goodness [cp. B 16:62].

Langland deliberately turns us away from further speculation. Sensing that Piers is displeased with his line of questioning, the Dreamer politely asks him to continue with his account of the fruit hanging on the Tree. Piers, the jovial farmer now, describes his moist fruit, his hybrid pears, and his clean angel-pears that ripen soonest and are 'sweet without swelling'. As I mentioned earlier, these three kinds of fruit are equivalent to the three grades of yield produced on good ground from the Sower's seed: in elaboration of the parable, the thirtyfold yield had become associated with a conjugal way of life, the sixtyfold with a widowed life, and the hundredfold with a virginal life. This exegetical connection has been pointed out by several scholars. Smith quotes a useful commentary from Denis the Carthusian to demonstrate that these different callings (*ordines*) with their different yields of fruit signify in ascending order the progress of souls towards perfection.[28] These stages in virtue sound very similar to Langland's Lives of Dowel, Dobet, and Dobest, but Langland, it must be noted, does not usually talk in terms of *ordines* or *status* either in distinguishing the Lives or in describing the Tree, nor does he call his angel-pears *perfecti*. (Bloomfield, I think, distorts the meaning of the Tree by calling it 'the Tree of Perfection'.[29]) Langland is altogether concerned to break down artificial distinctions between people and to emphasise the infinity of *caritas*: his Tree is a single and developing organism, and the Lives merge into one unfinished progress.

<h1 style="text-align:center">III</h1>

Will, still displaying curiosity, next asks Piers to pull down an apple and let him taste it. At this, all hell is let loose, in a manner of speaking. Will, wanting to *know* for himself the taste of the apple, enacts the primal sin. Piers's response is unexpected and violent. He does not pluck an apple: he hits and shakes the whole tree so that the fruit falls down. I am not aware that anyone has offered a satisfactory explanation of why the exemplary Piers should do this; the C-version, in which Elde, 'Old Age', brings the downfall of the fruit, makes a plain enough allegory of mortality, but the B-text presents an enigma even more astounding than the tearing of the Pardon. I want to offer a new approach to the explication of what Piers does, in the context of his role as prophet.

Will craves an apple. Piers shakes down both apples and (presumably) pears. The apples fairly obviously suggest the Tree of Knowledge; the pears, to a reader of the *Confessiones*, perhaps something else. Augustine, looking back over his youth, makes much of the fact that as a boy he once shook down the fruit from a neighbour's pear tree — not to eat it, but for devilment. As a mature man, he could find no explanation for such an act but an innate propensity to sin.[30] Courcelle describes his attitude to that prank as 'condamnation d'un vol qui est le mal pour le mal'.[31] If the teacher that Langland most admired could convict himself of 'evil for the sake of evil', clearly even Piers himself could not be exempt from that propensity: even the just man, acting wilfully, does sin. I think, therefore, that the actions of Will and Piers here present the bitter and the sweet consequences of the Fall: without recognising the bitter taste of the apple (the legacy of original sin), Will could not taste the sweetness of the Saviour's love, as he desired to do.[32]

However, the main significance of the dropping of the fruit must inhere in the allegory of the consequences of sin under the Old Law, which bring in their train the incarnation of *caritas*; only by comprehending the whole sacred history can Will begin to understand the boundless depth of *charite*. Under the Old Testament Law, Adam's posterity faced terrible penalties if they transgressed: stoning to death or being 'shaken out' of God's congregation.[33] In the historical allegory, Piers acts like the prophets visiting God's wrath upon sinners. He casts something at the topmost fruit and shakes down other fruit, so that a great lamentation goes up from every part of the Tree. As the fruit drops, the Devil waits to carry it off. Thus, the action initiated by Will's desire to know the savour of the fruit dramatises the Fall, the coming of death into the world, and the Law which condemns. But among the 'fruits' who die and are gathered up by the Devil are the prophets and *figurae* of the coming Saviour.

Little attention has been paid to the named men who fall as fruit from the Tree. The common confusion of this Tree of Charity with a genealogical tree has set readers thinking in mistaken ways about these people and about Piers's final action 'to go robbe that rageman' [cp. B 16:89]. It is often supposed that his seizing of the staff precipitates the Incarnation, because the next scene is of Gabriel's annunciation to Mary. But there can be no temporal sequence here: the facts entirely preclude it. John the Baptist is one of the 'fruits' of the Tree taken off by the Devil, and the Baptist's death occurred during the adult earthly life of Christ. The presence of John the Baptist implies two things: first, that the shaken Tree has its being in the era of Prophecy, which comes to an end with the Baptist's death;[34] second, that Piers's action in going after the apple-thief betokens the contest of Christ and Satan which culminates in the Harrowing of Hell.

The names of the patriarchs and prophets who appear on the Tree are not the forefathers of Christ (as they would be on a Jesse tree). They are Adam, father and corrupter of mankind, Abraham, father of the Chosen People who are to be redeemed, Isaiah, the prophet of Advent and of the Saviour's bloody battle with Satan, Samson, whose self-immolation in destroying the heathen temple prefigured the Harrowing of Hell. The last two figures are Samuel and John the Baptist. Traditionally, Samuel prefigures the sacrifice of the Lamb with his sacrificial offering before a battle with the Philistines. He also signals by his anointing of King David and his own retirement[35] that with the coming of the King who is son of David the voices of the prophets will become silent and the voices of the evangelists will in their turn preach the Kingdom of God. Bede explains Samuel's function in these terms and links this prophetic act with 'The Law and the Prophets were until John' [*Luc.* 16:16].[36] Thus the Tree tells in the voice of prophecy, over and over again, that the Saviour is coming: Will has the answer to his question.

The climax of the scene comes when Piers in righteous anger 'hits after' the Fiend who has robbed him of his fruit. Woolf has called attention to the everyday realism of the scene: the angry farmer throwing his stick at the thief running off with his armful of stolen apples.[37] Yet the lifelikeness of the action is a product of the reality of the Scriptures in Langland's mind. As we have seen, his imagination is fed by rumination on biblical texts and only secondarily by reflection on the problems of farmers. We must expect that this climactic action will have its proper biblical warranty.

I hope I have shown that the historical aspect of the Tree emblem, as symbolising the fulfilment of prophecy, makes an entirely fitting prelude to the gospel story which follows in the poem. Piers, miming in the fashion of the Hebrew prophets, rehearses the God-given signs of wrath and mercy, reminding Will of cruel justice and lamentations following on from the plucking of the apple in Eden, and foretelling the coming redemption through the loving self-sacrifice of God the Son. Piers's seizing of the second staff as a weapon against the Devil should also have a historical significance. It could mime one or both of two separate Old Testament incidents involving a prophet's staff. At God's command, Moses threw down his staff and it became a serpent: the sign is given in Exodus as a promise that God's people will be freed from bondage. The second incident I have in mind is also interpreted as presaging Christ's battle with the Devil for the souls in bondage: when Goliath challenged the Israelites, David took only his staff and sling to their single combat.[38]

Augustine, looking for the significance of the serpent-rod miracle, associates it with 'the rod of thy inheritance' (*uirga hereditatis tuae* [*Ps.* 73:5]) and says, 'If death came by the Serpent, the rod in the serpent is Christ in death'.[39] (He then recalls, as Jesus did, the brass serpent held up by Moses to heal the people who had been bitten by venomous serpents, and concludes that the obscure verse in *Ps.* 73 foretells the redemption of the Church, which inherits the promises given in the Old Testament.) The implication of guile, Christ putting on mortality to hide himself, and going against the Serpent with the deception of the serpent, to my mind makes this particular staff-throwing an apt precedent for Piers's gesture here: Langland's treatment of the Harrowing of Hell shows that this aspect of the defeat of the Devil very much appealed to him. However, we should perhaps regard Piers's action with the staff as a kind of gestural pun,[40] concurrently miming David's retaliation against Goliath, since Langland later presents Christ as son of David carrying his wooden cross as sign of his victory. (The exegetes were not slow to see the possible figural import of David's staff: it was, after all, the staff rather than the sling which excited Goliath's scorn – 'Am I a dog, that you come at me with staves?') Piers, seizing and hitting out with the staff that means 'the passion and the powere of oure prince Jesu', thus makes a sign with Old Testament wonders behind it, and the phrase Langland uses, 'happe how it myghte' [B 16:87], indicates that the way the prophetic sign will be realised in action is not yet fully disclosed. It creates an expectation which the jousting scene will expand and ultimately satisfy.

If I am right about the way Langland's mind was working in B Passus 16, the reader requires extrinsic knowledge for full appreciation of what is going on (though some mystification might suit the poet's book). Even in his own time, there must have been many readers who could not fathom the hidden sense. So, as in the case of the Pardon-tearing, it is likely that his readers' puzzled reaction (or perhaps his desire to reach a larger, less well-informed public) caused the poet to think again and to delete these enigmatic signs in favour of much more transparent and ordinary allegorical material. Yet, if we interpret as I have indicated, we perceive a *schema* of emblematic pointers to the way that Will must go and to the revelation that his dreams will bring. Will must proceed from fear of the Lord (under the threat of the first staff), to hope of redemption (holding on to the second staff), and finally to a union of his own *Liberum Arbitrium*, his healed self, with the Holy Spirit (the third staff being his constant defence against the Fiend). As he continues on his pilgrim's progress through the poem, he will see how Christ put on mortality to fight for the stolen fruit, and he will see him also as the princely son of David restoring the Kingdom by overcoming the Devil.

As we move into the next part of the narrative, other phrases confirm that

Piers speaks with a prophet's voice in this second epiphany of the B-text. The poet stresses that Jesus came 'in the fullness of time', quoting *plenitudo temporis* from *Gal.* 4:4 [cp. B 16:93]. He repeats the idea that the prophecies were being fulfilled in the line,

> And Piers the Plowman parceyved plener tyme
>
> [B 16:103]

casting Piers in the role of a tutor to the child Jesus who teaches him the craft of healing. The Pauline context of *plenitudo temporis* brings out the point that Jesus came 'made under the Law to redeem those who were under the Law'.[41] One sense, therefore, of the pedagogic relationship of Piers and Jesus is that the child Jesus was instructed in the Law and wisdom of the Jews. But more than this, Langland especially wishes to emphasise here that Jesus, Son of Justice, took on himself all the limitations of life in a human body. There is a delicate theological point at issue, since incarnate God cannot *need* instruction – yet there are passages in Isaiah which speak of the child Emmanuel learning to know good from evil [cp. *Isa.* 7:14-16]. (Jerome faces the question in his commentary on Isaiah and concludes that it is designed to let us know that Christ in the childhood of his human body did not use the divine Wisdom to make judgements before the proper time.[42]) Langland seems to have Isaiah at the back of his mind when he thinks of Jesus discovering how to keep the human body in health, since Isaiah is named in the C-text at this point. Isaiah himself was renowned as a medical man, since he successfully prescribed a poultice for a desperately sick king [cp. *Isa.* 38 *passim*], and Langland knows this; the C-text compares Jesus and Isaiah:

> That suche a surgien sethen ysaye was þer nevere
>
> [C 18:140]

The poet rather quaintly imagines the youthful Jesus practising his newly-learned skills on sick patients [B 16:104ff.; C removes the practising, cp. C 18:138ff.]. However, the over-riding sense of this passage in both versions is that God's providential plan, partially revealed to the prophets in the past, is about to be fulfilled at the destined time, and the final prophecies are being uttered: we think of Simeon in the temple and John the Baptist preaching in the desert [cp. *Luc.* 2:25ff. and 3:2ff.].

While in the B-text the role of Piers as prophet can be made out, in the C-text Piers has no part in the scene, with the effect that the moral aspect of the Tree symbol is clearer and uncomplicated, but the allegory is weakened. An awkwardness is left at the mention of *plenitudo temporis*. In B, when we read

> Til *plentitudo temporis* [tyme] comen were
> þat Piers fruyt floured and felle to be rype
>
> [B 16:93f.]

we know that these 'fruit' are the holy men and women of the Old Covenant who are awaiting the coming of the Messiah. The metaphor is taken up again in B 18:20 when Faith tells Will that Jesus is to joust for Piers the ploughman's fruit. The tinkering in the C-revision leaves us no hint that the fruit-tree is under Piers's care, so that the mention of Piers's fruit at the joust [C 20:18] does not connect with the apple-tree at all. Worse, the tree-symbol itself has been changed in C to accommodate a different image of mankind renewed — namely the 'ympe', the grafted branch which in Paul's language signifies the Church of the Gentiles growing out of the Jewish Synagogue, and for the individual soul the infusion of grace into Adam's stock. Smith puts the meaning of the C-version plainly: 'The full implication of the figure of the grafted tree, then, is probably that the tree of true love can only flourish when it is "grafted" with God's image, consummately personified in Christ'.[43] As a feature of the Tree of *Liberum Arbitrium*, the freed will, this is good, but it conflicts with the later account of the prophets on the Tree and forestalls the account of the *plenitudo temporis*. Elde's allegorical part is not well thought out, because he only does his shaking of the Tree *twice*, when by his nature he ought, like the 'winds', to be attacking the fruit unremittingly — and anyway, Age cannot be ordered about by any human *Liberum Arbitrium*. The alteration of the scene in the revision has the marks of a local second-thought; it disposes of the rather frightening Piers with his piercing look and wrathful actions, and at the same time destroys a good deal of the point of the scene. It takes away the dialogue between Will and Piers, removing all close contact between them, and so making Piers's role as guide to the pilgrim inadequate. In the C-text, Will makes his own way to Jerusalem without learning anything new from Piers. This may suggest some disillusionment in William Langland. It certainly shows that he valued the clarity of the message of his poem well above the artistry of its narrative form, at least in his later life.

71

VIII

CHRIST AND PIERS

In his Palm Sunday dream, Will finds himself with the crowds in Jerusalem watching a young man enter the city, riding barefoot on the back of a donkey. A herald standing up in a window announces him as 'Son of David' and the 'old Jews' greet him in song. Manifestly, the second David has come to fight, and the single combat foreshadowed in David's challenge to Goliath is about to take place. The poet imagines him, as he imagined David's 'mighty men' earlier in the poem,[1] as a medieval youth eager to prove his manhood in order to win his spurs and become a knight. The atmosphere of a tourney is deftly sketched, but the hymns, the hosannas and palm branches precede the coming of the rider, so that no reader will fail to place the contest in its biblical and liturgical setting. This entry to Jerusalem is the culmination of the ministry of Jesus in the gospels, and it is described by the evangelists so as to suggest that the prophecies of Isaiah and Zechariah about the coming King and Messiah are being fulfilled. Near the end of the Old Testament, Zechariah is inspired to say:

> Thus says the Lord of Hosts: I will return to Sion and dwell in the midst of Jerusalem, and Jerusalem shall be called the City of Truth and the mountain of the Lord of Hosts shall be called the Holy Mountain.
>
> [*Zach.* 8:3]

Jerusalem, he says, will rebuild the Temple, many nations will come to the city, and there will be rejoicing:

> See, your king comes to you, just and a saviour; himself poor, and mounted on a donkey and on a colt, the foal of a donkey.[2]
>
> [*Zach.* 9:9]

Many followers of Jesus believed, as they strewed their palm branches before his donkey, that they were welcoming this king and saviour.

It is therefore entirely appropriate that Will's visions of the way to Truth should bring him to Jerusalem and the prospect of the Holy Mountain, and to the sight of the Son of David on his donkey. But to the Dreamer the figure is not recognisable as Jesus; he sees him as

> Oon semblable to þe Samaritan, and somdeel to Piers the Plow[man]
>
> [B 18:10; C 20:8]

Will had been following the Good Samaritan, as his servant, but the rider galloped away like the wind and left him disconsolate [cp. B 17:85ff.; C 19:47ff.]. In the new dream, the rider is not quite the same as before; he now looks 'something like' Piers the ploughman. Will is uncertain who it is that he sees going to the joust, and has to ask Faith.

I have already referred (in Chapter 3) to the traditional identification of the Good Samaritan with Jesus himself. The Doctors invoke it without the need of prior explanation: as when Ambrose says that Adam had received a lethal wound which would have killed the whole human race, had not *Samaritanus ille descendens* cured the wound.[3] Augustine often thinks of Jesus as *medicus*, and in expounding John's gospel he prays to the Physician to be brought into the Inn:

Let us pray to the physician of the wounded man, let us be carried into the inn to be healed. He it is who promises health, he who had pity on the man who was left by the robbers half-dead on the road.[4]

The 'innkeeper', Augustine goes on to say, signifies 'the ambassadors of Christ' (he is here quoting *2 Cor.* 5:20) to whom he gave 'the two coins' which are to be expended in restoring the health of the wounded man. The two coins are then explained as the two commandments *in quibus tota lex pendet et prophetae.* (This phrase, Langland's readers will recall, is also the 'charm' to save many lives; it is carried by *Spes* in Will's dream of the Samaritan [cp. B 17:11f.; C 19:12ff.].) Augustine concludes his exposition of the parable by identifying the inn with the Church, in which the wounded man will be healed.

This discourse on the gospel begins by enquiring what is meant by 'knowing Truth'. I find this pertinent to our understanding of Langland's picture of the disguised Christ as part of Will's search for Truth:

And so there follows, *Et cognoscetis veritatem* [*Jo.* 8:32]. Truth is unchangeable. Truth is bread; it restores minds, it never fails them. It changes what it feeds; it is not itself changed into that which is fed by it. Truth is the very Word of God, the only-begotten Son of the God of Gods. This Truth put on flesh for our sakes, so that it was born of the Virgin Mary and fulfilled the prophecy, *Veritas de terra orta est* [*Ps.* 84:12]. Thus, when this Truth was speaking among the Jews, it was concealed in flesh; but it was concealed, not so that it should be denied, but so that it should be divulged; to be divulged, so that it should be revealed in the flesh; and revealed in the flesh, so that flesh should be redeemed from sin. And so our Lord Jesus Christ, standing before our sight in the infirmity of the flesh, with the majesty of his divinity hidden, said to those who believed him as he spoke: *Si manseritis in verbo meo, vere discipuli mei eritis* [cp. *Matt.* 10:22]. For he who endures to the end shall be saved. *Et cognoscetis veritatem*, which was hidden from you till now; and it speaks to you, *Et veritas liberabit vos.*[5]

By this train of thought Augustine identifies the Samaritan who succours the wounded man with Truth itself clothed in flesh, the liberator of those who believe and persevere in faith. The 'liberation', as he goes on to expound it, is from subjection to 'Caesar'.[6] The Jews, who thought themselves free, were paying tribute to Caesar, and Jesus therefore taught them through the sign of Caesar's penny. 'For, just as Caesar looks for his image on the coin, so God looks for his in man'.[7] Such teaching as this fed Langland's mind and issued in his strange and compelling vision of the hidden Truth which Will seeks, and sees, uncomprehending, in his dream.

It is the amplitude of the poet's vision which must amaze us. Uniquely, to the best of my knowledge, he fuses into one figure the Samaritan who is Truth disguised and the ploughman who reveals the Word to mankind.

That the jouster outwardly resembles Piers has caused some unnecessary bewilderment. When the crowds in Jerusalem cheered the man on the donkey, they thought he was a prophet. As Jerome puts it,

> When Jesus came in with a crowd, all the citizens of Jerusalem were moved, wondering at the throng, not knowing the truth, and saying *Quis est hic?* This, too, we read in another place that angels said: *Quis est iste rex gloriae?* While the others were doubting and enquiring, the crowd of common people confessed him, starting from the lesser titles that they might reach to the greater, and said: '*Hic est Iesus propheta a Nazareth Galileae*; the prophet whom Moses said would come like to himself . . .'.[8]

Will the Dreamer is among the crowd asking 'Who is he?' but, before Faith gives him his answer, the reader has been left in no doubt that the figure on the donkey is Jesus. What faith has to tell him is that the crowds who see the human body of David's line apparelled like a prophet see only the outward appearance of Jesus. Like a knight wearing another's blason, Jesus is in disguise. He *is* a prophet and an example, like the Piers-figures who have come into the earlier dreams: he looks like another David who opposes his frail human body to the might of the Philistine. Hence the poet can say,

> This Iesus of his gentries wol Iuste in Piers armes
> In his helm and habergeon *humana natura*.[9]
>
> [B 18:22f.; C 20:21f.]

(It will be remembered that David when he went out against Goliath had taken off the armour King Saul lent him; it might be said that his helmet and mailcoat were his own head and breast.[10]) So that Christ shall not be known for *consummatus deus* he wears a cloak:

> In Piers paltok þe Plowman þis prikiere shal ryde
> For no dynt shal hym dere as *in deitate patris*.
>
> [B 18:25f.; cp. C 20:24f.]

These words of Faith allude to the doctrine that God in his eternal Triune nature could not be injured. Christ who is equal with the Father had to 'empty himself' to redeem man.[11] However, it is not this difficult point of faith that Langland wishes to pursue: what fascinates him is the reason for the disguise. The devil has to be fooled — 'go gile ayein gile!' — so that the Law may be fulfilled.

The poem rises to a crescendo of triumph in the verbal battle between Christ and the devil. The devil claims law on his side: God gave him possession of the sons of Adam and God cannot use force to rob him. Yet it was by breaking into the Garden like a thief and by using deceit that he gained that possession, so his title is questionable. Knowing this, he has feared for years that Truth would come to take back those souls, and for the last thirty he has watched Jesus

74

walking about the earth and tried to trap him:

> I have assailed hym with synne and som tyme yasked
> Wheiþer he were god or goddes son; he [g] af me short answere.
>> [B 18:297f.; C 20:330f.]

He would have lengthened the life of Jesus had he been able, in order to prevent him from giving that life for Adam's life (and so making amends under the law for man's offence). Jesus offers his life to him, and so claims back his subjects:

> Thow, Lucifer, in liknesse of a luther addere
> Getest bi gile tho that God lovede
> And I, in liknesse of a leode, that Lord am of hevene
> Graciousliche þi gile have quyt — go gile ayein gile!
>> [B 18:354ff.; not in C]

This bold assertion that Truth employed dissimulation is toned down in the C-version. But the Doctors would not have found it scandalous; Ambrose too has his moment of glee at the way the devil was outwitted by guile. He uses the word *fefellit* 'he beguiled' with the same rhetorical excitement as Langland shows with *gile*, viewing the incarnation and ministry of Christ as governed by the need to keep the devil guessing.

> It is for no small reason that the virginity of Mary beguiled the prince of this world, who when he saw her espoused to a man, could not have supposed the birth suspicious. That the purpose of this plan was to beguile the prince of this world is made clear by the words of the Lord himself, when the apostles were told to keep silent about Christ, when the healed were forbidden to brag of the cure, when the demons were enjoined not to speak of the Son of God. To beguile, as I said, the prince of this world, the apostle too declared to be the purpose of this plan, saying: 'But we speak the wisdom of God hidden in a mystery, which none of the princes of this world knew; for had they known it, they would never have crucified the Lord of Glory' [*1 Cor.* 2:7f.]; that is to say, they would never have brought it about that I should be redeemed by the death of the Lord. He beguiled therefore for us, he beguiled that he should conquer, he beguiled the devil when he was tempted, when he was questioned, when he was called the Son of God, so that at no point did he confess his proper divinity. But yet more he beguiled the prince of this world: for though the devil sometimes had doubts, as when he said, 'If you are the Son of God, cast yourself down', assuredly, too late he recognised him and departed from him.[12]

Langland, with his strong — but distinctly medieval — sense of justice, insists that the price of sin has to be paid, both by God and man. There is no softness in his attitude towards wrongdoing of whatever kind, and for him consummate charity has a core of sternness. He does not choose the figure of the Good Shepherd (though shepherd-flock imagery is not absent from the poem), but rather the Good Samaritan, as his symbol of divine and human love. The Samaritan is apt for the poet's purpose because he can be seen as an unflinching physician pouring wine over festering wounds as well as being a supportive and compassionate friend. Just as the Tree of Charity had its rod and staff, the Samaritan has his *two* bottles, of wine and oil. This attribute of the figure, generally ignored by critics of the poem, is important in patristic thought, and it binds together the teaching about justice and mercy which pervades *Piers Plowman*. We recall that the secular king of the *Visio* was warned that, if he gave judgement according to the bare law, he would be judged according to the letter of the law [B Prol. 137; cp. C Prol. 151 ff.] : looking back, we are made newly aware that the mitigation of the full force of the law of God, the re-interpretation, as it were, of the unalterable decrees of Justice, is what is meant by the salvation of mankind.[13] Langland's secular example provides language for the theological doctrine: the doctrine in its turn puts a different perspective on the day-to-day judgements of the courts.

This sort of interaction between Christian preaching and secular institutions or relationships is very much the province of Gregory, and we can find in his *Moralia* similar advice to rulers — 'For discipline or mercy is much bared if one is upheld without the other' — supported by reference to the Samaritan's wine and oil (together with mention of the rod and manna of the Ark of the Tabernacle and of the rod and staff which comforted David).[14] Langland's poem is clearly intended to have practical effect on both rulers and commons and it is central to his whole endeavour that his readers should realise that the *salve* which the Samaritan offers stings as well as soothes.[15] He expects the Samaritan to return to the world with his salve [so, B 17:115 ff.; not in C], but in the meantime the work of spiritual healing is the responsibility of the Innkeepers. Within the Inn of the Church, the work of healing should be progressing, but instead, as Langland pictures it, the quack doctors are treating their patients' wounds with comforting but useless plasters and medicines [cp. B 20:377 ff.; C 22:78 f.] : 'contrition', which ought to be the Church's 'sovereign salve', has become an empty word. In this veritably desperate situation, Langland holds up 'Piers the ploughman', Truth's authentic messenger, as the only recourse for all those who want to get out of the maze and live good lives. His poem must be designed to pierce the complacency of uncaring priests, in particular. They have been given 'the salve' and yet ignore the needy all around them.

The sequence of Will's meetings with Abraham-Faith, Moses-*Spes* and Jesus-Samaritan unquestionably indicates, as Smith and others have pointed out, that the Samaritan represents *caritas* in the poem. What I have stressed is that this *caritas* is an uncompromising love inimical to any taint in the beloved; the Piers of all the epiphanies is a pattern of *justitia* embodied in the righteous living of God's messengers, a pattern of uncompromising justice which encompasses concern for the well-being of all. With the event of the jousting in Jerusalem we reach an interface where the Samaritan and Piers coalesce and the *imago dei* is revealed with a new intensity.

When the Christ of the Ascension comes into the vision he presents a new pattern, now that of martyrdom, self-sacrificing love:

> I fel eftsones aslepe — and sodeynly me mette
> That Piers the Plowman was peynted al blody,
> And com in wiþ a cros before þe comune peple
> And riȝt lik in alle [lymes] to oure Lord Ies[u].
> [B 19:4 ff.; C 21:6 ff.]

We have here a paradox, inherent in the biblical revelation of God, that the human body (Piers's 'paltok') is the *disguise* of the unapproachable Godhead and is at the same time the fullest *epiphany* of the divine ever to be given to 'the comune peple', the least-veiled image of *caritas*. Langland gives this vision a kind of iconic power by using the word 'peynted': this is not a suffering Jesus but an emblem of majesty and blood-brotherhood. We see a conqueror splashed with the grape-juice of God's Vine, recalling the words of Isaiah, 'Who is this who comes from Edom, with dyed garments from Bosrah?', which foreshadow the second coming of the King of the vine-harvest and the resurrection of all the dead [cp. B 18:369ff.; C 20:411ff.].[16]

For one brief moment in sacred history, the messenger Piers is co-extensive with the Word; he appears as an 'Angel' to declare Himself. The matter is expounded by Gregory in these words:

> For who is this Angel, but he who is called by the Prophet *The Angel of mighty counsel*? [*Isa. 9:6, Sept. vers.*]. For because 'to declare' is called 'evangelize' in Greek, the Lord in announcing himself to us is called Angel. And he well says, *If there shall be a messenger [or Angel] speaking for him* [*Job* 33:23]; because, as the Apostle says, He even intercedes for us. But let us hear what he says for us; *One of like things*. It is the way with medicine to cure disease sometimes by similar, sometimes by contrary, remedies. For it has frequently been wont to cure the hot by warm, and the cold by cold, applications; and on the contrary, the cold by warmth, the hot by cold. Our Physician then, on coming to us from above, and finding us oppressed with such great diseases, applied to our case something of a like, and something of a contrary, nature. For he came to us as Man to men, but as a Just One to those who were in sin. He agreed with us in the truth of His nature, He differed from us in the power of His righteousness. For sinful man could not be amended, except by God. But it was necessary that He who was healing him should be an object of sight; in order that he might amend our former sinful lives, by setting a pattern for us to imitate. But it was not possible that God could be seen by man; He therefore became man that He might be seen. The Holy and Invisible God appeared therefore as visible man, like ourselves, that while He seemed to be of like nature, He might teach us by His holiness. And while agreeing with our condition in verity of nature, He might put a stop to our sickness by the might of his skill.[17]

This passage, I venture to say, conveys discursively some of the meaning of Langland's Piers-Samaritan figure, and it may have helped him to crystallise that poetic image.

There is no break in the narrative to signal the final transformation of Piers: the transfer of power and god-likeness to mankind is explicit. Humankind is made like God: man is newly-stamped with the undoubted image of the King. The poet makes Conscience the spokesman who is now able to describe the pattern of Dowel, Dobet and Dobest: Christ is the pattern, and in this account of his ministry the characteristics of the earlier transformations of Piers are given fuller meaning.[18]

Christ in youth changed water into wine, and so began to Dowel. Conscience's words imply (as we have already noted[19]) that Christ changed the Old Law into the New: this is the traditional significance assigned to the miracle of the wine from water. My interpretation of the first Piers in the light of Augustine's personal experience of the change to a new life relates this miracle to the miraculous illumination of the too-much-earthbound Piers. Next, Conscience describes how Christ did 'doughty deeds' among the common people, earning the name of Dobet, son of David. Here we recall the powers of the old prophets, particularly of David, and the match which this phase of doughty deeds makes with the Piers-figure of *Passus Primus de Dobet* in the B-text, laying about him with the staff. The Jesus of Dobest is not, as might have been expected, the Jesus of the Crucifixion, but instead the Jesus who bestows pardon on mankind. This the patriarchs and prophets could not do, but this Jesus does, and Langland conveys his belief through the Samaritan-figure leaving wounded man to the healing care of the Innkeeper. The prophets had fed the hungry, upheld justice, given comfort, and even raised the dead: but none had presumed to forgive sins. The power to forgive sins is the mark of the *deus-homo*, and it was his claim to forgive sins which earned Jesus the hatred of the Jewish priests. For Langland, only the cleansing away of the defilement called sin can make man acceptable to God. Pardon is for him the essence of salvation, for without it the image on the coin cannot be restored and man cannot face God. For this reason the ultimate vision of his poem on salvation must revolve upon 'Piers power'.

Will's final vision of Piers follows on from Conscience's revelatory speech, which contains one other vital element:

> And whan þis dede was doon do best he [þouȝte],
> And yaf Piers [pardon, and power] he graunted hym,
> Myght [men] to assoille of alle manere synne[s],
> To alle maner men mercy and forȝifnesse
> In covenaunt þat þei come and kneweliche to paie
> To Piers pardon þe Plowman *redde quod debes*.
> Thus haþ Piers power, be his pardon paied
> To bynde and unbynde boþe here and ellis.
>
> [B 19:182ff.; C 21:182ff.][20]

The pardon is conditional on *redde quod debes* 'pay back what you owe'. Justice must continually be satisfied. In daily life the principle of making restitution for wrongs done is easily understood, and Langland has given many instances in the topical parts of his poem. In the spiritual life, the import of the phrase derives from the interpretation of Holy Church's 'Reddite *cesari . . . þat cesari* befalliþ, *Et que sunt dei deo* oþer ellis ȝe don ille'. Those who receive the pardon which Piers can rightfully bestow make it void unless they both satisfy earthly justice and offer their souls to God. Thus payment of the true coin is the requisite of salvation, and Langland's purpose is to make his contemporaries realise what a paltry substitute offering is Meed's money, when given for mass-pence or for a new church window.

Without warning or explanation the poet has replaced the name Peter by the name Piers. The change marks the raising of Peter to a new status as the Keeper of the Keys [cp. *Matt.* 16:19]; he is given this apostolic power as the founder of

78

Christ's Church. As Will the Dreamer listens to Conscience, he sees tongues of flame descend upon Piers and his fellow apostles. In fright, he shakes Conscience, wondering what that was:

> Quod Conscience, and knelede, This is Cristes messager
> And cometh fro the grete God — Grace is his name.
>
> [B 19:207f.; C 21:207f.]

So, in the vision of Pentecost, Piers-Peter is filled with Grace, now named as Christ's messenger. Will has seen in turn the patriarchal Piers who is an analogue of God the Father, and the battling Piers who is an analogue of the Son in contest with Sin, Death and the Devil; he now sees the Piers of the Holy Spirit, who lives on in the era of the saints as the steward of Grace. He has learnt from his vision of Christ the full import of Dobest and what it has to do with the pardon of Piers and the way to Truth.

IX

PIERS IN THE LAST AGE

I

The final epiphany of Piers is, appropriately, the least enigmatic. Piers comes into the era of Grace, which is the era of Christendom, and, according to medieval belief, the sixth and Last Age of the world. It is therefore also the era of Antichrist, as prophesied in the last book of the bible, and of forces gathering for the ultimate battle. The prophecies foretell a great harvest, one angel reaping the earth with his sickle, another gathering the ripe grapes from the Lord's vine; and this harvest is followed by the coming of the King of Kings, his vesture sprinkled with blood, to sit upon the throne of judgement.[1] Will sees the hosts of Antichrist in his dream, and his last vision of Christ also recalls these prophesies. The Piers who should guide the Christian folk in this era might have been portrayed as a shepherd (Dobest bears the bishop's crook[2]), but the calm prospect of green pastures and the safety of the sheepfold is not for Langland. His is a world of labour, conflict and need, disordered and ravaged by the powers ranged with Antichrist. His pattern-figure must toil with the rest for the great harvest, doing his best to make the Barn secure.

Piers takes on the work of the Apostle Peter. His task is to feed Christ's folk, to salve their wounds, and to spread the virtues over the earth. The imagery Langland uses is venerable; it was natural for the apostles to envisage their vocation in terms of the parables Jesus himself had used about the preparation for the Kingdom. They were the sowers of the seed, the labourers in the wheat-field, the vineyard workers earning their penny.[3] (Incidentally, Jesus speaks of 'healing' those who listen to his words, as he urges them to give ear to the parable of the Sower.[4]) Langland has inherited a mass of farming and harvesting metaphors associated with the spreading of the gospel and promoting the virtues. Unlike the ploughman of the *Visio*, the central character he creates for Will's last dream does not function figurally. He swings from the purely historical (Peter and the disciples in the upper room at Pentecost) to the purely allegorical (Piers harnessing the evangelists to his plough). Because he is *called* Piers the Plowman, he can still carry with him the scent of the fields, the hint that Langland's hoped-for spiritual renewal may originate among humble rural men rather than among well-read sophisticates, but his actions are those of a priest. In plain language, he is inspired by the Holy Spirit to preach the gospel and to give the sacraments to the growing Christian congregation. In the symbolism of the dream, he ploughs, harrows and sows, and builds the barn.

As we have already noted, following Barney, the metaphor of ploughing is particularly favoured by Gregory.[5] He speaks of priests as *agricolae* 'tillers of this land',[6] and he regards it as the duty of any man set in authority to ensure that 'the minds of those under him, like ploughed earth, may be made fruitful by the seed of his preaching'.[7] Langland is certainly thinking in a Gregorian way when he describes Piers's allegorical ploughing, though the germ of the symbolism obviously lies in the parables and in Paul. Patristic metaphor is often cerebral, a mnemonic code for a piece of doctrine, as it were, rather than something imaginatively envisaged, and Piers driving his 'beasts' is a case in point. Much significance is stored in the quaint image, as we shall see. The building of the 'barn' also has august antecedents, but it is Langland's genius that brings the place to life.

The description of the building of the Church ought to bring with it, according to the scheme of the *Vitae*, a vision of Dobest. On the face of it, Will's dream portrays no such thing, but we should look at the traditional underthought which governs the narrative. After the scenes of the Ascension and Pentecost, Will's dream is following the thought of Paul. It is Paul who writes of the variety of gifts given to men after the Ascension, and the use to be made of them in building *unity* and, mystically, creating the perfect man:

> And it is he who gave some to be apostles, and some to be prophets, and some evangelists, and some pastors and teachers, thus bringing the saints together for the work of the ministry, for the building of the Body of Christ, until we all, in the unity of the faith and the knowledge of the Son of God, constitute a perfect man [*in uirum perfectum*], to the full measure of the stature of Christ [*Eph.* 4:11 ff.].[8]

Langland has exploited the root concreteness of the word 'building' to make of 'unity' an edifice Will can see going up, but we need the whole passage from Paul in order to understand that they are all toiling to reach perfection: there can be no better life than what Piers and his helpers are working to achieve. Peter, like Paul, teaches the right use of the gifts, and in his writing this is part of a theory of 'stewardship'. The building of the Church required many apostles, evangelists and teachers to continue the work begun by him, and the Piers Langland next presents is the steward of Grace and an example for all those who have been given 'Peter's power'.[9] (Will, too, is no longer alone; he sings *Veni, Creator Spiritus* with many hundreds of other pilgrims. His private search for Truth has merged again with the quest of the folk.)

Langland naturally bases his account of the work of Piers in the Last Age on the writings of Peter himself about what should be done before the approaching end of the world. In the First Epistle, Peter imagines the Church as a building made with living stones [*1 Pet.* 2:4], and, preaching that the end of all things is near, he urges the faithful to work together in love, 'each one using whatever gift he has received to serve others, as good stewards of the manifold grace of God' [*1 Pet.* 4:10]. Though Langland *quotes* only Paul (*Divisiones graciarum sunt* [*1 Cor.* 12:4]) when he enumerates some of the gifts of Grace [cp. B 19:228; C 21:228], the complementary teaching of Peter pertinently explains why Piers is represented as a steward as well as a ploughman in the service of Grace.

Gregory, too, associates the building of the living Church with the giving of the manifold gifts, and the *Moralia* may channel this topic to Langland. What Gregory stresses in the following passage is the *charitatis necessitudo*, the close bond of charity, which makes the separate gifts the possession of all:

> Thus [God] regulates all things, so that while all have separate gifts, when the close bond of charity is put between them, the separate gifts become the property of all, and each man possesses in another what he did not receive himself, so that in humility he gives out to another the possession he had as his own. Hence it is said by Peter, 'Each one using whatever gift he has received to serve others, as good stewards of the manifold grace of God.'[10]

Gregory makes explicit here what Will the Dreamer should be perceiving in his Pentecostal dream. Will is being shown that Dobest means 'learning to love' without reservation; he is discovering what the mysterious 'cheyne of charite' signifies, and the nature of the 'dreury', the love-gift, which Holy Church said was as precious as God himself.[11] The life of Dobest for 'lered' and 'lewed' alike means using each one's talents to the full for the good of everyone, without pride or envy. But no one can expect to achieve this without the help of grace, because the adversary powers are fighting to disrupt unity. Will might now become 'a god bi the gospel . . . And ylik to oure Lord', as Holy Church promised when he set out, if it were not for his continuing vulnerability in face of the assaults of the world, the Flesh, and the Devil. He needs Piers not just as an example to follow, but as 'prowor', purveyor of Grace.

Langland strongly believes that the sacraments are necessary to heal and fortify the besieged army in its battle with evil. Through the sacraments grace is transmitted to the penitent, and this belief is plainly affirmed in Grace's proclamation at this point in the dream:

> For I make Piers þe Plowman my procurator and my reue
> And Registrer to receyue *redde quod debes*.
> My prowor and my Plowman Piers shal ben on erþe
> And for to tilie truþe a teeme shal he haue.
>
> [B 19:258ff.; cp. C 21:258ff.]

Piers (and, presumably, anyone to whom Piers delegates his powers) is given authority to judge, to administer the household, to collect the dues and purvey grace, i.e. to act as stewards. They are also to 'plough the earth'. Langland has shown in the passage about the gifts that every man, whatever his talent, is to be valued and given his proper dignity, but he accepts too that some men are chosen to minister in a special way and are given extraordinary powers and responsibilities. In treating the life of Dobest he must of course be concerned with the role of prelates in the Christian community, and he is likely to be addressing himself to such men (albeit circumspectly, through the medium of well-established allegory).

Jesus had several things to say about stewards and highly-placed servants who are given control over money and authority over other people,[12] and Langland's reiterated phrase *redde quod debes* is a reminder of one of them: that such trusted men will be called to account [cp. *Matt*. 18:23ff.]. In another place, the steward who gets drunk and abuses those under him is given as an example to be shunned: 'For from everyone who has been given much, much will be demanded; and of one to whom men have entrusted much, they will ask the more' [*Luc.* 12:48]. A third warning to stewards is concluded with the mysterious words,

Facite vobis amicos de mammona iniquitatis.

[*Luc.* 16:9]

Make yourselves friends of the mammon of iniquity.

This is a text which, like *redde quod debes*, has a fairly evident moral meaning to do with the right use of money, and Langland employed it with that sort of meaning in the *Visio*.[13] In the *Vita de Dobest*, however, the Dreamer has another perspective: the practical advice of the *Visio* has not been invalidated, but, in the spiritual life which the *Vitae* present, the 'inward' meaning of such texts must be scrutinised as well. It is on this level that we can descry what the allegorical steward and the allegorical ploughman have to do with the 'true treasure' Will has been seeking all this time. The unglossed gospel contrasts 'the mammon of iniquity' with 'the true riches'; Ambrose delves to find an inward meaning which involves the doctrine about the image and the coin which I have postulated to inhere in Langland's figure of Piers. Luke has:

If therefore you have not been trustworthy in the unrighteous mammon, who will commit to your trust the true riches?

And if you have not been trustworthy in that which is another man's, who will give you that which is your own?

[*Luc.* 16:11 ff.]

Ambrose explains that earthly wealth ('that which is another man's') is 'alien' to us because 'not born with us': in contrast with Christ, 'the true riches', who is 'our own' — ours because he is life.[14] In the argument of the poem, allusively conducted through linkage of the derived meanings of so many parables, to be an ordinary steward as in the *Visio* is to owe a due of almsgiving, etc., to others, and to do well in this sphere is to make a small move towards repaying what is owed to God. To be a steward in the *Vita de Dobest* is to have infinitely more responsibility and to have regard to the mystical sense of Paul's teaching that Christians must work together to promote that perfection which is the only complete repayment of what is owed to God.

Clerical readers who took these allusive points as reflections on themselves (or their colleagues) would also remember that the passage I have been quoting about the steward caused the Pharisees to sneer at Jesus, and that they were answered with the words,

The Law and the Prophets were until John: since that time the Kingdom of God is being preached and every man presses into it. It is easier for heaven and earth to pass away than for one letter to drop out of the Law.

[*Luc.* 16:16]

This is, in my view, an important text for Langland. While it affirms the Law and the fulfilment of Prophecy, it implies that the pharisaical fashion of reading the Law is no longer valid, and that other men will find another way to the Kingdom.

83

The whole of *Piers Plowman*, while affirming as Jesus does in this text that sacred history is marked by these three eras of progressive revelation, also hints at the rigidity of old institutions and the force of general feeling which may crack them. Langland is making his statement of faith in the apostolic Church, but the hint of 'taking heaven by storm' which ended the original poem [cp. A 11:293 ff.], the repeated quotations from *Ps.* 131 *Memento Domine David*, and, above all, the choice of a farm worker as the leader of mankind, combine to suggest a new and irresistible upward movement of all sorts and conditions of men pressing into the Kingdom, sweeping aside the neo-Pharisees of the established hierarchy. Langland himself, as I read him, shares the anger of the reformers, but his faith in unity and the bond of charity makes it impossible for him to countenance the anarchic consequences of rebellion against Holy Church herself. His anger gives energy to the Piers who tears the Pardon and lays about him with his staff; but it is his faith which creates the Piers who ploughs the whole earth and builds the barn Unity. The Piers of this final epiphany is energetic, too, but his energy is harnessed to the steady purpose of serving Grace.

Piers certainly has his helpers harnessed in that same service: the evangelists appear as the farmer's oxen pulling his plough, the Doctors as his horses, in the brief but highly significant allegory that follows [B 19:262 ff.; C 21:262 ff.]. Very little attention has been paid to its significance: the editors glumly recall that St Luke's emblem was an ox, which is really nothing to the point. We have come along the road to Dobest, and we find that it means emulating a draught-ox or a work-horse. Apostles, oxen? Bishops, horses? What sort of examples are these? Can a man who calls himself *presul*, *pontifex*, *metropolitanus*, *episcopus*, *pastor*, see himself as a horse in harness? [cp. B 15:42 f.] The answer is that perhaps he should, since Gregory the Great was not ashamed to see himself in that light. The Apostle Paul did not disdain to compare himself with an ox working on a farm. The first point to note is that these are not blundering beasts like the folk in the *Visio*, they are beasts harnessed in a team: they have submitted to discipline because this is the way the work will be done. The work is the allegorical ploughing and harrowing necessary for the spread of Christian teaching.

'To plough', in the exegetical language of the *Moralia* to which we have already referred, 'assuredly is to lay open the soil of the human heart with the ploughshare of the tongue, by assiduity in preaching'. (This is the phrasing that Langland casually echoed when he said that prelates and priests should travel the world

> To tulie þe erthe with tonge and teche men to louye
>
> [C 10:199].)

However, when Piers begins his missionary work, more than ordinary preaching is in the poet's mind. Piers first ploughs and then harrows the land, first with oxen and then with horses in his team. Langland has not invented the action; the harrowing and the horses, too, are apparently lifted from Gregory, and from the same piece of exegesis. Encouraged by Paul's metaphor of 'kicking against the pricks' [cp. *Act.* 9:5] and 'ploughing in hope' [cp. *1 Cor.* 9:10], Gregory imagines Paul as a farmer's beast working to break up the clods of earth which might have crushed the newly-sown seeds in the furrows. The 'clods' of his image are the harsh commands of the letter of the Law:

He [Paul] who by showing it to be wrong broke up the hardness of the Law in the humble minds of the faithful — what was he doing but 'breaking the clods in the valleys' after the Lord? [cp. *Job* 39:10] in order that the seed-grains which the furrow of the heart cut by the plough of faith was receiving, might not die because they were weighed down by observance of the letter.[15]

Though Gregory does not call it 'harrowing', the work he describes is that in all but name, since the field has already been ploughed and sown. In Langland's image the four Doctors are working like Paul to make hearts receptive to the Christian message, and also to make that message less stony. There is a double sense in the agricultural metaphor which comes from the two passages I have just excerpted from Gregory. The hearts of unbelievers are hard, the Jewish Scriptures have a hard surface: the business of Piers and his team is to open the hard hearts and to delve through the surface meaning of the Scriptures, and by so doing to promote love and goodness. Langland nicely translates Gregory's words into Gregory in action with the other Doctors, toiling to break down the hard passages in Scripture, and so playing his part in affecting the hearts of those who read him.

Gregory would by no means have been offended at being portrayed as a horse, for he is quite happy to think of himself as neighing when he preaches: in the following sentence [on *Job* 39:19], he explains how the example of a preacher's life and the tenor of his words together move men towards perfection:

The Lord declares that he gives both strength and neighing to this horse, because unless both life and teaching are in accord in his preacher, the virtue of perfection will never appear.[16]

It has to be admitted that the elaboration of this kind of metaphor into allegorical action makes unappealing poetry. The contrasting scene in the *Visio*, in which Liar's noisy cart is accompanied by jurymen, summoners, and the like, in the guise of saddle-horses and cart-horses, has the licence of satire to raise a laugh at the expense of the willing servitude of these people, but a smile would be quite out of place when Piers harnesses his mighty beasts. The fact that the symbolism of the ox goes back to the New Testament helps to give the action some gravity.

Paul's appropriation of the Mosaic 'Do not muzzle the ox' to himself and the other apostles has an underthought which leads back to the *redde-quod-debes*-theme, if we follow a Gregorian line of thought on the matter (as Langland pretty certainly does). Paul was talking about preachers getting their food from their congregations:

For it is written in the Law of Moses, 'Do not muzzle an ox while it is threshing'. Is God's concern with oxen? Or is this said about us? Assuredly, it was written about us, because he who ploughs should plough in hope, and he who threshes should thresh in hope of having some corn. If we have sown spiritual things among you, is it so much if we reap your carnal things?

[*1 Cor.* 9:1 ff.][17]

Gregory finds this a useful text to remember when he elaborates the thought that 'the land will cry out' against pastors who 'devour the Church's supplies with dumb mouths': such pastors, he says, exact what is owed to their bodies, but do not 'pay what they owe' to the hearts of their charges.[18]

The imaging of the evangelists and apostles and the great bishops as obedient beasts is therefore far from being a rather unfortunate concomitant of the imaging of Piers as the Sower preparing his field. It is a way of emphasising, and particularly for clerical readers, the humility and complete lack of personal ambition in those who were chosen to found and spread the Church. *Sotto voce*, as it were, because of traditional elaboration of Paul's text, it reinforces other warnings of proud, greedy and slack pastors who give small return for what they receive from their congregations.

The work of the four Doctors as Piers's team can now be seen as an essential constituent part of the Christian mission, from Langland's point of view. Their exegetical work is designed to make the bible a sharper implement with which to break down hardness of heart and to promote fear and love of Truth.[19] They break the hard clods of the Old Testament by combing it with the harrow of the New, and the texts thrown up by this process are used as tools with which to soften the laws of Moses. They know what they are doing and why. Gregory is quite clear as to why he is working like a horse; drawing apposite allegorical meaning out of 'Wilt thou give the horse strength?' [*Job* 39:19] *twice over, in different ways*, he explains,

> The word of God is earth which produces fruit more plentifully the more the labour of the enquirer turns it over in his mind. Therefore, the meaning of Holy Scripture should be sifted with manifold enquiry, for the earth which is often turned by the plough is made ready to produce a more abundant crop.[20]

The two Testaments, their surface turned over and over by the great Doctors, are thus made ready to be used in Piers's missionary endeavours. It is quite obvious from the scene of the 'harrowing' that Langland had no wish to encourage a return to an unglossed bible, as some reformers did. He condemned only that self-interested 'glossing' which Augustine himself condemned: he had interpreted 'the sellers of oxen' cast out from the Temple as preachers who 'sell the apostles' by using the Scriptures to gain honours and praise for themselves rather than to bring people to Truth.[21]

II

After the preparing of the ground by Piers and his team comes the sowing of seed; not, as might have been expected, the seed of the Sower parable, but instead the natural virtues. Langland is still following Augustine and Gregory, in treating the four cardinal virtues as necessary foundations of the Christian life on earth. Gregory calls them the four corners of the house on which the whole

86

structure of good practice is raised. Like Langland, he describes them as coming from God:

> For the gift of the Spirit, which first forms, in the mind it has worked on, prudence, temperance, fortitude, justice, next gives due proportion of the seven virtues to that same mind, so that it may be educated to withstand any kind of temptation.[22]

There might seem to be some inconsistency of thought in the ascription of the natural (pagan) virtues to Grace, but the way these two Doctors saw the matter was that the infusion of these natural virtues was part of the renewal of man brought about by the Atonement.[23] It is Augustine's doctrine that grace is the mending of nature; righteous pagans demonstrate that the imprint of God's image in their creation has not been entirely effaced, but none the less,

> It is the work of the Spirit of grace to renew in us the image of God in which we were naturally made, for the flaw in man is contrary to his nature, and it is that which grace heals.[24]

So the word *Spiritus* is added to the names of the natural virtues and they are associated with the gifts of the Spirit named by Isaiah [*Isa.* 11:1 ff.]. The work of Piers as sower is therefore to be understood as the starting of the process of renewal in the minds of the early Christian converts. Gregory's teaching (quoted above), that the Spirit first prepares and then strengthens the mind to equip it to face temptations, indicates another feature of Piers's activity in the field: he is preparing the hearts of his followers for the assaults which Grace has said will come.[25] In the final passus the poet will show how much these fundamental virtues are needed in contemporary England.

The four cardinal virtues are of course only a foundation upon which the theological virtues may rest, and the supreme virtue of love is the plant that Piers wants to nurture. The natural virtues, once propagated, must not be choked by weeds: this time it is not the 'apostolic mattocks' but the doctoral 'harrows' that are brought into play. The moral teaching of the four Doctors is now described as doing a different kind of harrowing, namely, pulling up the weeds, the vices, which spring up with the plants:

> For comuneliche in contrees cammokes and wedes
> Foulen þe fruyt in þe feld þer þei growen togideres;
> And so doon vices vertues — [f] orþi, quod Piers,
> 'Hareweþ alle þat konneþ kynde wit by conseil of þise docto[urs],
> And tilieþ [to] hir techynge þe Cardinale vertues!
> > [B 19:312ff.; C 21:313ff.]

Thus, as he turns to his allegorical account of the building of the Church, Langland makes an unusually plain acknowledgement of the unrivalled importance, in his eyes, of the four Latin Doctors as moral guides to those who can read them, and of their value as aids to the preacher doing his ploughing and tending of the human heart.

It remains for Piers to prepare the Barn for the harvest, and here Christ's second parable of the Sower naturally comes to mind: in it, the field is the world, in which wheat and tares grow together until the end of the age, when the weeds will be tied in bundles to be burned, and the ripe wheat placed in the barn [cp. *Matt.* 13:24-43]. Langland does not choose to dramatise this parable, though it would be the obvious climax to the ploughing scene and to the larger scheme of the Ages of sacred history. It would also fit very satisfactorily into the plan of the three Lives, since, as we have already noted, the three stages of growth in virtue could be represented in the metaphor of maturing wheat.[26] But the image of the ripe ears of wheat carried into the barn, like the image of the burnished coin received into the treasury, is one that Langland's purpose forces him to abandon. The wheat and the corn are inert, symbols indeed of the perfectibility of man's soul, but not symbols of activity. *Piers Plowman* is a poem to stir men to action; it is not to be rounded off with visions of the angel-harvesters, but instead with a scene in a sick-bay set in a great house under siege — a scene in which there is grim work to be done and where wounded men need nursing. Piers's Barn, therefore, is not the heavenly barn of the parable, but instead the 'grange *lex-christi*' which the poet introduced into the story of the Samaritan, the place of healing into which the wounded man was carried.[27] (The change of the name to *Unite* scarcely calls for explanation, since the Law of Christ is *caritas* and the Church is united 'in the bond of charity'.) Smith has indicated the importance of Langland's unusual interpretation of the *stabulum* of the parable as both *hostrye* and *grange*, which 'looks forward to the great configurations in Passus XIX of the building of the barn'.[28] By this bold amalgamation, Langland turns the Second Coming of Christ from a potentially terrifying scene of reaping and burning into a scene of tenderness and restoration:

> And alle that feble and feynt be, þat Feiþ may noȝt teche,
> Hope shal lede hem forþ with loue as his lettre telleþ,
> And hostele hem and heele þoruȝ holy chirche bileue
> Tyl I have salve for alle sike, and þanne shal I turne
> And come ayein bi þis contree and conforten alle sike
> That craueþ it [or] coueiteþ it [and] crieþ þerafter.
>
> [B 17:119 ff.; not in C]

This comforting passage, wholly in keeping with Langland's belief in the mercy of the Judge towards the contrite, has been misunderstood by some modern critics as an 'apparently heretical allusion to universal salvation'; but, as Smith makes clear, 'it is the sick who crave, covet, and cry after the Good Samaritan's cure who will receive this benefit'.[29] Perhaps some contemporaries of the poet similarly misread what he was saying, for this valuable section is excised from the final revision.

The house that Grace builds for Piers is founded upon mercy (just as the Tree of Charity is rooted in mercy), the passion and cross of Christ are its strength, and it is roofed with Holy Writ. Within the walls, Piers makes the blessed bread which is God's Body, the food which the Samaritan once told Will the sick man must have if he were ever to be strong again.[30] Only those who have received Piers's pardon and fulfilled *redde quod debes* are permitted by Conscience to eat this bread, and he calls on the Cardinal Virtues and the Paternoster to support his stand. People are brought into the Barn by the 'caples' Contrition and Confession, but Langland reiterates that the debt of sin must be paid, before the life-giving food is dispensed to the penitents. The practical religious teaching of the poem has its focus here: there is unbounded mercy for the asking, but justice must be satisfied; the Law has been transformed, but not destroyed. Will's questioning has brought him back to the simplicity of the Paternoster: 'Thy Kingdom come' and 'Forgive us our debts as we forgive our debtors'. The Dobest which he has been seeking through the three *Vitae* has been revealed as the life of true love. In earthly affairs this means living in hope, not in fear, of the coming of the Kingdom, holding to the confidence of a will conformed to the will of God. Langland's last look at Piers echoes the Sermon on the Mount, and also, I believe, the ninth of Augustine's Homilies on John's epistle, which seem to have contributed so much to the theme of *charite* in the poem:

> A[c] wel worþe Piers the plowman that pursueþ God in doynge
> *Qui pluit super Iustos et iniustos* at ones
> And sent the sonne to saue a cursed mannes tilþe
> As brighte as to þe beste man or to the beste womman.
> Right so Piers the Plowman peyneth hym to tilye
> As wel for a wastour and wenches of the stewes
> As for hymself and hise seruauntz, saue he is first yserved.
> [So blessed be Piers þe Plowman þat peyneþ hym to tilye],
> And travailleþ and tilieþ for a tretour also soore
> As for a trewe tidy man alle tymes ylike.
> And worshiped be he þat wroȝte al, boþe good and wikke,
> And suffreþ þat synfulle be [til some tyme þat þei repente].
>
> [B 19:430ff.; C 21:430ff.]

Expounding the meaning of John's words 'In this God's love is made perfect in us, that we may have confidence in the day of judgement' [*1 Jo.* 4:17], Augustine too speaks of the pattern of loving the good and the bad provided by God himself:

> What gives us confidence in the day of judgement? *Because, as he is, so are we in the world.* We must take this to refer to Love itself, and understand what is being said ... If, therefore, he bids us love our enemies, from whom does he give us an example? From God himself. For he says, 'that you may be sons of your Father who is in heaven'. How does God do that? He loves his enemies, for 'he makes his sun rise upon the good and the evil, and sends rain upon the just and the unjust' [*Matt.* 5:44f.]. If, therefore, God calls us to this perfection, that we love our enemies as he himself has loved his own, that is our confidence in the day of judgement, *because, as he is, so are we in the world*; because just as he loves his enemies, making his sun to rise upon the good and the evil and sending rain upon the just and the unjust, so we, though we cannot furnish our enemies with sun and rain, can give them our tears when we pray for them.[31]

In the poem, it is a 'lewed vicory' who has taken to heart the message of Piers the Plowman 'that pursueth God in doynge', and it is he who has the confidence to speak out against the Pope who funds those who are killing Christian people:

> Inparfit is that Pope that al peple sholde helpe
> And [soudeþ hem] þat sleeþ [swiche as] he sholde save.
>
> [B 19:428f.; C 21:428f.]

The horror of Langland's times is that even 'Piers', the pattern of perfect love, has been ousted by an unworthy simulacrum, the cardinal virtues by greedy cardinals, the priest's cart of the Christian Faith has been covered like a bandwagon with meretricious decoration; even the sacraments can be bought, and the disorderly friars are making a mockery of 'salvation'. Yet this vicar or 'curatour' — holder of a cure of souls — prays for the Pope who is spilling Christian blood and for the cardinals who love wealth above 'wealth of soul'. It is he who lives according to the pattern of charity which is the Image of God, and like the true son of Piers he will 'Lat God yworthe'.

We cannot doubt that William Langland was an angry man. One part of him would certainly like to take a stick to cheats, spongers and corrupters, and double-dealers of every kind — especially if they walk under the protection of a tonsure and a habit. It is the more to his credit that he does not consign them to the inferno. They, too, are his neighbours, and the part of him which would be Piers aims to live by the Sermon on the Mount. The tension between his wrath and his brotherly love is nowhere more evident than in the 'coals of fire' passage put in the mouth of Piers:

> Quod Piers the ploghman, *'Pacientes vincunt.*
> Byfore perpetual pees y shal preue þat y saide
> And avowe byfore god, and forsaken hit neuere,
> That *disce, doce, dilige deum*
> And thyn enemy helpe emforth thy myhte.
> Caste hote coles on his heued of alle kyn speche,
> Fond thorw wit and word his loue to wynne,
> ʒef hym eft and eft, euere at his nede,
> Conforte hym with thy catel and with thy kynde speche,
> And ley on hym thus with loue til he lauhe on þe;
> And bote he bowe for this betynge, blynde mote he worthen'.
> [C 15:138ff.; cp. B 13:130ff.]

Like Augustine before him, he finds the only hope for mankind in the kind of loving that wills the good of every other person, because it is based on the love of Love itself.[32] When he reads his daily psalms, he is moved as Augustine was by the voice of the people crying out, 'Who will show us any good?'. His response is to work over many years at his poetry, to show what he understands by the psalmist's mysterious answer: *Signatum est super nos lumen vultus tui, Domine.* He brings some of the brightness of that Image into the contemporary world in the figure of Piers Plowman.

NOTES

Chapter I Piers and the Modern Reader

1 My quotations are taken from *Piers Plowman: the A-version*, edited by George Kane (Athlone Press, London, 1960), from *Piers Plowman: the B-version*, edited by George Kane and E. Talbot Donaldson (Athlone Press, London, 1975), and (since the *C-Version* in this series is not yet available) from *Piers Plowman by William Langland: An Edition of the C-text*, edited by Derek Pearsall (Arnold, London, 1978). Also to be recommended are the complete edition of the B-text, *The Vision of Piers Plowman*, edited by A. V. C. Schmidt (Dent, London, 1978), and the edition of part of the B-text, *Piers Plowman: Prologue and Passus I- VII*, edited by J. A. W. Bennett (Oxford, 1972). My practice is to quote from the earliest version, with cross-reference to the other texts, except in those instances in which a reading peculiar to one text is in question. It is generally supposed that the final revision of the poem was completed about 1385, after about twenty-five years of reflection on the original theme. Exact dating of the three versions is not germane to my study, so I refer the reader to the editions for information on the question.

2 Pearsall (*ed. cit.*, p.11) finds the C-text 'substantially successful in achieving its overall purpose of reshaping and clarifying the general outline of the poem . . . C may be less exciting, but it makes better sense'. It will be my contention that the B-text, though often cryptic, has in fact a firmer conceptual structure than C. The value of the C-text is that it shows the working of the poet's mind more openly.

3 For the authorship controversy, see George Kane, *Piers Plowman: The Evidence for Authorship* (London, 1965).

4 David Aers, *Piers Plowman and Christian Allegory* (London, 1975), p.78f. The opposite view is presented by E. Vasta, *The Spiritual Basis of Piers Plowman* (The Hague, 1965).

5 The Lady's speech occupies almost the whole of Passus I in all three versions. (The poem is divided into *passus* 'steps', in place of cantos, in all the texts.)

6 Piers speaks to Will in his 'love-dream' of B Passus 16: 20ff.

7 The A-version concludes with Will's attempt to learn from Dame Study and from Scripture where in the world Dowel, Dobet and Dobest may be found. In the B and C-versions Will's search for these steps on the way to perfection of life is much extended. In some MSS a scribal rubric distinguishes the *Passus de visione* from the *passus de Dowel*, etc. Though the latter quest is a continuation of Will's earlier enquiry, it is convenient sometimes to keep this distinction under the heads of *Visio* and *Vitae*.

8 Since Jesus, according to John, said, 'I am the Way, the Truth, and the Life' [*Jo*. 14:6], it was common for homilists and commentators upon the bible to prefix a quotation from the gospels with the words *Veritas ait*, 'Truth says'. At the same time, it was emphasised that Truth's words were arcane and opaque to the worldly. [cp. Theology's view of the matter in the

91

probably spurious Passus 12 which concludes the poem in some A-text MSS; he says that 'God' holds his tongue when Pilate asks *'Quid est veritas?'*]

9   In bringing exegetical material to the reader's notice in order to explicate Langland's thought, I make no attempt to evaluate the biblical criticism contained in the quotations. My purpose is to demonstrate beliefs which impinge upon Langland's subject-matter, and to use texts and interpretations of scripture available at that date. My task, as I see it, is to further understanding of Langland's inherited beliefs, and neither to promote nor to denigrate them as beliefs.

My reference to 'haphazard plenty' glances particularly at D. W. Robertson and F. Huppé, *Piers Plowman and Scriptural Tradition* (Princeton, 1951), a book stored with information (some pertinent, some not) and often mined by other critics; but their critical methods are questionable and their views often unacceptable. I have gone afresh to the source-material and made no attempt to correlate their findings with my own.

10   The 'harrowing' is described in B 19: 269 ff., C 21: 269 ff.; Clergy's praise of Gregory is in A 11: 201, B 10: 298 (not in C); Scripture's eulogy of Augustine is in A 11: 302 ff., B 10: 458 ff., C 11: 289 ff. The works of Ambrose and Augustine are served as dishes at table in B 13: 37 ff., C 15: 43 ff. Augustine is called 'dyvynour of þe trinite' by Scripture [A 11: 302, B 10: 458, cp. C 11: 288]. Wit, after quoting several scriptural texts, puts the Four Doctors as witnesses to the truth of his doctrine alongside Luke (cp. B 9: 74 f.); he does not need to name them.

11   The fullest account of this theme in *Piers Plowman* is given by S. A. Barney, 'The Plowshare of the Tongue', *MS* 35 (1973), 261-93. He states: 'I believe Gregory's great *Moralia in Job* is the most important 'source' for the conception of the figure of Piers' (p. 268). I shall attempt to show that Augustine is even more important as a source of the concept, while also further substantiating Barney's opinion that Langland was greatly influenced by the *Moralia*.

12   Schmidt, 'Langland and Scholastic Philosophy', *MAE* 38 (1969), pp. 134-53, notes some of the means by which 'Augustinian' teaching might have reached Langland. He tends to the opinion that Langland's manner resembles more closely the pre-scholastic 'Augustinian' dialogues than scholastic disputation (p. 144). The extent of Langland's reading is still very much in dispute. R. Adams (*SP* 73, 1976, pp. 266 ff.) has demonstrated that evidence supposed to indicate Langland's reliance on the Breviary for scriptural texts is quite flimsy. T. D. Hill (*NQ* 123, 1978, p. 200 f.), in a brief but telling note, has observed that a reference to 'three garments' of Jesus (*PP*, C 11:193) shows that Langland knew an exegetical elaboration of *Luc.* 23:11 stemming from Ambrose, in which the Roman soldiers were said to clothe Jesus in a white, a scarlet, and a purple robe. Hill remarks that the casual use of the phrase implies 'that Langland's readers understood this "language" of exegesis' (p. 202). Several points used in my argument in this book indicate such understanding.

13   M. W. Bloomfield, *'Piers Plowman' as a Fourteenth Century Apocalypse* (New Jersey, 1963) has argued that 'it is in the older monastic view of man that we can best find the intellectual framework of *Piers Plowman*' (p. 153). He indicates in a general way the importance of Augustine and Gregory in preserving monastic philosophy and theology for the West, and his footnotes are full of useful information for the student of fourteenth-century and earlier religious thought. His concern with apocalyptic and with the political and social aspects of perfection takes his study in a rather different direction

from mine, and (as I believe) to a wrong view of The Tree of Charity, as will be indicated below.

14 For the quarrel, see A 8: 89 ff.; B 7: 107 ff.; C 9: 282 ff. The matter is more fully discussed in Chapter 5, below.

15 *Si enim per legem iustitia, ergo Christus gratis mortuus est*; mortuus enim Christus est, ut inpleret iustitiam. (Ambr., *In Luc. CCSL* 14, 142)

16 The expression *sol justitiae* is taken from the Messianic prophecies of *Malachios* 4: 2 and was well known as a name for Christ. The pseudo-Bernardine *Meditationes Piissimae* (*PL* 184, 485 ff.) quoted by Scripture (B 11: 3) ends with the hope that the reader who learns to know himself, to love God and overcome the world, the flesh and the devil, will leave the shadows of this life to see the Sun of Justice: videas etiam meridianum solem justitiae, in quo sponsum cum sponsa prospicies unum eumdemque Dominum gloriae qui vivit et regnat per infinita saecula. (508)

17 It must be noted that the numbering of the Psalms in the Latin Bible is one behind the A.V. numbering from Ps. 10 onwards (Ps. 9 being divided in the English versions). In the quoted verse (Ps. 36: 24) the verb *collidetur* is translated 'bruised' in the Douay version.

18 Quomodo igitur dominus iustitias dilexit neque uidit Dauid iustum derelictum aut quae ista aequitas, si iustus relinquitur, peccator adsciscitur, nisi intellegas quod eos iustos dicit qui ex lege praesumant et euangelii gratiam non requirant? Nemo autem iustificatur ex lege sed redimitur ex gratia. (Ambr., *In Luc.*, *CCSL* 14, 141)

19 J. F. Goodridge, *Piers the Ploughman*, translated into modern English prose (Penguin, 1959), p. 237. See also his Introduction, p. 58.

20 J. A. Alford, 'The Role of the Quotations in *Piers Plowman*', *Speculum* 52 (1977), 80-99, postulates that Langland's biblical quotations create the structural framework of the poem, which the narrative fills out. This over-simplifies the matter, but it is not going too far to say that the outline of the conceptual structure came to Langland from Latin material.

21 See R. E. Kaske, '*Ex vi transicionis* and Its Passage in *Piers Plowman*', *JEGP* 62 (1963), 32-60 (rev. and repr. 1969 in *Blanch*); Ben H. Smith, *Traditional Imagery of Charity in 'Piers Plowman'* (The Hague, 1966); and Anne Middleton, 'Two Infinites: Grammatical Metaphor in *Piers Plowman*', *ELH* 39 (1972), 169-88.

22 Augustine compares the 'plural' *faciamus* [Gen. 1: 26] and its accompanying *imaginem et similitudinem nostram* 'in *our* image and likeness' with the 'singular' forms in the next verse, *Et fecit deus hominem ad imaginem dei*, using the two texts together as proof that man was made in the image of the Trinity [cp. *De Trinitate*, *CCSL* 50, 360]. Langland, as Schmidt rightly notes (*ed. cit.*, 327), also stresses the contrast between *faciamus* 'let us *make*' used of the creation of man, and *dixit et facta sunt*, 'he *spoke* (and they were made)' [Ps. 148: 5] used of the creation of the physical world.

23 For a useful consideration of the figural mode of writing, see E. Salter, 'Medieval Poetry and the Figural View of Reality' (*PBA* 54, 1958, 73-92). Since Piers is neither a biblical nor yet a wholly non-biblical character, the legitimacy of reading his actions in a figural (i.e. typological) manner is open to question. The matter is discussed more fully in Chapter 2.

24 Quotations are taken from *De Trinitate*, ed. W. J. Mountain and Fr. Glorie, *CCSL* 50 and 50A (Turnhout, 1968). For Gregory, I have used the *CCSL* edition, Vols. 143 and 143A, ed. M. Adriaen (Turnhout, 1979) as far as it goes, and *PL* 76, ed. J. P. Migne, Paris, 1878. Quotations from Augustine's *Confessiones* are taken from *S. Aurelii Augustini Confessionum Libri XIII*,

ed. M. Skutella (Stuttgart, 1969), and for the homilies on the First Epistle of John I have used *In Epistolam Joannis ad Parthos Tractatus Decem*, ed. J.-P. Migne, *PL* 35, 1977ff. (Paris, 1902). For other patristic writers I have used the *CCSL* editions, or, failing these, the *Patrologia*.

25 P. Courcelle, *Les Confessions de Saint Augustin dans la Tradition Littéraire* (Paris, 1963).

26 For discussion, see C. D. Benson, 'An Augustinian Irony in *Piers Plowman*', *NQ*, n.s. 23 (1976), 51-4.

27 Scripture is replaced as speaker by Rechelesnesse in the C-text, and the lines read:

> For he þat most sey and saide of the sothfaste trinite
> Was Austyn þe oelde þat euere man wiste,
> Saide thus in his sarmoun for ensaumple of grete clerkes:
> *Ecce ipsi idiote rapiunt celum ubi nos sapientes in inferno mergimur.*

28 Pearsall's note on these lines (*ed. cit.*, p. 200) doubtfully cites *Conf.* 13:7 as the incident referred to. Langland may, however, have been thinking also of the spiritual ecstasy of *Conf.* 9:10, and of the insights summed up in the last paragraphs of *De Trinitate*, which Augustine presents as truths manifested by God's light to his inward eye [cp. *De Trin.*, *CCSL* 50A, 532]. Schmidt (p. 348) relates the 'books' mentioned by Scripture to the 15 books of *De Trin.* (*ed. cit.*, p. 331), and also notes that B 16: 223 adapts material from *De Trin.*, 10.12.19 and 15.21.41.

29 This comprehensive answer appears in C; the corresponding lines in B mention only the evangelists as 'auctour', quoting Jo. 14:10 and Jo. 14:9 as the testimony that Christ is one Person of the Trinity. As in other places, Langland here reveals his underlying thought more openly in the C-text.

30 See Aers (1975), pp. 77ff., for a short, sharp survey of the various published theories about the significance of the figure. I shall not attempt a summary of the extensive literature on this topic.

31 The importance of the coin-metaphor in *Piers Plowman* has been sketched by B. Raw, 'Piers and the Image of God in Man', in Hussey, *'Piers Plowman': Critical Approaches*, pp. 143-79. This valuable article defines a central religious theme in the poem, though the extent and variety of the patristic interpretation of the coins mentioned in the gospels is only touched upon.

32 Lady Holy Church does not explain to Will the significance of her foundation-text *Deus caritas* and its relation to her affirmation that the man who is true 'is a god by þe gospel' [cp. A 1: 83ff., B 1: 85ff., C 1: 81ff.], but the teaching of Augustine is quite clear on this matter. As Pearsall notes (*ed. cit.*. p. 46), it would be wrong to conclude from this reference to the doctrine of deification that Langland is writing a mystical poem: 'The most that can be said is that Langland is aware of such doctrines and that, as often, he is trying to adapt the language of contemplative devotion to a more general concept of the Christian life'. Augustine makes no distinction of active and contemplative callings in expounding his understanding of *caritas*, and it might be more appropriate to say that Langland is returning to a more general, older concept of the Christian life. In the homiletic sequence which includes the metaphor of planting the tree *caritas*, Augustine also tells his hearers that the word of scripture affirms this doctrine: Non audeo dicere ex me, Scripturas audiamus: *ego dixi, Dii estis, et filii Altissimi omnes*, 'I would not dare to say it on my own authority, but we hear the Scriptures: "I have said, you are gods, and you are all the sons of the Highest" (Ps. 81: 6).' (*Tract. in I Jo.* 2, *PL* 35, 1977.)

Chapter 2 The Epiphanies of Piers

1 Piers does not come on the scene until A 6: 25, B 5: 537, C 7: 182; the names of his wife, son, and daughter are given in A 7: 70ff.; B 6: 78ff.; C 8: 80ff. Their significance is discussed more fully below.

2 His name only recurs in A in the unauthenticated passus which ends the version, in passing reference to 'oþer werkes boþe of peres þe plowman' [A 12: 96f.].

3 Redi ergo mecum et consideremus cur diligamus apostolum. Numquidnam propter humanam speciem quam notissimam habemus eo quod credimus eum hominem fuisse? Non utique; alioquin nunc non est quem diligamus quandoquidem homo ille iam non est; anima enim eius a corpore separata est. Sed id quod in illo amamus etiam nunc uiuere credimus; amamus enim animum iustum. Ex qua ergo generali aut speciali regula nisi quia scimus et quid sit animus et quid sit iustus? *De Trin.*, 8.6 (*CCSL* 50, 279)

4 Quem ibi uidet cum uidet et dicit quid sit animus iustus, nec alibi quam in se uidet, cum ipse non sit animus iustus? An illud quod uidet ueritas est interior praesens animo qui eam ualet intueri? Neque omnes ualent, et qui intueri ualent hoc etiam quod intuentur non omnes sunt, hoc est non sunt etiam ipsi iusti animi sicut possunt uidere ac dicere quid sit iustus animus. Quod unde esse poterunt nisi inhaerendo eidem ipsi formae quam intuentur ut inde formentur et sint iusti animi . . . Homo ergo qui creditur iustus ex ea forma et ueritate diligitur quam cernit et intelligit apud se ille qui diligit; ipsa uero forma et ueritas non est quomodo aliunde diligatur. *De Trin.*, 8.6 (*CCSL* 50, 282f.)

5 Quapropter non est praecipue uidendum in hac quaestione quae de trinitate nobis est et de cognoscendo deo nisi quid sit uera dilectio, immo uero quid sit dilectio. Ea quippe dilectio dicenda quae uera est, alioquin cupiditas est; atque ita cupidi abusiue dicuntur diligere quemadmodum cupere abusiue dicuntur qui diligunt. Haec est autem uera dilectio *ut* inhaerentes ueritati *iuste uiuamus*, et ideo contemnamus omnia mortalia prae amore hominum quo eos uolumus iuste uiuere. *De Trin.*, 8.7 (*CCSL* 50, 284)

His phrase *iuste vivamus* is quoted from Tit. 2:12. *Dilectio* is used as a synonym of *caritas*; later he quotes *Deus dilectio est* in place of the Vulgate text of *Jo.* 8:16.

6 Ecce, *deus dilectio est*. Vtquid imus et currimus in sublimia caelorum et ima terrarum quaerentes eum qui est apud nos si nos esse uelimus apud eum? Nemo dicat: 'Non noui quod diligam'. Diligat fratrem et diligat eandem dilectionem; magis enim nouit dilectionem qua diligit quam fratrem quem diligit. Ecce iam potest notiorem deum habere quam fratrem, plane notiorem quia praesentiorem, notiorem, quia interiorem, notiorem quia certiorem. *De Trin.*, 8.8 (*CCSL* 50, 286)

7 Quanto igitur saniores sumus a tumore superbiae tanto sumus dilectione pleniores. Et quo nisi deo plenus est qui plenus est dilectione? 'At enim caritatem uideo, et quantum possum eam mente conspicio, et credo scripturae dicenti: *Quoniam deus caritas est, et qui manet in caritate in deo manet*.' *De Trin.*, 8.8 (*CCSL* 50, 287)

8 The text *Qui manet in caritate*, etc., is not quoted in C, but its thought is paraphrased in C 10:156f. The phrase 'when we are healed of the cancer of pride' occurs in the first sentence of the quotation given in Note 7 above: cp. *De Trin.*, (*CCSL* 50, 360)

9 The 'love-dream' is the vision of the Tree of Charity in B Passus 16. Some MS read *lone dreem*: K-D read *louedreem*, Schmidt *lone dreem*. Schmidt's

note is worth quoting: 'The original reading of *lone/loue* cannot be settled on palaeographical or, indeed, semantic grounds. 'Love-dream' consorts well with 'pure joy' (18) while 'lone dream' highlights the solitary, interior and mystical quality of the inner vision' (*ed. cit.*, p. 292). Augustine's doctrine of love inclines me to prefer the former.

10 Ita et ipsorum uitam facit a nobis diligi formae illius dilectio secundum quam uixisse creduntur, et illorum uita credita in eandem formam flagrantiorem excitat caritatem ut quanto flagrantius diligimus deum, tanto certius sereniusque uideamus quia in deo conspicimus incommutabilem formam iustitiae secundum quam hominem uiuere oportere iudicamus. *De Trin.*, 8.9 (*CCSL* 50, 290)

11 Restat etiam hinc ascendere et superius ista quaerere quantum homini datur. Sed hic paululum requiescat intentio non ut se iam existimet inuenisse quod quaerit, sed sicut solet inueniri locus ubi quaerendum est aliquid. Nondum illud inuentum est, sed iam inuentum est ubi quaeratur. Ita hoc dixisse suffecerit ut tamquam ab articulo alicuius exordii cetera contexamus. *De Trin.*, 8:10 (*CCSL* 50, 291)

12 The opinion that Piers is ideal earthly perfection has sometimes been advanced; e.g. by Vasta (1965), p. 132ff.

13 Et exclamabam legens haec forus et agnoscens intus haec nolebam multiplicari terrenis bonis devorans tempora et devoratus temporibus, cum haberem in aeterna simplicitate aliud frumentum et vinum et oleum. *Conf.*, 9.4.

14 E. B. Pusey, *The Confessions of St. Augustine* (London, 1938), p. 197. Tobie Matthew's translation was repr. London 1923; see p. 213.

15 T. P. Dunning, 'The Structure of the B-text of *Piers Plowman*', *RES*, n.s. 7 (1956), 225-37 (repr. *Blanch*).

16 There is considerable MSS support for the reading *bely ioye* [B 7:123] (so Schmidt 1.119) but K-D have preferred to emend to *bilyue* 'sustenance'. The phrase *bely ioye* occurs in the A-text eight lines later (ed. Kane, 8:112) in connection with Luc. 12:22, but varr. of *belyve* or *liflode* occur in the line corresponding to B 7:123.

17 *Nam et si ambulem in medio umbrae mortis.* Nam et si ambulem in medio uitae huius, quae umbra mortis est . . . *Virga tua et baculus tuus, ipsa me consolata sunt.* Disciplina tua tamquam uirga ad gregem ouium, et tamquam baculus iam ad grandiores filios et ab animali uita ad spiritalem crescentes, ipsa me non afflixerunt, magis consolata sunt; quia memor es me. Aug. *En. in Ps.* (*CCSL* 38, 134f.)
The text *Virga tua*, etc., is quoted by Wit in connection with the dread felt by Dowel and the suffering felt by Dobet in A 10:87 (B and C differ).

Chapter 3   Images and Transformations

1 In the Epistle to the Hebrews, the Son is called *splendor gloriae et figura substantiae ejus* (*Heb.* 1:3; cp. *Col.* 1:15). In modern times the authorship of Hebrews by Paul and of the Apocalypse by John (The Revelation of St. John the Divine in A.V.) has been disputed, but for Langland these books had the authority of apostolic utterances.

2 In both B and C-texts, the jouster bears Piers's arms, 'his colours and his cote Armure' [B 19:12f.; C 21:12f.]; in C only, Faith adds 'plate-armour':

In Pers plates the plouhman this prikiare shal ryde

[C 20:24]

3 cp. *Matt.*, 4:18f.
4 The four Doctors' scriptural exegesis is founded upon their belief that much of the bible is arcane and full of hidden significance. The adapted text *audivi arcana verba* [cp. 2 *Cor.* 12:4], 'I heard secret words', quoted by Langland [B 18:397; C 20:438], is linked by Gregory (*Moralia, PL* 76, 630, on *Job* 39:29) with the constantly-quoted *Videmus nunc per speculum (et) in aenigmate* (cp. 1 *Cor.* 13:12), ' we see now in a mirror (and) in an enigma' (i.e. a dark allegory). To Gregory, these texts signify Paul's recognition that the mysteries of the Godhead into which he himself had been given insight were not communicable in his preaching. Gregory deduces that the Church herself feeds upon contemplation of Christ's divinity, but she satisfies her young with preaching about the crucified Lord. Langland's use of the *arcana verba* text is ambiguous: it seems to be uttered by Christ himself (though it may be an authorial parenthesis). I believe the intention is to remind readers that, though Christ is speaking as man's blood-brother, he is in fact only a half-brother — a point more obviously expressed in C 20: 436. (For a different view, see Schmidt, *ed. cit.*, p.352.) The *per speculum* text appears in variant forms: Augustine, who returns to it constantly, gives his own interpretation of it in *De Trin.*, 15.9 (*CCSL* 50A, p.480ff.).
5 *Nonne ex denario conuenisti mecum?* Denarius figuram regis habet. Recepisti ergo mercedem quam tibi promiseram, hoc est imaginem et similitudinem meam. Jer., *In Math.* (*CCSL* 77, 176)
6 Non otiosum etiam quod mulier illa dragma laetatur inuenta. Non mediocris haec dragma est, in qua principis est figura. Et ideo imago regis census ecclesiae est . . . dragmae sumus, habeamus pretium; filii sumus, festinemus ad patrem. Ambr., *In Luc.* 7, (*CCSL* 14, 287)
   The Greek *drachma* (*dragma*) is equivalent to the Roman *denarius*, so Ambrose connects the woman's lost *drachma* with God's 'penny'.
7 See Raw, in *Hussey* (1969), p.156f.; and my comment on p.10, and Ch.1, Note 31, above.
8 See, for instance, Jer., *In Math.* (*CCSL* 77, 106)
9 The derived meanings are fully set out by B. H. Smith, *Traditional Imagery of Charity in Piers Plowman* (The Hague, 1966), pp.74-93. Smith quotes exegetes more nearly contemporary with Langland. The interpretation of the four Doctors may be gathered from Ambrose, *In Luc.*, (*CCSL* 14, 237ff.).
10 O tu, anima mea, ubi te esse sentis, ubi iaces aut ubi stas donec ab eo qui propitius factus est omnibus iniquitatibus tuis sanentur omnes languores tui? Agnoscis te certe in illo esse stabulo quo samaritanus ille perduxit eum quem reperit multis a latronibus inflictus uulneribus semiuiuum. *De Trin.* (*CCSL* 50A, 531f.)
11 For example, Augustine, *Tract. in Ioh.*, 17.6 (*CCSL* 36, 173).
12 Smith (1966), p.78, points out a similar merging of images between the 'grange *lex christi*' (B 17:71) and Piers's Barn in B Passus 19. See also p.88, below.
13 Ambrose takes for granted the application of these words to the Passion of Christ 'whose clothes Isaiah saw were red' (*cuius Esaias ruborem uidit uestimentorum*). *In Luc.*, 3.23 (*CCSL* 14, 87).
14 The significance of the wife's name escapes the editors. Pearsall notes, '*Worch-when-tyme-is*, i.e. not on the sabbath' quoting *Ex.* 20:9 (*ed. cit.*,

p.149). However, the echo of Galations can hardly be fortuitous, given the setting of agricultural work as a metaphor for the good life in both instances. Langland's version of the text, quoted at A 11:245; B 10:204, is *Dum tempus est operemur bonum ad omnes* . . . (but the MSS show variants, and Schmidt reads *habemus* for *est*).

Piers's son's name is a corollary of the text quoted five lines later, *Michi vindictam*, etc.; the daughter's name I take to emerge from I *Pet.* 1:14, 2:13, 2:18 (the thoughts 'issue' from Peter).

15 The Latin *signatum est* is peculiarly difficult to render appropriately in this doctrinally important verse. The basic sense of *signare* is 'to set a mark on (as with a seal or a stamp)'; it can also mean 'to adorn'. Augustine's interpretation requires that *signatum est* be taken as God's identifying mark on the soul of man, which the questioners seeking for good things outside themselves have failed to appreciate. The A.V. reading, 'Lord, lift thou up the light of thy countenance upon us', admits no such exegesis.

16 Sacrificate sacrificium justitiae, et sperate in Domino (*Ps.* 4:5f.).

17 See Smith (1966), pp.49ff. Smith points out that *Ps.* 4 was read daily at the Office of Compline in the Sarum Use.

18 It is interesting to note that Augustine's discourse on this psalm also brings in the text *Reddite Caesari*, adding one more item to the train of thought shared by Langland and Augustine. That Langland had pondered the meaning of this psalm is shown by his quotation of *Vt quid diligitis vanitatem et queritis mendacium?* (Ps. 4:3) and his exhortation to 'ye grete clerkes' to go to the gloss (B 15:82).

19 A similar point is made by Raw (1969), p.159. She stresses that the coin is a passive symbol.

20 See *Act.* 2:1-4, and cp. B 19:200ff.; C 21:200ff.

21 See, for example, Raw (1969), p.163f. She goes so far as to say that in B Passus 16 'Piers is still in the pre-incarnation era', and that when 'he strikes out with the second prop' in this scene he 'causes the incarnation' (p.165).

22 See p.17f. and Ch.2, Note 13, above.

23 (Sed si non possunt adhuc), interim uel temporalia bona non desiderent, nisi ab uno Deo, sic et in Veteri Testamento seruiant, ut ad Nouum peruentiant. Aug., *En. in Ps.* (*CCSL* 38, 331f.)

24 For a general survey of the theme in early literature, see J. E. Cross, 'Aspects of Microcosm and Macrocosm in O.E. Literature' in *Brodeur Studies*, ed. S. B. Greenfield, Oregon, 1963, pp.1-22.

The chief authority for the *comparatio* of the life of the microcosm and the history of the macrocosm (as recorded in the bible) was Augustine (cp. *De Genesi contra Manicheos* 1, 23f., *PL* 34), but Isidore, Gregory and Bede helped to make the theory well known in England from Anglo-Saxon times onward.

25 Quemadmodum Caesar a nobis exigit impressionem imaginis suae, sic et Deus, ut quemadmodum illi redditur nummus, si Deo reddatur anima lumine vultus eius illustrata atque signata. (Bede, *In Marc.* [*PL* 92, 253]; quoted by Raw, p.157. The translation is hers.)

26 Ambrose, *In Luc.* (*CCSL* 14, 133). The miracle is recorded in *Matt.* 17:24ff.

27 The gospel text is from *Matt.* 22:21. Kane's A-text, quoted here, differs slightly from Skeat. (In my epigraph to the book I have deviated from my general practice in quoting, since the lines in Schmidt's B-text used there are more familiarly spelt and punctuated.)

28 The speech is analysed in some detail by Smith (1966), pp.21-40.

29 The compound *deus-homo* 'god-man' was first used by Augustine. See, for example, *Tract. in Ioh. (CCSL* 36, 236); Langland translates it literally as 'god man' (B 11: 206; C 12: 112). See also Ch. 8, Note 11, below.

Chapter 4   Piers, Peter and the Law

1 In C the passage is rewritten: it discusses the difference between 'mede' and 'mercede', using grammatical metaphors for the relation of payer and recipient of reward. However, *Matt.* 6: 2 is still a central text in the argument (cp. C 3: 332ff.).
2 See *Marc.* 10:17-21; *Luc.* 18:18-23. The man insisted that he had observed the commandments from his youth, and Jesus told him to give all that he possessed to the poor and then to follow him. The disciples were astonished when he taught that the rich could not enter the Kingdom, saying among themselves, 'Who can be saved, then?' The reply given by Jesus was 'For men it is impossible, but not for God; for God everything is possible.'
3 *Nemo bonus*, 'No one is good'. Ambrose states plainly that no man can be immaculate:

> Videmus impossibile esse ut perfecte quis immaculatus esse possit in corpore constitutus, cum etiam Paulus imperfectum se dicat.
> (Ambr., *In Esai.* [*CCSL* 14, 407])
> We see that it is impossible for anyone while set in the body to be perfectly immaculate, since even Paul calls himself imperfect.

He goes on to quote 1 *Cor.* 13:10 and also *uidemus nunc per speculum in aenigmate, tunc autem facie ad faciem*. The passage is taken up by Augustine in his anti-Pelagian writings. I return to Ambrose's commentary when considering Langland's use of the text in C 15: 136 (see p. 55, below).
4 The phrases *si dolum proximo meo fecero* and *si locutus non fuero ueritatem* from *Ps.* 14: 2f. come, unmarked, into his list of good works to be done and evils to be avoided (in the expectation of the Lord's coming to demand fruit from his tree). It is incidentally of interest that Ambrose here [cp. *Luc.* 3: 9] refers to Christ as *bonus ille cultor agri* 'that good farmer of the field' (Ambr. *In Luc.* [*CCSL* 14, 64]).
5 See A 5:11ff.; B 5:11ff. In C, the passus begins with the poet's personal 'confession' of time wasted and his hope in the end to win grace. He quotes both *Matt.* 13:44 and *Luc.* 15:10 in reference to himself, hinting his hope that, like the lost coin, he will eventually be received into heaven (cp. C 5: 98ff.). The dream then follows, with Reason preaching and Conscience acting as cross-bearer. (The quotation from *Isa.* 14: 5f. occurs at C 5:177.)
6 Aug. *Conf.* 8.2.3 (*narravi ei circuitus erroris mei*). This interpretation of Langland's *mase* seems more appropriate than that of Bennett (*ed. cit.*, p. 105). He compares the miniature mazes found in some cathedral floors, which supposedly typified man's life and spiritual progress.
7 See A 3: 260ff.; the prediction is developed in B 3: 284ff.; C 3: 436ff.
8 Quoted above, p. 8.
9 See p. 25, and Ch. 3, Note 26.
10 For references, see Pearsall's note, *ed. cit.*, p. 121; for the relation of restitution and justice, see Bloomfield (1963), p. 131f.

11 The Ciceronian definition is included in Augustine's consideration of the *forma justitiae*, already quoted in Chapter 2 above: I include the whole passage as it bears on the *forma justitiae*:

> Cum enim dico et sciens dico: 'Iustus est animus qui scientia atque ratione in uita ac moribus *sua cuique distribuit*,' non aliquam rem absentem cogito sicut Carthaginem aut fingo ut possum sicut Alexandriam, siue ita sit siue non ita; sed praesens quiddam cerno et cerno apud me etsi non sum ipse quod cerno, et multi si audiant, approbabunt.   *De Trin.* (*CCSL* 50, p. 282)
>
> For when I say and mean 'A soul is righteous [*justus*] when it is one which with purpose and reason in life and conduct *apportions to each his own*' I am not thinking of some absent object such as Carthage, or imagining, as I can, something like Alexandria, whether it is so or not; but I see something present and I see it in me, although I am not myself what I see, and many people, if they hear me, will concur.

12 As we have seen (above, p. 16) both these texts were important in Augustine's theory of true love; each occurs more than twenty times in *De Trinitate*. In C, the text *qui manet*, etc., is replaced by *Ego in patre, et pater in me* (*Jo.* 14: 9 f.).

13 Similar instances occur in Meed's trial; first when that warlike lady swears that she could win a kingdom, 'be marie of heuene!' and, next, when the king is persuaded by her specious arguments to accept her domination, 'be crist!' [cp. A 3: 188, 215; B 3: 201, 228; C 3: 283].

14 Piers swears by St Peter in A 7: 3 and 7: 27; in B and C the oath is by St Peter of Rome [B 6: 3; C 8: 2]. See also Bennett, *ed. cit.*, p. 189, Note 544.

15 Bede, for example, repeats this 'etymological' interpretation (*CCSL* 120, 133), and so does Anselm (*PL* 158, 602).

16 Peter was brought up as a Jew and was divinely directed, first at the Transfiguration, then through the gift of tongues at Pentecost, and lastly through a vision of creatures held by Jewish law to be 'unclean' (cp. *Act.* 10: 9ff.), to relinquish some exclusive tenets of Judaism and promulgate the New Law of Jesus to non-Jews. In a fourth-century Christian fresco in the catacombs of Rome he is depicted holding the scroll of the New Law, but such a picture is misleading, since a fundamental contrast has been made since the time of Paul between the written law of Moses and the law of Jesus which is 'written on the heart' of the believer. For the contrast Langland constantly draws between formal, outward, Pharisaical religion and true worship founded on inward commitment, the transformation of Peter's beliefs would be a uniquely authoritative example. For the typological parallel with Moses, see L. Réau, *L'Iconographie de l'Art Chrétien*, Vol. 2 (Paris, 1956), p. 204; for iconography and Peter, J. Lees-Milne, *Saint Peter's* (London, 1967).

17 cp. p. 27, above.

18 Sed non capit humana condicio in hoc corruptibili, in hoc mortali corpore facere tabernaculum deo. (Ambr., *In Luc.* [*CCSL* 14, 221])

19 Inde apparent Moyses et Helias, hoc est lex et propheta cum uerbo; neque enim lex potest esse sine uerbo neque propheta nisi qui de dei filio prophetauit. Et illi quidem filii tonitrui corporali gloria Moysen quoque et Heliam speculati sunt, sed etiam nos cotidie uidemus Moysen cum dei filio; uidemus enim legem in euangelio, cum legimus: *diliges dominum deum tuum*, uidemus Heliam cum dei uerbo, quando legimus: *ecce uirgo in utero accipiet*.   (Ambr., *In Luc.* [*CCSL* 14, 218])

Then there appeared Moses and Elias, that is, the Law and the Prophet, with the Word: nor can the Law exist without the Word, nor yet the Prophet except as one who prophesied about the Son of God. And the Sons of Thunder [James and John] looked on Moses and Elias in their corporeal glory, but even we today see Moses with the Son of God; for we see the Law in the Gospel, when we read 'thou shalt love thy God', we see Elias with the Word of God when we read 'Behold, a virgin shall conceive in her womb' [*Isa.* 7:14].

20 Ambr., *In Luc.* (*CCSL* 14, 216).

21 Transcendamus igitur opera mundi, ut possimus faciem ad faciem deum uidere. *Ascende in montem qui euangelizas Sion* . . . tres autem soli et tres electi ducuntur ad montem. Putarem in tribus mystice genus hominum conprehensum, quia ex tribus filiis Noe genus omne defluxit humanum, nisi electos cernerem. (Ambr., *In Luc.* [*CCSL* 14, 217])

22 Et hodie Moyses docet et hodie Helias loquitur et hodie in maiore gloria Moysen uidere possumus. Quis enim non potest, quando et populus Iudaeorum eum uidere potuit, immo uidit? Vidit enim in gloria faciem Moysi, sed uelamen accepit, sed in montem non ascendit et ideo errauit. Qui solum Moysen uidit, dei uerbum simul uidere non potuit. Reuelemus igitur nos faciem nostram, *ut reuelata facie gloriam dei speculantes in eandem imaginem reformemur.* (Ambr., *In Luc.* [*CCSL* 14, 218])

23 Will, asking what Charity is, and where he might find him, complains that he has never come across him, nor has he seen Christ:

> Clerkes kenne me þat crist is in alle places
> Ac I seiȝ hym neuere sooþly but as myself in a Mirour.
> *[Hic] in enigmate, tunc facie ad faciem.*
> > [B 15:161 ff.; cp. C 16: 294 f.]

Anima praises Charity, and tells Will that he will never find him without the help of Piers the ploughman, *'Petrus id est Christus'* [cp. B 15: 212]. The whole difficult passage is rewritten in C, though the association of Piers and God-in-Christ is retained [C 16: 337 f.].

24 The interpretation of *per speculum in aenigmate* (and particularly the translation of *per speculum*) is important to the theme of *De Trinitate*; Augustine is quite specific on the matter:

> Incorporalem substantiam scio esse sapientiam et lumen esse in quo uidentur quae oculis carnalibus non uidentur, et tamen uir tantus tamque spiritalis: *Videmus nunc,* inquit, *per speculum in aenigmate, tunc autem facie ad faciem.* Quale sit et quod sit hoc speculum si quaeramus, profecto illud occurrit quod in speculo nisi imago non cernitur. Hoc ergo facere conati sumus ut per hanc imaginem quod nos sumus uideremus utcumque a quo facti sumus tamquam *per speculum.* Hoc significat etiam illud quod ait idem apostolus: *Nos autem reuelata facie gloriam domini speculantes in eandem imaginem transformamur de gloria in gloriam tamquam a domini spiritu.*
> > (*De Trin.* [*CCSL* 50A, 479])

I know that wisdom is an incorporeal substance and a light by which things are seen which are not seen by the eyes of the flesh, and yet [Paul], so great and so spiritual a man, said, 'We see now *per speculum in aenigmate,* but then face to face'. If we ask what kind of mirror [*speculum*] and what mirror, it is at once apparent that in a mirror nothing but an image can be seen. And so we have tried to use this 'image' which we ourselves *are*, to see in some way or another him by whom we were made, as though 'in a mirror' [*per speculum*]. This too is the meaning of another saying of the same apostle, 'But we with face revealed beholding as in a glass [*speculantes*] the glory of the Lord, are changed into the same image from glory to glory even as by the Spirit of the Lord' [*2 Cor.* 3:18].

25 Gregory, *Moralia* (*CCSL* 143A, 1126, on *Job* 31:37). Langland uses the Latinate word *spiek* (Gregory, following Vulgate, uses *spica*) for the 'ear' of wheat, which strikes me as a clerk's, rather than a countryman's, term [cp. C 12:179]. See also the rather similar passage in *Hom. in Ezech.* (*PL* 76, 960f.), where Gregory describes the steps in virtue with the same gospel text [*Marc.* 4:28] in mind. Langland makes the same association in:

> Or as whete out of weed waxiþ, out of þe erthe,
> So dobest out of dobet & dowel gynneþ springe.
>
> [A 10:126f.]

26 Barney (1973), pp. 227, 282. See also Chapter 1, Note 11, above.

Chapter 5 Piers and the Pardon

1 *Habebat enim legem et iuxta uiam erat quia non credebat in via.* Jer., *In Math.* (*CCSL* 77, 190). (The A.V. text differs, reading 'in the way' for 'beside the way', so the interpretation would not apply.)

2 J. A. Burrow, 'The Action of Langland's Second Vision', *EC*, 15 (1965), pp. 247-68, emphasises the positive value of the agricultural work and the social improvements effected by Piers, and concludes that the pilgrimage has been rightly superseded by the work on the half-acre. Such an interpretation accounts for Truth's Pardon, but not for the tearing of it, nor for Piers's decision to change his way of life.

3 'In an even larger sense, Piers as a farmer suggests archetypal man in the terms used of his creation in Genesis . . . The farmer is also the emblem of man bearing and responding to the effects of the Fall . . . Thus, Piers raises the two most basic questions about man: what was he meant to be, and what has he become in the world in which he must now define himself?' (E. Kirk, *The Dream Thought of Piers Plowman*, London, 1972, p. 73.

4 Augustine's application of the Samaritan story to his own case, quoted above, p. 21, would show that such an interpretation by no means conflicts with our view that Piers is an example to the Christian reader. Langland's use of the strange word *semyvif* [B 17:58; C 19:55] indicates the importance he attached to the *semivivus* 'half-alive' of the Vulgate narrative [*Luc.* 10:30]. The use of the parable in the liturgy for the 13th Sunday after Trinity is remarked by Pearsall (*ed. cit.*, p. 308). The sequence of prayers and readings accompanying the parable includes Moses' prayer for pardon and the promises given to Abraham's people.

5 cp. C 7:292ff. and *Luc.* 14:16-24 (cp. *Matt.* 22:1-10).

6 Nec [regnum caeli possit adipisci] ille qui emat boues, cum Helisaeus occiderit et populo diuiserit quos habebat. Et ille qui ducit uxorem cogitet quae mundi sunt, non quae dei, non quo coniugium reprehendatur, sed quia

ad maiorem honorem uocetur integritas . . . Ambr., *In Luc.* (*CCSL* 14, 283).
Nor [can he attain to the Kingdom of Heaven] who [in the parable of the
Great Feast] buys oxen, since Elisha slaughtered and distributed to the
people those which he owned. And the man who was taking a wife had his
mind on worldly matters, not those of God — not that marriage is
reprehensible, but because chastity may be called to a greater honour . . .

7   Iudaei autem corporali ministerio iuga sibi legis inponunt et ideo secundum
prophetam *disrumpamus uincula eorum et abiciamus a nobis iugum ipsorum*;
Christum enim recepimus, qui ceruicibus nostris pietatis suae iugum mite
suspendit. Quinque autem iuga sunt uerborum decem uel quinque libri
ueteris legis . . . Ambr., *In Luc.* (*CCSL* 14, 283)
But the Jews in their corporeal service impose the yoke of the Law upon
themselves, and so let us, according to the prophet, 'break their bonds and
cast off from ourselves their yoke' [*Ps.* 2: 3]; for we have received Christ,
who hangs the yoke of his compassion gently upon our necks. But the
'five yokes' [of the oxen in the parable] are the Ten Commandments or
the Five Books of the Old Law.

8   Ergo et ille qui uillam emit alienus a regno est — ementes enim atque
uendentes Noe, ut legisti, tempore diluuia sorbuerunt — et ille qui iugum
potius legis quam gratiae munus elegit et ille qui propter ducendam excusat
uxorem. Ambr., (*In Luc.* (*CCSL* 14, 284)
And so that man, too, who buys a farm [*villa*] is alien to the Kingdom — for
in the time of Noah, as you have read, buyers and sellers were drowned in the
floods — so, too, that man who chooses the yoke of the Law rather than the
gift of Grace, and that man who excuses himself because he is taking a wife.

9   H. Meroney, 'The Life and Death of Longe Wille', *ELH* 17 (1950), 1-35, is,
I believe, the first critic to notice the similarities between Moses and the
Piers of the *Visio*. Several critics have noted that Piers's anger as he divides
the Pardon in two is similar to the anger of Moses as he breaks the tablets of
the Law (cp. *Exod.* 32:19). The Doctors teach that the Law had to be
'broken' or 'abolished' in one sense, in being renewed. [See e.g. Aug., *Quaest.
Exod.* (*CCSL* 33, 147f.)]

10 See p. 23, above, and Chapter 3, Note 14 [cp. A 7: 70ff.]. Augustine too
ignores the word *bonum* 'good' in appropriating Paul's words in a sermon on
spiritual ploughing: *Tempus est, operemur, laboremus* . . . (cp. *PL* 40, 685ff.,
esp. 687). Note that Augustine uses *est* 'is' rather than *habemus* 'we have',
as Langland does.

11 For example, Lady Meed quotes half a text to her own advantage; Conscience
taxes her with not having read to the end [cp. B 3: 330ff.; C 3: 487ff.].

12 The accusation of self-indulgence is sufficient to disprove some critics'
contention that Piers is 'ideal perfection'. See also my note on *bilyve* and
bely joye (Ch. 2, Note 16). It is perhaps of interest that over-eating is a vice
that Augustine finds harder to give up than other sins of the flesh
(cp. *Conf.*, 10: 31).

13 Jesus exhorts Peter to watch and pray: 'The spirit is willing, but the flesh is
weak' [*Matt.* 26: 41].

14 *Ergo qui in tecto est non descendat et qui in agro est non reuertatur retro.
Vnde intellegam quid sit ager, nisi ipse me doceat Iesus dicens: nemo
mittens manum in aratrum et respiciens retro aptus est regno caelorum?*
. . . *Ara igitur agrum tuum, si uis dirigi ad dei regnum. Floreat tibi bonorum
seges fecunda meritorum.* Ambr., *In Luc.* (*CCSL* 14, 312f.)
'And so the man who is on the roof should not come down, or the man who
is in the field turn back.' Whence should I come to know what the 'field' is,

103

unless Jesus himself teaches me, saying, 'No man setting his hand to the plough and looking back is fit for the Kingdom of Heaven' . . . Till your field, therefore, etc.

15   Ergo directus ad dei regnum opes et patrimonium non requiras. Noui et aliam scriptam tunicam, de qua nos hortatur apostolus, ut *exspoliantes ueterem hominem cum actibus eius induti nouum* superioris tunicam non requiramus erroris. Ambr., *In Luc.* (*CCSL* 14, 313)

And so, on your way to the Kingdom of God you should not look for wealth and patrimony. I know, too, of another scriptural 'tunic', concerning which the apostle exhorts us to 'put off the old man with his deeds and put on the new' and not to look back for the tunic of our former error.

16   Ergo ita exerceamus et colamus agrum nostrum in istius culturae munere constituti, ut in illa superiore Hierusalem, ubi legis custodia uera celebratur, habeamus similaginem de manipulis nostris, quos beati qui potuerint congregare, ut *uenientes ueniant in exsultatione tollentes manipulos suos*. Isti igitur fructus sunt spiritales et felices ueri prouentus laboris, qui nullo inutili imbre madefiant; fructus autem carnis corruptelae obnoxius, et ideo qui carnalia seminauerit, carnalia metet. Ambr., *In Luc.* (*CCSL* 14, 317f.)

And so let us exert ourselves and cultivate our field, while we are placed in this agricultural employment, so that in the heavenly Jerusalem, where the true keeping of the Law is celebrated, we may have the finest flour from our sheaves, which the blessed will be able to bring together, so that 'coming, they come in exultation bearing their sheaves'. Those fruits, therefore, are spiritual and the blessed produce of true labour, not dampened by any unproductive rain; but the fruit of the flesh is liable to corruption, and so those who sow in the flesh reap in the flesh.

Ambrose weaves into his exposition *Gal.* 4: 26 and 6: 8; his quotation is from *Ps.* 125: 6.

17   Tamen, fratres, ante omnia custodite hereditatem nostram, de qua securi sumus nos in testamento Patris nostri esse: non in aliqua charta frivola alicuius hominis, sed in testamento Patris nostri. Inde securi sumus, quia qui fecit testamentum, uiuit; qui fecit testamentum heredi suo, ipse indicabit de testamento suo. Aug., *En. in Ps.* (*CCSL* 38, 379f.)

18   Sed peccatori, inquit, dicit Dominus: *Vtquid tu adsumis testamentum meum per os tuum?* . . . sed in quemlibet dicat hoc Dominus, ideo dicit, quia peccatori non prodest quando legem Dei loquitur. Aug., *En. in Ps.* (*CCSL* 38, 381)

The association of the Old Covenant and the will or testament of God is also made in *Gal.* 3:15; Augustine, in his commentary, accepts the paradox that the Testator died and yet lives. By the death of Christ the promises made to the seed of Abraham are confirmed (i.e. the will is proved). The heirs are the spiritual, not the carnal, seed of Abraham (cp. *PL* 35, 2121).

19   Bennett sees an ambiguity in the word 'purchaced' which would be very much in keeping with the notion that the Old Testament has a double significance, its secondary meaning being confirmed by the death of Christ, which both confirms the inheritance and ransoms the faithful (i.e. 'buys the indulgence'). (See Bennett, *ed. cit.*, p.216.) The promise of pardon and of the Kingdom is obtained by 'Piers' under the Old Dispensation, but the promises are given their full meaning when Jesus pays the price. Only by destroying the literal meaning of Truth's document can Piers become the spiritual heir of Abraham.

20   '*For hym and for his heires*: a legal formula . . . It thus confirms the impression that a document of some kind is to be envisaged — though as no papal

pardon presumed to extend its benefits to a man's children it is evident that this pardon is of no ordinary kind.' (Bennett, *ed. cit.*, p. 216 f.)

21 *Et semen eius in benedictione erit.* Et hic non occurat carnalis cogitatio . . . Semen eius reliquiae eius, unde hic seminat, et postea metet. Namque apostolos dicit: *Bonum autem facientes non deficiamus: tempore enim suo metemus indefatigabiles. Itaque dum tempus habemus, ait, operemur bonum ad omnes.* Hoc est semen tuum, quod erit in benedictione. Aug., *En. in Ps. (CCSL* 38, 373)
Augustine concludes his explication of this verse by quoting the passage about the exultant reapers bearing their sheaves [*Ps.* 125: 6] which we have noted above in Ambrose's imaging of life as a field to be sown, not carnally but spiritually (cp. Note 16).

22 Langland shows particular disgust at unprofitable talk about theological matters, dinner-table conversation on sacred subjects which chiefly displays the cleverness of the speakers:

> Thus þei dryuele at hir deys þe deitee to knowe,
> And gnawen god [in] þe gorge whanne hir guttes fullen.
> [A 10: 57 f.; B 10: 56 f.; C 11: 40 f.]

An extended example of such hypocritical talk is given by the Doctor of Divinity over his meal at B 13: 99 ff.; C 15: 107 ff. It is to be noted that Conscience and Patience on that occasion feed upon:

> sondry metes manye
> Of Austyn, of Ambrose, of [alle] þe foure Euaungelistes:
> *Edentes & bibentes qui apud eos sunt.*

23 This is the formulation from the *Quicunque vult*, 'Whoever will be saved' . . ., part of the Athanasian Creed; it is based on the words of Jesus [cp. *Matt.* 25: 46]. The Doomsday prophecy is paraphrased in the poem at B 19: 192 ff., C 21: 192 ff., where the man who *reddet quod debet* will be rewarded, it is said, and the man who does not pay will be punished with endless woe.

24 Frank, *'Piers Plowman' and the Scheme of Salvation* (New Haven, 1957), surveys various interpretations of the gesture; see also R. Woolf, 'The Tearing of the Pardon' in *Hussey* (1969), p. 50 ff., and P. Martin, *Piers Plowman: The Field and the Tower* (London, 1979), p. 159 f.

25 See O. E. D. s.v. teen sb. 1, 2 and 3.

26 Piers's resolution to give up ploughing presents great difficulty to those critics who approve his decision to give up the pilgrimage for the farming, taking the latter to be an allegorical image of the good life.

27 See p. 8, above.

28 *'Irascimini et nolite peccare.'* (A. V. reads 'Stand in awe and sin not.') Paul quotes this same verse when he writes of 'putting off the "old man"' [*Eph.* 4: 26] and no doubt Augustine remembers this association.

29 Legebam: irascimini et nolite peccare, et quomodo movebar, deus meus, qui iam didiceram irasci mihi de praeteritis, ut de cetero non peccarem . . . nec iam bona mea foris erant nec oculis carneis in isto sole quaerebantur. Aug., *Conf.* 9: 4.

30 Ibi enim, ubi mihi eratus eram, intus in cubili, ubi compunctus eram, ubi sacrificaveram, mactans vetustatem meam, et inchoata meditatione renovationis meae, sperans in te, ibi mihi dulcescere coeperas et dederas laetitiam in corde meo. *Ib*.

31 See p. 17, and Chapter 2, Note 13, above. The Pauline passage is read as the Epistle for the nineteenth Sunday after Pentecost.

32   Augustine offers this as the second of alternative interpretations: *Aut, agite paenitentiam; id est,* irascimini uobis ipsis de praeteritis peccatis, et ulterius peccare desinite. Aug., *En. in Ps. (CCSL* 38, 16)

33   *Fructus etenim terrae absque pecunia comedere* est ex Ecclesia quidem sumptus accipere, sed eidem Ecclesiae praedicationis pretium non praebere. De qua uidelicet praedicatione auctoris uoce dicitur: *Oportuit te committere pecuniam meam nummulariis, et ueniens ego recepissem utique quod meum erat cum usura. Moralia (CCSL* 143A, 1132) on *Job* 31: 39.

For to 'eat the fruit of the land without money' is to receive indeed our expenses from the Church, but not to give our money's-worth of preaching to that same Church. Concerning this same preaching, it is said by the Creator's voice, 'You ought to have entrusted my money to the exchangers, and then at my coming I should have received what was mine with interest.'

For the general theme in Gregory, see p.4, and Chapter 1, Note 11, above.

34   Eia, non tibi uenit in mentem seruus ille qui abscondit talentum, et noluit erogare? Numquid enim accusatus est quia perdidit, et non quia sine lucro seruauit? Sic ergo audite, fratres mei, ut non quiescatis. Aug., *Tract. in Ioh.* 10. 9 *(CCSL* 36, 106)

Come! don't you naturally think of that servant who hid the talent and did not want to pay it out? For surely he was not blamed because he had lost it, but rather because he kept it safe without profit? Hear this then, brethren, so that you don't rest inactive.

Chapter 6   Patience and Piers the Palmer

1   . . . *iis qui secundum patientiam boni operis, gloriam et honorem et incorruptionem quaerunt, vitam aeternam* [*Rom.* 2: 7].

2   This continuity of the Old and the New Laws is the central theme of R. M. Ames, *The Fulfillment of the Scriptures: Abraham, Moses, and Piers* (Evanston, 1970).

3   Quia enim amor Dei amorem proximi generat, dicturus per legem Dominus: *Diliges proximum tuum*, praemisit dicens: *Diliges Dominum Deum tuum*, ut scilicet in terra pectoris nostri prius amoris sui radicem figeret quatenus per ramos postmodum dilectio fraterna germinaret. *Moralia (CCSL* 143, 352f., on *Job* 6:14) It will be noticed that this passage also uses the image of a Tree or plant of love: I will revert to this again in Chapter 7.

4   Sed nec ab homine uinci potest, qui uitia sua uicerit. Non enim uincitur, nisi cui eripitur ab aduersario, quod amat. Qui ergo id amat solum, quod amanti eripi non potest, ille indubitanter inuictus est nec ulla cruciatur inuidia . . . Diligit enim deum ex toto corde, ex tota anima, ex tota mente et diligit proximum tamquam se ipsum . . .

Diligamus, ergo, ut praeceptum est, etiam inimicos nostros, si uere inuicti esse uolumus. Non enim per se ipsum quisquam hominum inuictus est, sed per illam incommutabilem legem, cui quicumque seruiunt soli sunt liberi. Sic enim eis quod diligunt auferri non potest, quae res una inuictos facit et perfectos uiros. Aug., *De uera religione (CCSL* 32, 243f.)

5   Qui ergo diligit aliquem tamquam se ipsum, hoc in eo debet diligere, quod sibi ipse est. Corpora uero non sunt, quod nos sumus. Non ergo in homine corpus est expetendum aut desiderandum. Valet enim ad hoc etiam, quod

praeceptum est: *Ne concupiscas rem proximi tui.* Quapropter quisquis in proximo aliud diligit quam sibi ipse est, non eum diligit tamquam se ipsum . . . Quapropter cur iste non sit inuictus hominem diligendo, cum in eo nihil praeter hominem diligat, id est creaturam dei ad eius imaginem factam, nec ei possit deesse perfecta natura quam diligit, cum ipse perfectus est? Aug., *De uera religione* (*CCSL* 32, 245 f.)

6   The medieval MSS sometimes use spellings with c for the classical t in such words as *transitio, patientes.* I have normalised the spelling except when actually quoting a passage from the text.

7   R. E. Kaske, '*Ex vi transicionis* and Its Passage in *Piers Plowman*', *JEGP* 62 (1963), 32-60, repr. in *Blanch*, 228-63. Ben H. Smith, 'Patience's Riddle, *Piers Plowman* B XIII', *MLN* 76 (1961), 675-82. See also his discussion in *Traditional Imagery* (1966). J. F. Goodridge has an appendix on the riddle in his Penguin translation, pp. 299-308.

8   A similar point is made by R. Ames (1970): 'Like the prophets, Patience can speak only in riddles; indeed, his riddle is a prophecy' (p. 176). However, Ames also says that Patience's package contains 'the Passion of Christ' and that his prophecy includes 'the calling of the Gentiles', and there we differ.

9   Haec est autem uera dilectio *ut* inhaerentes ueritati *iuste uiuamus*, et ideo contemnamus omnia mortalia prae amore hominum quo eos uolumus iuste uiuere . . . Cum enim duo praecepta sint *in quibus tota lex pendet et prophetae, dilectio dei* et *dilectio proximi*, non immerito plerumque scriptura pro utroque unum ponit . . . et pleraque alia reperimus in litteris sanctis in quibus sola dilectio proximi ad perfectionem praecipi uidetur et taceri de dilectione dei cum in utroque praecepto lex pendeat et prophetae, sed et hoc ideo quia et qui proximum diligit consequens est ut ipsam praecipue dilectionem diligat. *Deus* autem *dilectio est, et qui manet in dilectione in deo manet.* Consequens ergo est ut praecipue deum diligat. *De Trin.* (*CCSL* 50, 284 f.)

See also p. 11, Chapter 2, Note 5, above.

10   Quia cum diligimus caritatem, aliquid diligentem diligimus propter hoc ipsum quia diligit aliquid. Ergo quid diligit caritas ut possit etiam ipsa caritas diligi? Caritas enim non est quae nihil diligit. Si autem se ipsam diligit, diligat aliquid oportet ut caritate se diligat. Sicut enim uerbum indicat aliquid, indicat etiam se ipsum, sed non se uerbum indicat nisi se aliquid indicare indicet; sic et caritas diligit quidem se, sed nisi se aliquid diligentem diligat non caritate se diligit. Quid ergo diligit caritas nisi quod caritate diligimus? Id autem ut a proximo prouehamur frater est. *De Trin.* (*CCSL* 50, 287)

11   Imago uero quae *renouatur* in spiritu mentis *in agnitione dei* non exterius sed interius *de die in diem*, ipsa perficietur uisione quae *tunc* erit post iudicium *facie ad faciem, nunc* autem proficit *per speculum in aenigmate.* Propter cuius perfectionem dictum intellegendum est: *Similes ei erimus quoniam uidebimus eum sicuti est. De Trin.* (*CCSL* 50A, 457)

12   Sanctus itaque spiritus de quo dedit nobis facit nos in deo manere et ipsum in nobis. Hoc autem facit dilectio. Ipse est igitur deus dilectio. Denique paulo post cum hoc ipsum repetisset atque dixisset: *Deus dilectio est*, continuo subiecit: *Et qui manet in dilectione in deo manet, et deus in eo manet*, unde supra dixerat: *In hoc cognoscimus quia in ipso manemus et ipse in nobis quia de spiritu suo dedit nobis.* Ipse ergo significatur ubi legitur: *Deus dilectio est.* Deus igitur spiritus sanctus qui procedit ex deo cum datus fuerit homini ascendit eum in dilectionem dei et proximi, et ipse dilectio est. non enim habet homo unde deum diligat nisi ex deo. *De Trin.* (*CCSL* 50A, 506)

13   Smith (1966), p. 48; see also *MLN* 76 (1961), pp. 676 ff.

14   Chastite wiþoute Charite worþ cheynide in helle
      It is as lewid as a laumpe þat no liȝt is inne.
                              [A 1:162f.; B 1:188f.; C 1:184f.]

15   The A. V. translation has 'candle' here, but *lucerna* implies a lamp.

16   Qualis in me tunc erat nesciente alio lumine illam inlustrandum esse, ut sit
      particeps veritatis qui non est natura veritatis, quoniam *tu inluminabis
      lucernam meam, domine, deus meus inluminabis tenebras meas.* Aug.,
      Conf., 4.15.

17   See *En. in Ps.* (*CCSL* 38, 862 [on *Ps.* 17:29]; *CCSL* 39, pp. 641 and 861).

18   For the contrast between those who are given light, as in Psalm 17, and the
      worldly-wise whose hearts are dark, see Augustine, *Sermo* 67 (*PL* 39, 436).
      The idea of the darkened heart stems from *Rom.* 1:21f.

19   Si tamen legem perficitis regalem secundum Scripturas: Diliges proximum
      tuum sicut teipsum, bene facitis; si autem personas accipitis, peccatum
      operamini . . . [*Jac.* 2:8f.]
      Patientes igitur estote, fratres, usque ad adventum Domini. Ecce agricola
      expectat pretiosum fructum terrae, patientes ferens donec accipiat
      temporaneum et serotinum. [*Jac.* 5:7]
      Exemplum accipite, fratres, exitus mali, laboris et patientiae, prophetas, qui
      locuti sunt in nomine Domini. [*Jac.* 5:10]
      P. M. Kean, 'Justice, Kingship and the Good Life in Part II of *Piers Plowman*',
      in *Hussey* (1969), 94 and Note 27, has also noted resemblances to the
      Epistle of James.

20   Kaske (1963) thinks that Patience sums up 'the whole complex of virtues'
      (p. 49) but this would not be consistent with the role of this character in
      relation to Will's progress.

21   A curious cross-connection of the 'lamp-line' and the Passover is suggested
      by Jerome's commentary on the Wise and Foolish Virgins and their lamps.
      He gratuitously adds to his interpretation that the expected coming of
      Christ (the Bridegroom of the parable) would be in the middle of the night,
      as, *in that time in Egypt when the paschal meal was celebrated*, the death-
      bringer came, the Lord passed through the tents, and the blood of the Lamb
      consecrated the doorposts. (my italics) Jer., *In Math.* (*CCSL* 77, 237)

22   Et si mihi digito ostendatur ipse homo, studes mihi coniungere, notum
      facere, amicitia conligare. Itaque si facultas datur, accedo, alloquor, sermonem
      confero, affectum meum in illum quibus uerbis possum exprimo, uicissimque
      in eo fieri quem in me habeat atque exprimi uolo, spiritalemque complexum
      credendo molior quia peruestigare tam cito et cernere penitus eius interiora
      non possum. *De Trin.* (*CCSL* 50, 302, and cp. 308, 27f.)

23   In this matter too, the teachings of Jesus bring out what was earlier implicit:
      Ps. 50 *Miserere mei, Deus* includes a contrast between the offering of praise
      from a contrite heart and burnt offerings [cp. *Ps.* 50:17-19]. This psalm is
      mentioned as part of the food served to Patience at the dinner-party [B13:
      54; cp. C 15:63].

24   Pax enim nostra ex desiderio conditoris incohatur, ex manifesta autem
      uisione perficitur. Greg., *Moralia* (*CCSL* 143, 322, on *Job.* 5:24)

25   See my earlier reference to this text on p. 28, above.

26   Ambr., *In Luc.* (*CCSL* 14, 322).

27   Non est qui faciat bonitatem, non est usque ad unum. [*Ps.* 13:3]

28   Candor est enim lucis aeternae
                    et speculum sine macula Dei majestatis,
                    et imago bonitatis illius.   [*Sap.* 7:26]

108

29   Quia uera perfectio de patientia nascitur, statim post patientiam, uiarum perfectio subinfertur. Greg., *Moralia* (*CCSL* 143, 241, on *Job.* 4: 6)
Since perfection is born of patience, immediately after 'patience', 'the perfection of his ways' is mentioned [Gregory's comment on 'Where is your fear, your strength and the perfection of your ways', *Job.* 4: 6].

30   Quoniam servasti verbum patientiae meae, et ego servabo te ab hora tentationis, quae ventura est in orbem universum tentare habitantes in terra. Ecce venio cito: tene quod habes, ut nemo accipiat coronam tuam. [*Apoc.* 3: 10f.]

31   Goodridge (1959), p. 306.
The washing of hands before the meal (B 13: 28) almost certainly suggests more than polite manners, in view of the pharisaical character of the chief guest. Jesus was rebuked by a Pharisee for *not* washing his hands before eating, and made this an occasion for contrasting external with internal cleanness (*Luc.* 11: 38). The clerical reader might also have remembered Heb. 9: 9f., which contrasts the food and drink and ceremonial washings of the old observance, the externals of good behaviour, with the cleansing sacrifice of the new order, which purges the conscience.

32   Goodridge (1959), p. 207; and cp. Ames (1970), p. 175f.

Chapter 7   *Piers and the Tree*

1   The faculty of *Liberum Arbitrium* in discussed by Schmidt, *MAE* 38 (1969), 134-56; see esp. p. 155. My own observations here, following the practice I have laid down, depend upon the theory of Augustine. He was much imitated, as Schmidt points out. Schmidt's opinion is that Langland has more affinity with the pre-scholastic 'Augustinian' treatises on the soul than with the disputations of the schoolmen.

2   See also Schmidt (1969), p. 151.
Haec igitur trinitas mentis non propterea dei est imago quia sui meminit mens et intelligit ac diligit se, sed quia potest etiam meminisse et intellegere et amare a quo facta est. Quod cum facit sapiens ipsa fit. Si autem non facit, etiam cum sui meminit seque intellegit ac diligit, stulta est. Meminerit itaque dei sui *ad* cuius *imaginem* facta est eumque intellegat atque diligat. *De Trin.* (*CCSL* 50A, 442f.)

3   Cum ergo sit mens interior, quodam modo exit a semetipsa cum in haec quasi uestigia multarum intentionum exerit amoris affectum. Quae uestigia tamquam imprimuntur memoriae quando haec quae foris sunt corporalia sentiuntur ut etiam cum absunt ista, praesto sint tamen imagines eorum cogitantibus. Cognoscat ergo semetipsam, nec quasi absentem se quaerat, sed intentionem uoluntatis qua per alia uagabatur statuat in se ipsa et se cogitet. *De Trin.* (*CCSL* 50, 325)

4   Sed per legem cognitio peccati, per fidem inpetratio gratiae contra peccatum, per gratiam sanatio animae a uitio peccati, per animae sanitatem libertas arbitrii, per liberum arbitrium iustitiae dilectio, per iustitiae dilectionem legis operatio. [cp. *Rom.* 3: 20] Aug., *De Spiritu et Littera* (*CSEL* 60, 208)
See also Schmidt (1969), pp. 141ff.

5   See p. 33, above.

6   Quasi agrum invenit corda hominum: sed quomodo invenit? Silvam invenit,

exstirpat; si agrum purgatum invenit, plantat. Plantare ibi vult arborem, charitatem. Et quam silvam vult exstirpare? Amorem mundi. Audi exstirpatorem silvae. Aug., *Tract. in 1 Jo.*, 2. (*PL* 35, 1993f.)

7 Gregory also uses this passage from John's Epistle, speaking of *rooting-out* the thorns of the world, but his metaphor is of a crop (*messis*), not of a tree:

Unde Ioannes apostolos sciens inter spinas amorum saecularum supernae caritatis messem germinare non posse, priusquam aeterni amoris semina proferat, de audentium cordibus sancta verbi manu amorum saecularium spinas eradicat, dicens: *Noli diligere mundum, etc.*   *Moralia* (*CCSL* 143A, 896, on *Job.* 27:10)

8 See p. 49, Chapter 6, Note 3, above. The image in this passage is of a plant like a tree or a vine, but it does not come as close to Langland's description as the Augustinian image.

9 Non ergo intuendum est si uineae floreant, sed si flores ad partum fructuum conualescant; quia mirum non est si quis bona incohet, sed ualde mirabile si intentione recta in bono opera perduret ... Cum itaque hoc in se fidelis anima ostendit quasi oliua florem protulit. Sed cum quidam ex talibus rursus coeperint mundi gloriam quam contempserant quaerere, et terrenis rebus quas spreuisse uidebantur insatiabiliter inhiare, uacare iurgiis, proximorum laesiones exquirere, nimirum proiecit oliua florem quem proposuit, quia rudimenta boni studii ad perfecta opera non perduxit. Sed sciendum est quia haec semper eis eueniunt qui Deum puro ac simplici studio non sequuntur. *Moralia* (*CCSL* 143, 666, on *Job.* 15:33)

10 The edd. hesitate over the readings *pure/pore/pouere* in this line. Since 'pure simple' is another name for the Tree, also called Patience, we might gloss it with Gregory's 'pure and single aim' (*purum et simplex studium*), implying simplicity of heart and perseverance in seeking for Truth.

11 See Smith (1966), p. 65f., and Aers (1975), pp. 79ff.

12 Omnino sic se tenet ista dilectio: quomodo ipsa compaginata est in unum, sic omnes quae ex illa pendent, unum facit, et quasi conflat illos ignis. Aug., *Tract. in 1 Jo.*, 10. (*PL* 35, 2056)

13 Sonus verborum nostrarum aures percutit, magister intus est. Nolite putare quemquam aliquid discere ab homine. Admonere possumus per strepitum vocis nostrae; si non sit intus qui doceat, inanis fit strepitus noster ... Magisteria forinsecus, adjutoria quaedam sunt, et admonitiones. Cathedram in coelo habet qui corda docet. Aug., *Tract. in 1 Jo.*, 3. (*PL* 35, 2004)

14 Aers (1975), pp. 79-84.

15 Aers (1975), p. 83.

16 Bede (*CCSL* 119A, 360f.; cp. *Neemia* 5:13). Interpreting *Neemia* as *consolator*, Bede sees the prophet as a type of the Comforter who comes in our own times to turn our hearts from error and kindle them with divine love. This teaching would bring together, as in Langland's scene, the Law, the fruits of the Law, and the advent of divine love.

17 Quam cito duritiam Iudaeorum superbiamque causas esse sterilitatis agnouit! ... Pollicetur dura cordis eorum apostolicis ligonibus esse fodienda ... Ambr., *In Luc.* (*CCSL* 14, 272)

How quickly he recognised that the hardness and pride of the Jews were causes of barrenness ... He promises that the hard places of their hearts are to be dug over with apostolic mattocks ...

18 Et sexta aetate generis humani *filius dei uenit* et factus est *filius hominis* ut nos reformaret *ad imaginem dei*. Ea quippe nunc aetas agitur siue milleni anni singulis distribuantur aetatibus, siue in diuinis litteris memorabiles

atque insignes quasi articulos temporum uestigemus ut prima aetas inueniatur ab Adam usque ad Noe, inde secunda usque ad Abraham, et deinceps sicut Mattaeus euangelista distinxit *ab Abraham usque ad Dauid, a David usque ad transmigrationem in Babyloniam*, atque inde usque ad uirginis partum. Quae tres aetates coniunctae illis duabus quinque faciunt. Proinde sextam inchoauit natiuitas domini, quae nunc agitur usque ad occultum temporis finem ... Iuxta quippe est in eodem euangelii loco arbor quoque illa ficulnea cuius miseram sterilitatem etiam tertius annus arguebat. *De Trin*. (*CCSL* 50, 169f.) And in the Sixth Age of mankind *the Son of God came* and was made *the Son of Man* in order to reform us *in the image of God*. That is now the present Age (whether a thousand years make up each Age or whether we find tokens of memorable and notable people in Holy Writ as turning points in time, so that the First Age is seen as from Adam up to Noah, next the Second up to Abraham, and then, as the evangelist Matthew made the distinction, *from Abraham up to the crossing into Babylon* and next up to the Virgin Birth). Thus the nativity of the Lord started the Sixth, which is now current until the hidden end of time ... And next to this in the same place in the gospel is that fig-tree whose wretched barrenness was proved by the third year as well.

19 See p. 28, Chapter 4, Note 4, above, for the passage in question.
Bonus ille cultor agri interueniet pro nobis infecundis, pro nobis infructuosis ... Ambr., *In Luc*. (*CCSL* 14, 64)
May the good Farmer of the field intervene on our behalf, barren and unfruitful as we are.
Jerome also sees this tree as full of empty leaves signifying the traditions of the Pharisees (*In Math*. [*CCSL* 77, 190]). Cp. also p. 37, above.

20 Vidit itaque Zacchaeum sursum; iam enim sublimitate fidei inter fructus nouorum operum uelut fecundae altitudine arboris eminebat ... Zacchaeus in sycomoro, nouum uidelicet noui temporis pomum, ut in hoc quoque conpleretur illud: *arbor fici produxit grossos suos*; ad hoc enim Christus aduenit, ut ex lignis non poma, sed homines nascerentur. Ambr., *In Luc*. (*CCSL* 14, 331)
And so he saw Zacchaeus on high: for already he stood out in the loftiness of his faith among the fruits of new works as by the height of the flourishing tree ... Zacchaeus was in the sycomore-fig tree, that is, a new fruit of the new era, so that in it this too should be fulfilled: 'the fig tree has formed its early figs' [*Cant*. 2:13], for Christ came to it so that the tree should bear, not fruits, but men.

21 Namque aliae florem ferunt ante quam fructum pomaque uentura praenuntio sui flore designant, haec sola ab initio germinat poma pro floribus. In aliis flos decutitur et poma nascuntur, in hac poma decidunt, ut poma succedant. Ambr., *In Luc*. (*CCSL* 14, 270)
For other [trees] bear flowers before fruit and mark out with presaging flowers where the fruits will come, but this [tree] alone from the beginning grows fruits instead of flowers. In others the flower is shaken off and fruits are put forth, but in this the fruits fall that fruits may follow.

22 *Regio deserti* est cor infidelium quod dum Creator deserit, nullus inhabitator colit. *Ventus* autem *vehemens* quid aliud quam temptatio fortis accipitur? *Moralia* (*CCSL* 143, 92, on *Job* 1:19)

23 Quid est enim homo nisi folium, qui videlicet in paradiso ab arbore cecidit? Quid est nisi folium, qui temptationis vento rapitur et desideriorum flatibus levatur? Mens quippe humana quot temptationes patitur, quasi tot flatibus movetur. *Moralia* (*CCSL* 143A, 619, on *Job* 13:25)

24 Aers (1975), p.91 f. On the barren fig tree, see p.63, Note 19, above, and also Ambr., *In Luc.* (*CCSL* 14, 353).

25 Rursum per lignum incarnata Dei Sapientia figuratur sicut de ea scriptum est: Lignum vitae est his qui apprehenderint eam ... (*CCSL* 143A, 631, on *Job* 14:7)
Augustine, quoting the same text, adds, *Ecce Dominus tuus factus est tibi quasi baculus* ... 'See, your Lord is made your staff, as it were ...' *En. in Ps.* 32, s.3 (*CCSL* 38, 267)

26 *'Vade retro me, Satanas!'* (*Matt.* 16:23). These words, apparently spoken to Peter by Jesus, are explained by the commentators as in fact spoken to the Devil, since Peter had just been solemnly blessed and given the keys of the Kingdom. (So Jerome: *'Vade post me satana,'* diabolo dicitur, *In Math.* [*CCSL* 77, 144]). The echo of the phrase in the mouth of Piers thus recalls the incident in which Satan was prompting Peter to go against God's will, in trying to prevent the death of Jesus, but was overcome.

27 The comparison of the Trinity with the wood of a tree is to be found in Augustine's *De Fide et Symbolo*: the analogy is to root, trunk and branch, distinct parts and yet one wood. Augustine is careful to say that no corporeal example can bear real resemblance to the divine nature, but that the tree illustrates the doctrine of Three Persons with one Substance. *De Fide et Symbolo* (*CSEL* 41, 19f.)

28 Smith (1966), p.68.

29 Bloomfield (1963), p.74.

30 Augustine, *Confessiones*, 2:4.9.

31 Courcelle (1963), p.214.

32 For other views of the action, see Aers (1975), p.84, Note 40, and pp.101ff.

33 The consequences of the Fall also include the stoning of just men, e.g. Naboth (*Nabuth*). Ambrose comments on the killing of the prophets in exposition of *Luc.* 20:10, in which God the *agricola*, owner of a vineyard, sends his servants for the fruit (*Et tempore fructum seruulos suos misit*) only to have them wounded by the tenants; Naboth [cp. *3 Reg.* 21:13] he takes to be a prophet, not in what he says, but in what was done to him. (*In Luc.*, [*CCSL* 14, 340])

34 See *Matt.* 14:10, and for the end of the era of prophecy *Matt.* 11:11-13, *Luc.* 16:16.

35 See *Jud.* 16:30 for the death of Samson, *1 Reg.* 7:9ff. for Samuel's sacrifice, *1 Reg.* 16:13 for the anointing of David.

36 Bede relates Samuel and David with John the Baptist and Jesus:
Impleto unctionis officio Samuhel domum redit quia ueniente iam domino qui praenuntiabatur venturus, prophetarum praeconia siluerunt. *Lex enim prophetae usque ad Iohannem, ex eo regnum Dei euangelizatur.* Bede, *In 1 Sam.* (*CCSL* 119, 141)
Samuel, having fulfilled his function of anointing, returned to his home, because now that the Lord was coming whose advent had been foretold, the herald voices of the prophets became silent. The Law and the Prophets were until John; since that time the Kingdom of God is preached.

37 R. Woolf, 'The Tearing of the Pardon', in *Hussey* (1969), p.73.

38 cp. *Exod.* 3:15; *1 Reg.* 17:43.

39 Quid significat? non enim frustra factum est. Interrogemus litteras Dei. Quid serpens persuasit homini? Mortem. Ergo mors a serpente. Si mors a serpente, uirga in serpente, Christus in morte. *En. in Ps.* 73 (*CCSL* 39, 1008)
Augustine also uses the rod-serpent transformation in *De Trin.* among *examples of God's way of speaking to man*: Ergo *uirga in serpentem,*

Christus in mortem, et serpens rursus *in uirgam*, Christus in resurrectionem
. . . *De Trin.* 3:9 (*CCSL* 50, 148)

It is to be remembered that John conjoins the very similar prophetic sign (the brass serpent on the raised staff of Moses) with the expression of God's great love for the world (cp. *Jo.* 3:14-16). That gospel conjunction of Moses's symbolic staff and God's love shown in the Passion makes Langland's figural use of the staff in his presentation of 'charite' less extraordinary.

40   The postulated piling of symbolic sense upon symbolic sense would be a compression of a series of O.T. signs of the coming Saviour's contest with Death and the Devil, all signifying to Will the power of God's love. Such linking of prophetic signs is common in patristic commentary.

41   At ubi venit plenitudo temporis, misit Deus Filium suum, factum ex muliere, factum sub lege, ut eos qui sub lege erant redimeret, ut adoptionem filiorum reciperemus. *Gal.* 4:4f.

42   Et hoc dicatur, ut veritas humani corpus approbetur: tamen adhuc pannis involutus et butyro pastus ac melle, habebit boni malique judicium ut reprobans mala, eligat bona. Non quod hoc fecerit aut reprobaverit, vel elegerit, sed quod scierit reprobare et eligere, ut per haec verba noscamus, infantiam humani corporis divinae non praejudicasse sapientiae. Jerome, *In Isa.* (*PL* 24, 112f.)

And let this be said, that Truth may be shown in a human body: while yet wrapped in swaddling clothes and fed on curds and honey, he will possess judgement of good and evil (so that rejecting the wrong, he may choose the right). Not that he will have *done* this, *viz.*, rejected or chosen, but that he will have known how to reject and choose; so by these words we may learn that the infancy of the human body did not prematurely make judgements of the divine Wisdom.

(Jerome's tenses are difficult to render in this piece, because he is postulating what Isaiah's words will mean when Jesus has become a child and Truth is seen by mankind.)

43   Smith (1966), p. 60.

Chapter 8   Christ and Piers

1   cp. A 1:96f.; B 1:98f.; C 1:101f., and *3 Reg.* 14:43.
2   Haec dicit Dominus exercituum: Reversus sum ad Sion, et habitabo in medio Jerusalem; et vocabitur Jerusalem civitas veritatis, et mons Domini exercituum mons sanctificatus. [*Zach.* 8:93]
Ecce Rex tuus veniet tibi justus, et salvator; ipse pauper et ascendens super asinam et super pullum filium asinae. [*Zach.* 9:9]
3   Ambr., *In Luc.* (*CCSL* 14, 239)
4   Precemus medicum saucii, portemur in stabulum curandi. Ille est enim qui promittit sanitatem, qui miseratus est in uia semiuiuum a latronibus derelictum. Aug., *In Ioh.* (*CCSL* 36, 365)
cp. also his mention of the Inn at the end of *De Trin.* (above, p. 21).
5   Ideo sequitur: *Et cognoscetis ueritatem*. Veritas incommutabilis est. Veritas panis est, mentes reficit nec deficit; mutat uescentem, non ipsa in uescentem mutatur. Ipsa est ueritas Verbum Dei, Deis apud Deum unigenitus Filius. Haec ueritas carne induta est propter nos, ut de Maria uirgine nasceretur, et

impleretur prophetia: *Veritas de terra orta est.* Haec ergo ueritas cum Iudaeis loqueretur, latebat in carne; latebat autem non ut negaretur, sed ut differretur; differretur, ut in carne pateretur; in carne autem pateretur, ut caro peccati redimeretur. Stans itaque conspicuus secundum infirmitatem carnis Dominus noster Iesus Christus, et secundum maiestatem diuinitatis occultus, dixit ad eos qui ei, cum haec loqueretur crediderant: *Si manseritis in uerbo meo, uere discipuli mei eritis.* Qui enim perseuerauerit usque in finem, hic saluus erit. *Et cognoscetis ueritatem*, quae modo uos latet, et loquitur uobis. *Et ueritas liberabit nos.* Aug., *In Ioh.* (*CCSL* 36, 357)

6   Langland takes up the idea of liberation in the speech he puts in the mouth of Conscience, explaining the meaning of the name 'Christ': those who become Christians, he says, are franklins and free men [cp. B 19:38f.; C 21:38f.].

7   Quia sicut quaerit Caesar in nummo imaginem suam, sic Deus quaerit in homine suam. Aug., *In Ioh.* (*CCSL* 36, 358) cp. p.25, Note 25, above.

8   *Et cum intrasset Hierosolymam commota est uniuersa ciuitas dicens: Quis est hic?* Introeunte Iesu cum turba, tota Hierosolymorum ciuitas commouetur, mirans frequentiam, nesciens ueritatem et dicens: *Quis est hic?* Quod quidem et in alio loco dicentes angelos legimus: *Quis est iste rex gloriae?* Aliis autem uel ambigentibus uel interrogantibus, uilis plebicula confitetur a minoribus incipiens ut ad maiora perueniat et dicit: *Hic est Iesus propheta a Nazareth Galileae.* Propheta quem et Moyses similem sui dixerat esse uenturum . . . Jer., *In Math.* (*CCSL* 77, 186)

9   The phrase 'of his gentries' reminds the reader that Jesus is of noble birth, descendant of King David.

10 Dixitque David ad Saul: Non possum sic incedere, quia non usum habeo. Et deposuit ea, et tulit baculum suum, quem semper habebat in manibus . . . [*1 Reg.* 17:39f.].

11 Schmidt, *ed. cit.*, p.350, Note 22, comments: '. . . like such knights as Lancelot, he [Christ] disguises his divinity in the form of the humble ploughman, *habitu inventus ut homo*, "in habit found as a man" (Phil. 2:7)'. However, since Langland imagined David's followers as knights, it seems more probable that he thinks of Jesus as coming to knightly combat like another David, with the outward appearance of a young man from the country who is also a prophet.
The first half of the verse quoted by Schmidt is also pertinent:

> Qui cum in forma Dei esset, non rapinam arbitratus est esse se aequalem Deo; sed semetipsum exinanivit, formam servi accipiens, in similitudinem hominum factus, et habitu inventus ut homo.
>
> [*Phil.* 2:7]

Paul's words 'emptied himself, taking the form of a servant' lead into the phrase 'made in the likeness of men' which lies behind Christ's words in *Piers Plowman*:

> And I in liknesse of a leode, þat lord am of heuene,
> Graciousliche þi gile haue quyt: go gile ayein gile!
>
> [B 18:356; not in C]

Thus, Lucifer's guile in descending to the form of a serpent was matched by Christ's taking the form of a man. Augustine often quotes *Phil.* 2:7 in his commentary on John's gospel; it underlies his doctrine of *deus-homo* 'god-man' (see Chapter 3, Note 29, above).

12 Non mediocris quoque causa est, ut uirginitas Mariae falleret principem

114

mundi, qui cum desponsatam uiro cerneret, partum non potuit habere suspectum. Fallendi autem principis mundi fuisse consilium ipsius domini uerba declarant, cum apostoli iubentur tacere de Christo, cum sanati prohibentur gloriari de remedio, cum daemones praecipiuntur silere de dei filio. Fallendi, ut dixi, principis mundi fuisse consilium etiam apostolus declarauit dicens: *sed loquimur dei sapientiam in mysterio absconditam, quam nemo principum istius saeculi cognouit. Si enim cognouissent, numquam dominum maiestatis crucifixissent*; hoc est: numquam me redimi domini morte fecissent. Fefellit ergo pro nobis, fefellit ut uinceret, fefellit diabolum, cum temtaretur, cum rogaretur, cum dei filius diceretur, ut nusquam diuinitatem propriam fateretur. Sed tamen magis fefellit principem saeculi; diabolus enim etsi aliquando dubitauit, cum diceret: *si filius dei es, mitte te deorsum*, tamen uel sero cognouit et discessit ab eo. Ambr., *In Luc.* (*CCSL* 14, 31)

The passage is influenced by Origen, *Homiliae in Lucam* 1, 6, 37 f., but the rhetorical play on *fefellit* is Ambrose's addition.

13 Among modern critics, Bloomfield (1961) has most plainly stated that justice is Langland's theme: 'It is certainly true that Langland values justice as much as love and, because of the crisis of his own time, probably rated it higher. Justice without love is deficient, but love without justice is equally deficient; and indeed without justice there can be no society in which man can be perfected' (p. 130).

14 Disciplina enim uel misericordia multum destituitur, si una sine altera teneatur. Sed circa subditos suos inesse rectoribus debet et iuste consulans misericordia, et pie saeuiens disciplina. Hinc est quod semiuiui illius uulneribus, qui a Samaritano in stabulum ductus est, et uinum adhibetur et oleum. *Moralia* (*CCSL* 143A, 1012, on *Job* 29:25)

15 The 'salve' is traditionally associated with the spiritual healing offered by the sacrament of penance, the 'wine' being the penance enjoined by the confessor. This sacrament is clearly of great importance to Langland, and the corruption of the sacrament is the ground of his frequent denunciation of venal friars and pardoners.

16 Quis est iste, qui venit de Edom, tinctis vestibus de Bosra? . . . Quare ergo rubrum est indumentum tuum, et vestimenta tua sicut calcantium in torculari? [*Isa.* 63:1 f.]

17 Quis enim est iste angelus, nisi ille qui per prophetam dicitur: *Magni consilii angelus* (*Isa.* 9:6, *sec. LXX*)? Quia enim Graeca lingua evangelizare denuntiare dicitur, semetipsum nobis annuntians Dominus angelus vocatur. Et bene ait: *Si fuerit pro eo angelus loquens*, quia, sicut ait Apostolus, etiam interpellat pro nobis (*Rom.* 8:34). Sed quid pro nobis loquatur, audiamus: *Unum de similibus*. Mos medicinae est ut aliquando similia similibus, aliquando contraria contrariis curet. Nam saepe calida calidis, frigida frigidis; saepe autem frigida calidis, calida frigidis sanare consuevit. Veniens ergo ad nos desuper medicus noster, tantisque nos inveniens languoribus pressos, quiddam nobis simile, et quiddam contrariam apposuit. Ad homines quippe homo venit, sed ad peccatores justus. Concordavit nobis veritate naturae, sed discrepavit a nobis vigore justitiae. Vitiosus enim homo corrigi non poterat nisi per Deum. Videri autem debuit qui corrigebat, ut praebendo imitationis formam, anteactae malitiae mutarent vitam. Sed videri ab homine non poterat Deus; ergo homo factus est, ut videri potuisset. Justus igitur atque invisibilis Deus, apparuit similis nobis homo visibilis, ut dum videtur ex simili, curaret ex justo; et dum veritate generis concordat conditioni, virtute artis obviaret aegritudini. *Moralia* (*PL* 76, 287, on *Job* 33:23)

115

18 Conscience's long speech occurs at B 19:26-198; C 21:26-198.
19 See p.18, above.
20 Schmidt rightly notes that Langland's reference here to *Matt.* 16:19 'is not in itself an affirmation of the medieval doctrine of the Pope's "plenitude of power" in things earthly and heavenly, though it is the ultimate source of that doctrine' (*ed. cit.*, p.354).

Chapter 9   *Piers in the Last Age*

1 For the harvest of the earth, see *Apoc.* 14:14ff.; cp. B 18:369ff.; C 20:411ff.
2 Dobest is aboue hem boþe & beriþ a bisshopes croce [A 9:86; B 8:96; C 10:92].
3 For the Sower, see *Matt.* 13:3ff.; Labourer in the field, *Matt.* 13:27ff.; Workers in the vineyard, *Matt.* 20:1ff.; 21:33ff.
4 Jesus, referring to those whose ears are open, says *et sanem eos* 'and I will heal them' [*Matt.* 13:15]; the Parable of the Sower begins three verses later.
5 Barney (1973), p.268f.
6 Agricolae quippe huius terrae sunt hi qui minori loco positi, quo ualent zelo, quanto possunt opere, ad eruditionem sanctae Ecclesiae in praedicationis gratia cooperantur. *Moralia* (*CCSL* 143A, 1133, on *Job* 31:39)
I hesitate to use the word 'ploughman' here, since *agricola* is a word of more general meaning: the work described is 'ploughing', but *agricola* implies a man with more authority than our 'ploughman' has today.
7 Ad hoc quippe diuina dispensatione ceteris unusquisque praeponitur, ut subiectorum animus, quasi substrata terra, praedicationis illius semine fecundetur. *Moralia* (*CCSL* 143A, 1131, on *Job* 31:38)
8 The last phrases of the quotation are very difficult to translate. The Jerusalem Bible (*La Sainte Bible*, Paris, 1955) reads '. . . et à constituer cet Homme parfait dans la force de l'âge, qui réalise la plénitude du Christ'. Paul's chapter also includes the metaphor of 'putting off the "old man"' [cp. vv. 22ff.].
The passage about the gifts was elaborated by the homilists; in the C-text more gifts are listed [cp. C 21:225ff.].
9 See B 19:260; C 21:258. For the power given to Peter see also B 19:385ff.; C 21:385ff.
10 Sic cuncta moderatur, ut dum singula quaeque sunt omnium, interposita quadam charitatis necessitudine, fiant omnia singulorum, et unusquisque sic quod non accepit in altero possideat, ut ipse alteri possidendum quod accepit humiliter impendat. Hinc enim per Petrum dicitur *unusquisque sicut accepit gratiam*, etc. *Moralia* (*PL* 27, 461, on *Job* 38:4)
11   Whanne alle tresours arn triȝed treuþe is þe beste;
                   I do it on *Deus caritas* to deme þe soþe.
                   It is as derworþi a dreury as dere god hymseluen.
                              [A 1:83ff.; B 1:87ff.; C 1:81ff.]
For the 'cheyne of charite', see p.15, above.
12 cp. *Luc.* 12:42ff. and 16:1ff.; *Matt.* 18:23ff. and *Marc.* 13:34ff.
13 cp. B 6:228f.; C 8:236f. Augustine stresses that we are all inevitably in debt to *caritas* [cp. *En. in Ps.* 36, *s.*3 (*CCSL* 38, 379)].
14 Et ideo ait: *facite uobis amicos de iniquo mamona*, ut largiendo pauperibus

angelorum nobis ceterorumque sanctorum gratiam conparemus. Nec reprehenditur uilicus, in quo discimus non ipse esse domini, sed potius alienarum uilici facultatum. Et ideo licet peccauerit, tamen quia sibi in posterum ex indulgentia domini quaesiuit auxilia, praedicatur. Pulchre autem iniquum mamona dixit, quia uariis diuitiarum inlecebris nostros auaritia temtabat adfectus, ut uellemus seruire diuitiis. Vnde ait: *si in alieno fideles non fuistis, quod uestrum est quis dabit uobis*? Alienae nobis diuitiae sunt, quia praeter naturam sunt neque nobiscum nascuntur neque nobiscum transeunt, Christus autem noster est, quia uita est. Ambr., *In Luc.* (*CCSL* 14, 297)

15 The first quotation, already brought to notice by Barney, is from *PL* 76, 574. Barney (1973), p. 269, comments that the phrase 'by the plowshare of the tongue' (*linguae uomere*) turns up again and again in Gregory. There are, however, variations in the metaphor and its application. Here Gregory imagines Paul tamed and harnessed, drawing the plough of preaching (*aratrum praedicationis trahat*), teaching those who believed in Christ that they should no longer keep the Jewish observances:

> Qui ergo in humili mente fidelium legis duritiam redarguendo contrivit, quid aliud quam in valle post Dominum glebas fregit? ne videlicet grana seminum quae excisus aratro fidei sulcus cordis exciperet per custodiam litterae pressa deperirent.
> *Moralia* (*PL* 78, 591, on *Job* 39:10)

The 'furrows' have already received the 'seeds', so the work Paul is doing is more akin to harrowing than to actual ploughing. He is (like Gregory himself) shaking off the weight of the 'letter' of scripture by 'breaking up the clods'.

16 Hoc itaque loco equi nomine sanctus praedicator accipitur . . . Huic equo Dominus et fortitudinem et hinnitum se dare testatur, quia in praedicatore ejus nisi et vita et sermo convenerint, nequaquam virtus perfectionis apparebit. *Moralia* (*PL* 76, 597, on *Job* 39:19)

17 It is a point of interest that Aers selects for his hypothesis about Piers a verse from the end of this same chapter, 'I became all things to all men that I might save all' (Aers, 1975, p. 78) but he seems oblivious to the context of spiritual and carnal ploughing in the chapter.

18 Quid ad haec nos pastores dicimus, qui adventum districi judicis praecurrentes, officium quidem praeconis suscipimus, sed alimenta ecclesiastica muti manducamus? Exigimus quod nostro debetur corpori, sed non impendimus quod subjectorum debemus cordi. *Moralia* (*PL* 76, 246, on *Job* 31:39)

19 Piers, in sowing the virtues, has to 'cleave the soil of the human breast by preaching' [cp. B 19:275; C 21:275]; for the quotation from Gregory and its context, see p. 84 and Note 15, above (on *Job* 39:10). Barney quotes *Moralia* on *Job* 31:38-40 on this matter.

20 Terra est verbum Dei, quam quanto labor inquirentis exigit, tanto largius fructum reddit. Debet ergo intellectus sacri eloquii multiplici inquisitione ventilare, quia et terra, quae saepius arando vertitur, ad frugem uberius aptatur. *Moralia* (*PL* 76, 589, on *Job* 39:9)

21 Qui tamen sunt qui uendunt boues? ut in figura quaeramus mysterium facti . . .
Qui ergo boues uendunt? Boues intelleguntur qui nobis scripturas sanctas dispensauerunt. Boues erant apostoli, boues erant prophetae . . . [Augustine quotes *1 Cor.* 9:9f.]
Isti autem de scripturis ipsis fallunt populos, ut accipiant ab ipsis honores et laudes, et non conuertantur homines ad ueritatem. Aug., *Tract. in Ioh.*

10, 7, (*CCSL* 36, 104f.)

22 This passage follows the account of the 'great wind' of temptation quoted above, p.64, and Chapter 7, Note 22.

In quattuor uero angulis domus ista consistit quia nimirum solidum mentis nostrae aedificium, prudentia, temperantia, fortitudo, iustitia sustinet. In quattuor angulis domus ista subsistit quia in his quattuor uirtutibus tota boni operis structura consurgit. Moralia (CCSL 143, 105, on *Job* 1:19)

Donum quippe Spiritus quod in subiecta mente ante alia prudentiam, temperantiam, fortitudinem, iustitiam format, eamdem mentem ut contra singula quaeque tentamenta erudiat in septem mox uirtutibus temperat . . . Ib., 106.

23 On the importance of the cardinal virtues in the Christian life, see also Aug., *De Trin.* (*CCSL* 50A, p.438). A useful account of the Christianisation of the virtues is given by R. Tuve, *Allegorical Imagery* (N.J., 1966), 91ff.

24 *Hoc enim agit spiritus gratiae, ut imaginem dei, in qua naturaliter facti sumus, instauret in nobis. Uitium quippe contra naturam est, quod utique sanat gratia . . .* Aug., *De Spiritu et Littera* (*CSEL* 60, 201)

25 Gregory's phrase '*in subiecta mente*', which I have translated 'in the mind it has worked on', refers, I think, to the metaphor of God the cultivator (*cultor*) mentioned in his previous paragraph. The hint would be sufficient to inspire Langland's allegory of the preparation of the earth to receive the seeds of the virtues given by Grace.

26 For the metaphor, see p.34 and Chapter 4, Note 25, above.

27 So in B 17:74ff. In C, the image is somewhat confused by the addition of *lavacrum-lex-dei* for the baptismal font (C 19:71) though the significance is clear.

28 Smith (1966), p.78f.

29 Smith (1966), p.92.

30 cp. B 17:100; C 19:87.

31 *Unde ergo nobis datur fiducia in die judicii? Quia sicut ille est, et nos sumus in hoc mundo.* Debemus hoc referre ad ipsam charitatem, et intelligere quid dictum sit . . . Si ergo iubet nos diligere inimicos nostros, unde nobis dat exemplum? De ipso Deo: ait enim, 'Ut sitis filii Patris vestri qui in coelis est'. Quomodo illud facit Deus? Diligit inimicos suos 'qui facit solem suum oriri super bonos et malos, et pluit super justos et injustos' (*Matt.* V, 44-6). Si ergo ad hanc perfectionem nos invitat Deus, ut diligamus inimicos nostros sicut et ipse dilexit suos; ea nobis fiducia est in die judicii, *quia sicut ille est, et nos sumus in hoc mundo*: quia sicut ille diligit inimicos suos, faciendo solem suum oriri super bonos et malos, et pluendo super justos et injustos; ita nos quia inimicis nostris non possumus praestare solem et pluviam, praestamus lacrymas, cum pro illis oramus. Aug., *Tract. in 1 Jo.* (*PL* 35, 2047)

32 Augustine's word *adhaerere* which I have translated 'to cling to' is not anthropomorphic; he is remembering *Mihi adhaerere Deo bonum est* (*Ps.* 72:28) which he relates to the sticking of wax to a signet ring:

> Ergo quisquis ita uult esse similis Deo . . . non ab illo recedat, ei cohaerendo signetur tamquam ex anulo cera, illi affixus habeat imaginem eius, faciens quod dictum est: *Mihi adhaerere Deo bonum est*, uere custodit similitudinem et imaginem ad quam factus est.
>
> Aug., *En. in Ps.* 70, *s*.2 (*CCSL* 39, 965)

> Therefore, whoever wishes thus to be like God . . let him not move away from him; adhering to him, let him be stamped as wax is by the ring, let him have his image fixed upon him, doing as is written, 'It is

good for me to cling to God'; truly he is keeping the likeness and image to which he was made.

In this discourse, too, Augustine quotes the passage about the rain on the just and the unjust [*Matt.* 5:46], adding, *Qui ergo bene uult inimico suo, Deo similis est: nec ista superbia, sed oboedientia est. Quare? Quia ad imaginem Dei facti sumus . . . Ib.*, 964.

Therefore, he who wishes his enemy well is like God. This is not pride, but obedience. How? Because we were made in the image of God.

SELECT BIBLIOGRAPHY

The list is confined to works referred to in the course of the book.

A EDITIONS OF TEXTS

1 *Editions of* Piers Plowman *(listed chronologically):*

The Vision of William concerning Piers the Plowman, in Three Parallel Texts, ed. W. W. Skeat (Oxford, 1886, repr. 1954, with additional bibliography by J. A. W. Bennett)

Piers Plowman: The A Version. Will's Vision of Piers Plowman and Do-Well, ed. G. Kane (The Athlone Press, University of London, 1960)

Langland, *Piers Plowman.* The Prologue and Passus I-VII of the B-text, ed. J. A. W. Bennett (Oxford, 1972)

Piers Plowman: The B Version. Will's Visions of Piers Plowman, Do-Well, Do-Better and Do-Best, ed. G. Kane and E. T. Donaldson (The Athlone Press, University of London, 1975)

The Vision of Piers Plowman: A Complete Edition of the B-Text, ed. A. V. C. Schmidt (London and New York, 1978)

Piers Plowman by William Langland: an edition of the C-Text, ed. Derek Pearsall (York Medieval Texts: second series) (London, 1978)

(*Note*: The numbering of passus in the C-Text does not coincide in the editions of Skeat and Pearsall.)

2 *Editions of other texts principally quoted (listed alphabetically):*

Ambrose	*Expositio Euangelii secundum Lucam*, et *Fragmenta in Esaiam*, ed. M. Adriaen (*CCSL* 14) Turnhout, 1957
Augustine	*Confessionum Libri XIII*, ed. M. Skutella, Stuttgart, 1969
	Enarrationes in Psalmos (*CCSL* 38, 39, 40), edd. D. E. Dekkers and J. Fraipont, Turnhout, 1956
	De Fide et Symbolo (*CSEL* 41), ed. J. Zycha, Vienna, 1900
	In Iohannis Euangelium Tractatus CXXIV (*CCSL* 36), ed. D. R. Willems, Turnhout, 1954
	De Libero Arbitrio (*CCSL* 29), ed. W. M. Green, Turnhout, 1970
	De Spiritu et Littera (*CSEL* 60), ed. C. F. Urba and J. Zycha, Vienna, 1913
	Tractatus X in Epistolam Joannis ad Parthos (*PL* 35), ed. J.-P. Migne, Paris, 1902
	De Trinitate (*CCSL* 50, 50A), edd. W. J. Mountain and Fr. Glorie, Turnhout, 1968
	De Vera Religione (*CCSL* 32), ed. J. Martin, Turnhout, 1962
Gregory	*Homilia in Ezechielem* (*PL* 76), ed. J.-P. Migne, Paris, 1878

Gregory	*Moralia in Iob, Libri I-XXII* (*CCSL* 143, 143A), ed. M. Adriaen, Turnhout, 1979
	Moralium Liber (continuatio) (*PL* 76), ed. J.-P. Migne, Paris, 1878
Jerome	*Commentariorum in Isaiam prophetam Libri XVIII* (*PL* 24), ed. J.-P. Migne, Paris, 1863
	Commentariorum in Matheum Libri IV (*CCSL* 77), edd. D. Hurst and M. Adriaen, Turnhout, 1969

B   CRITICAL WORKS

1   *Collections of Critical Essays*

E. Vasta, ed. *Interpretations of Piers Plowman* (Notre Dame, 1968)

R. J. Blanch, ed. *Style and Symbolism in Piers Plowman* (Knoxville, 1969)

S. S. Hussey, ed. *Piers Plowman: Critical Approaches* (London, 1969)

2   *Critical Studies*

D. W. Robertson and B. F. Huppé, *Piers Plowman and Scriptural Tradition* (Princeton, N.J., 1951)

P. Courcelle, *Les Confessions de Saint Augustin dans la tradition littéraire* (Paris, 1963)

M. W. Bloomfield, *Piers Plowman as a Fourteenth Century Apocalypse* (New Brunswick, N.J., 1963)

G. Kane, *Piers Plowman: The Evidence for Authorship* (London, 1965)

E. Vasta, *The Spiritual Basis of Piers Plowman* (The Hague, 1965)

B. H. Smith, *Traditional Imagery of Charity in Piers Plowman* (The Hague and Paris, 1966)

R. Tuve, *Allegorical Imagery* (Princeton, N.J., 1966)

R. M. Ames, *The Fulfillment of the Scriptures: Abraham, Moses and Piers* (Evanston, 1970)

E. D. Kirk, *The Dream Thought of Piers Plowman* (New Haven, 1972)

D. Aers, *Piers Plowman and Christian Allegory* (London, 1975)

3   *Critical Articles*

T. P. Dunning, 'The Structure of the B-text of Piers Plowman', *RES*, n.s. 7 (1956), 225-37

B. H. Smith, 'Patience's Riddle', *MLN* 76 (1961), 675-82

J. A. Burrow, 'The Action of Langland's Second Vision', *EC* 15 (1965), 247-68

E. Salter, 'Medieval Poetry and the Figural View of Reality', *PBA* 54, London, 1968, 73-92

B. Raw, 'Piers and the Image of God in Man', in *Hussey* (1969), q.v., 143-79

A. V. C. Schmidt, 'Langland and Scholastic Philosophy', *MAE* 38 (1969), 134-56

J. S. Wittig, '*Piers Plowman* B IX-XII: Elements in the Design of the Inward Journey', *Traditio* 28 (1972), 211-80

A. Middleton, 'Two Infinites: Grammatical Metaphor in Piers Plowman', *ELH* 39 (1972), 169-88

S. A. Barney, 'The Plowshare of the Tongue: The Progress of a Symbol from the Bible to Piers Plowman', *MS* 35 (1973), 261-93

R. E. Kaske, '"*Ex vi transicionis*" and Its Passage in *Piers Plowman*', *JEGP* 62 (1963), 32-60; also in *Blanch*, q.v. (1969)

R. Adams, 'Langland and the Liturgy Revisited', *SP* 73 (1976), 266-84

J. A. Alford, 'The Role of the Quotations in *Piers Plowman*', *Speculum* 52 (1977), 80-99

4   *Translation*

Piers the Ploughman, translated into modern English prose by J. F. Goodridge (Penguin, 1959, 2nd edn. 1966)

INDEX

Abraham, 14, 24, 41, 68, 76
Adam, 14, 21, 24, 26, 33, 34, 38,
    45, 63, 65-8, 71, 74
  wound of, 73
Advent, 68
Aers, D., 2, 60, 61, 64, 94, 117
Ages of Man, 24, 81, 88, 110
'agnus Dei', 50, 53
Agricultural imagery, 3, 4, 8, 14, 22,
    34, 35, 38-40, 42, 43, 46, 47,
    59-65, 80, 82, 84-7, 99, 104,
    117
Alford, J. A., 93
Allegory, 3, 7, 20-2, 24, 26, 48, 60,
    61, 67, 69, 70, 80-2, 84-7, 118
Allusion, 22
Ambrose, 3, 4, 6, 8, 21, 25, 28, 30,
    32, 33, 35, 36, 38, 40, 55, 56,
    63, 73, 75, 83
Ames, R. M., 106, 107, 109
Amor mundi, 36
Ananias, 35
Angels, 10, 77, 115
Anima, 5, 15, 33, 53, 58-60, 64, 65
Annunciation, 68
Antichrist, 80
Apostles, 9, 10, 13, 15, 22, 24, 26,
    31, 32, 34-7, 41, 47, 61, 75,
    77, 79-81, 84, 86
Apostolate, 35, 36
Ascension, 76, 81
Athanasian Creed, 105
Atonement, 6, 45, 87
Augustine, 3, 4, 8, 10, 19, 22-6, 28,
    30, 32-4, 40-3, 45, 46, 48, 59,
    65, 69, 73, 78, 86, 87, 90
  Confessiones, 8, 9, 17, 18, 23, 29,
    44, 48, 53, 67
  De Spiritu et Littera, 59
  De Trinitate, 8, 9, 15-17, 21, 51,
    52, 54, 58, 63, 94
  De Vera Religione, 49, 50
  doctrine of deification, 94
  Enarrationes in Psalmos, 23, 44,
    45, 53
  Tractatus in 1 Ep. Joannis, 8, 60,

    61, 89, 94
  Tractatus in Ioh. Evang., 46, 73,
    106, 113, 114, 117

Barn, the allegorical, 35, 80, 87, 88
Barney, S. A., 35, 80, 92, 117
Bede, 4, 25, 68, 100
  In Ezram et Neemiam, 62
Bennett, J. A. W., 42, 104
Benson, C. D., 94
Bible, 3, 10, 17-19, 32, 48, 56, 68,
    72, 80
  interpretation of, 3, 4, 20, 22, 24,
    42, 60, 86, 97
  versions of, 6
Bishops, 47, 58, 80, 84, 86
Bloomfield, M. W., 67, 92, 99, 115
Burrow, J. A., 102

'Caesar', 10, 25, 26, 38, 73, 78
Cana, marriage at, 18, 78
Cardinals, 20, 90
Caritas, 5, 16, 18, 30, 50, 52, 59, 60,
    64, 67, 76, 77, 88
Carnal man, 18, 23, 39, 40, 65
Charity, 15, 17, 24, 33, 36, 48, 52,
    53, 58, 60, 67, 75, 89, 90
  bond of, 82, 84, 88
Christ, 6, 13, 14, 16, 18, 20, 21,
    24-8, 30-3, 35-8, 42, 43, 45-9,
    54-6, 60-3, 66-71, 73-9, 82,
    84, 88, 97
  'Sun of justice', 6, 70, 93
Christian life, 24
Church, 2, 40, 41, 60-3, 71, 73, 76,
    79, 81, 84, 86, 87, 88
  doctrines of, 2, 4, 6, 10, 60
Cicero, 30
Clergy, 3, 8, 9, 12, 26, 28, 48, 49,
    55, 56, 57
'coals of fire', 49, 50, 54, 55, 90
Coin image, 10, 11, 20, 21, 23-6, 30,
    33, 45, 47, 73, 78, 83, 88
Concupiscentia carnis, 59
Concupiscentia oculorum, 59
Confession, 34

123

126

127

J